ELECTRICAL CONTROL
OF FLUID POWER

THIRD EDITION

Electric and Electronic Control Circuits for Hydraulic and Air Fluid Power Systems

Prepared by Charles S. Hedges
Assisted by the Technical Staff of Womack Machine Supply Company

Sponsored by Robert C. Womack
Member Fluid Power Society and Fluid Power Educational Foundation

Published by

Womack Educational Publications

Department of Womack Machine Supply Company

2010 Shea Road • Dallas, Texas 75235 • Phone: 214-357-3871
Mailing address: P. O. Box 35027, Dallas, TX 75235 • Telefax 214-350-9322

Publisher's Information

ELECTRICAL CONTROL OF FLUID POWER

Third Edition ©1987 by Womack Machine Supply Company — All Rights Reserved
This is the Ninth Printing of the Third Edition — November 1999
Library of Congress Catalog Card No. 77-156777
ISBN No. 0-9605644-9-7
Printed in the U.S.A.

LIABILITY DISCLAIMER

Please read this before using the book.

We have taken great care in the preparation of this edition to see that all information is accurate. It has been checked and re-checked. However, any segment of information may apply on one application, and for one reason or another may not apply on another application which seems to be similar. This may be due to differences in environment, personnel, operating conditions, materials, and components. And, no matter how carefully the material is checked there is always the possibility of printing errors, or errors in circuits, tables, or text. For this reason we are offering this book only for educational usage, to illustrate principles and techniques, and we do not assume any liability for the safe and/or satisfactory operation of any machine or installation designed from information in this book.

To avoid accidents, please observe all safety precautions mentioned in the text.

PURPOSE OF THIS BOOK

All material in this book is specifically related in one way or another to electrical circuits for controlling air and hydraulic fluid powered machines. Starting with a simple explanation of some of the common components, it ends with a study of servo valves, proportional solenoid valves, and electronic programmable controllers. No attempt is made to cover theory or laws of electricity. All material is on a practical basis, with laws, theory, and mathematics avoided as much as possible.

This book has been prepared for those who already understand the basics of fluid power itself but have had limited experience with electrical control circuits. Fluid circuits have been described in our other books.

This is a book of ideas and control principles. Practical ways are shown in which switches, relays, solenoid valves, controllers, and other electrical components can be connected to control fluid powered machines. Hopefully the student can take these ideas and combine them into a complete circuit exactly right for his particular machine.

In this Third Edition, most of the material from previous editions has been retained but has been slightly rearranged. To this has been added chapters on servo valves and on proportional solenoid valves.

— The Author

HOW TO ORDER WOMACK TEXTBOOKS

Whether you are an individual, a company, a library, or a bookstore, you may order textbooks from the publisher using the address on the title page. See Page 257 for descriptions of other Womack books. We discourage book stores from carrying books in stock because they are frequently revised or updated and may get out-of-date on a bookstore shelf. We carry a large inventory at our warehouse in Dallas for immediate shipment, and can ship in 1 to 3 days after receiving your order.

Individuals please send personal check with order or request C.O.D. shipment. Texas residents please add appropriate sales tax. For the latest prices, request Bulletin S-105 for domestic prices and/or Bulletin S-103 for foreign prices.

Companies, schools, libraries and book stores may order by letter, phone or FAX on net 30-days billing. You will be billed for shipping charges.

For additional information or to get our most recent price list, please contact the Womack Educational Publications office at (214) 357-3871 or FAX us your requests or questions at (214) 350-9322.

Thank you for your purchase of our books.

Topics Covered in this Book

This is a brief resume of some of the more important topics covered in this book. A complete index will be found on Page 256. Reference design data starts on Page 244.

Special safety circuits include two-hand press operation; emergency and panic buttons; de-activating pushbuttons after cycle starts; automatic discharge of an accumulator; warning signals; unloading a pump before starting the motor or engine.

Start and stop control; fuse and disconnect boxes; manual and magnetic motor starters; NEMA motor designs; effects of high and low voltage; effects of incorrect frequency (Hz); how to measure HP on motor; duty cycle of motor, etc.

Electronic control of fluid power machines using programmable controllers; comparison of electric and electronic control; ladder diagrams acceptable to a controller; terms and abbreviations used with controllers; circuit components; circuit logic for controllers; permanent storage of programs, etc.

Comparison of servo valves with other solenoid valves; pressure and flow in a servo circuit; actuators for servo systems; open and closed loop systems; electro-hydraulic servo valves; position finding application; speed and pressure control systems, etc.

Comparison with standard solenoid valves; suitable applications; control of proportional valves; selection of valve size; amplifiers; direct-acting and pilot-operated types; pressure and flow control applications; joystick control, etc.

A collection of useful data especially for designers of electrical circuits. Much additional information will be found in our other publications such as our Fluid Power Data Book, our Bulletin W-144 set of design data sheets, and the appendices of our other books. These publications are listed on our current price list.

Note: This book is frequently reprinted, and is revised, if necessary, at each printing to keep it current with the latest technology of industrial fluid power. Our authors and editors are closely associated with the National Fluid Power Association (NFPA) standards work. They keep the text up-to-date with the latest terms and symbols adopted by one or more of the standardization agencies including the NFPA, the ANSI (American National Standards Institute), and the ISO (International Standards Organization).

CHAPTER 1

Popular Fluid and Electrical Components

In most air and hydraulic fluid power circuits, three kinds of valves are used to (1), control direction of fluid flow; (2), rate of fluid flow; and (3), to limit maximum level of pressure in either the pump line or in a branch circuit. Control valves for these functions can be purchased with solenoid actuators, and it is the purpose of this book to present electrical circuits for directional, speed, and pressure control of cylinders and fluid motors. With electrical control, machine cycles can be set up for automatic sequencing of various parts of the machine, and operator control can be exercised from a remote location.

For directional control, 4-way solenoid valves are the ones most often used, although combinations of two or more 2-way or 3-way valves can be used. For speed control, deceleration, step level pressure control, pump unloading, and pressure control, 2-way solenoid valves are primarily used.

Four-way air valves and 4-way hydraulic valves operate in much the same way but electric control circuits for the two media are usually different because different kinds of valves are used. For example, most air circuits use single solenoid valves or may use double solenoid valves without a center neutral. A center position is undesirable for most air circuits. Hydraulic 4-way valves, on the other hand, are nearly always the double solenoid type with a center neutral position.

In this section we will briefly describe some of the electrical components (switches, relays, etc.) for controlling fluid power. The ones described here, while being the more popular ones, are only a part of the wide variety available to a designer. The physical appearance of each component will vary with the brand, size, and type, and we cannot cover the full range of brands available.

7

Directional Control Valves — 4-Way . . .

A directional control valve is defined as one which controls the direction of flow in a fluid, either liquid or air in the case of fluid power. This is usually for the purpose of controlling the direction in which an output actuator moves, extension or retraction in the case of a cylinder, and clockwise or counter-clockwise in the case of a fluid motor. Except in special applications, one directional valve is required for each cylinder, or group of cylinders, connected in parallel to the same mechanism.

Four-way directional valves are usually considered standard for operation of double-acting cylinders. A 4-way valve has four connections to the circuit — a pressure inlet, an exhaust, and two work ports. They are built in a wide range of sizes and pressure ratings according to the volume of fluid to be handled and to the pressure level required in the system. Many will vary in appearance from the sketches shown here.

Solenoid controlled directional valves respond to an electrical signal for shifting their spool or poppet, to provide a choice of flow paths through the internal passageways to the outlet or work ports. Most directional valves are 4-way, and some can be optionally used as 2-way, 3-way, and even 5-way valves. For a more detailed description, refer to the Womack Industrial Fluid Power textbooks listed inside the rear cover.

Single Solenoid 4-Way Valves. Figure 1-1. On this type, one solenoid is used. The valve spool shifts when the solenoid is energized, and will remain shifted as long as current is maintained on the solenoid. It will return to normal position by spring force when the solenoid is de-energized. The valve has "maintained" electrical action. Circuits designed for its use must maintain current on the solenoid to keep the spool shifted. It is not possible to have a center neutral position.

A. Typical Single Solenoid Air Valve.

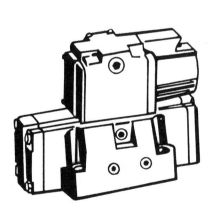

B. Typical Single Solenoid Hydraulic Valve.

C. Single Solenoid Air Valve
Direct-Acting Type

D. Single Solenoid Air Valve
Pilot-Operated Type

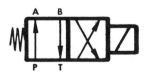

E. Single Solenoid Hydraulic Valve
Direct-Acting Type

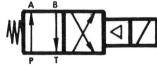

F. Single Solenoid Hydraulic Valve
Pilot-Operated Type

P is the pressure port; T is tank return on hydraulic valves;
E is exhaust on air valves; 1 and 2 are cylinder (work) ports.

FIGURE 1-1. Examples of single solenoid valves.

Action of Single Solenoid Valve. Figure 1-2. The basic action of a single solenoid valve in controlling a standard double-acting cylinder is shown in the two illustrations below. A pushbutton is wired in series with the valve coil to the 115v A-C (or other) power source. During the time the button is not actuated (upper sketch), the valve spool is held in its normal position by an internal spring, and fluid pressure is directed to the rod end of the cylinder, causing it to retract, then to hold against the rear end cap with full pressure. Note: If fluid lines 1 and 2 connecting valve to cylinder were to be reversed, the cylinder would return to fully extended position.

When the button is pressed, Part B of Figure 1-2, the solenoid will shift the valve spool to its opposite side position, and fluid pressure will be directed to the blind end of the cylinder causing its piston rod to extend, eventually holding the piston against the front (or rod end) cap with full pressure. However, if at any point in the piston stroke the button is released, the valve spool will be returned to its normal position and the cylinder will immediately start its retraction stroke even though its forward stroke has not been completed.

Since there can be no neutral position on a single solenoid valve, there is no electrical means by which the piston can be stopped between its extremes of travel.

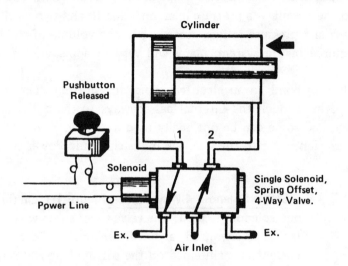

A. Cylinder retracts when normally open electric pushbutton is released.

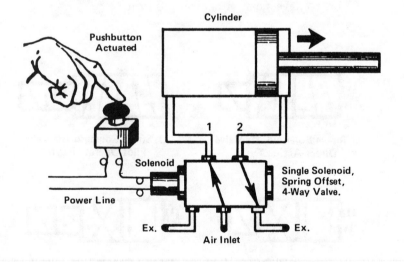

B. Cylinder extends when normally open electric pushbutton is pressed.

FIGURE 1-2. Pushbutton control of an air cylinder with a 4-way single solenoid valve.

Double Solenoid 4-Way Valve. Figure 1-3. A double solenoid valve can be identified by its having two solenoid coils, usually on opposite ends of the valve body. However, a visual inspection may not reveal whether the valve has 2 positions or 3 positions with a center neutral. This can be determined by its model number as listed in the manufacturers catalog, or by a physical inspection, removing an end cap to look for centering springs.

Valves with no centering springs on the main spool are called "2-position, no-spring" models. Those with centering springs are called "3-position, spring centered". However, some large hydraulic valves may use hydraulic pressure instead of springs to center the main spool.

Typical Air Valve

Typical Hydraulic Valve

FIGURE 1-3. EXAMPLES OF DOUBLE SOLENOID 4-WAY VALVES

Two-Position, Direct-Acting Type

Two-Position, Pilot-Operated Type

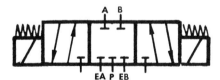

Closed Center, 3-Position, Direct-Acting Type

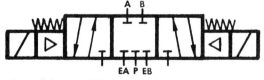

Closed Center, 3-Position, Pilot-Operated Type

Two-Position, Direct-Acting Type

Two-Position, Pilot-Operated Type

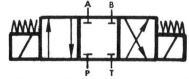

Closed Center, 3-Position, Direct-Acting Type

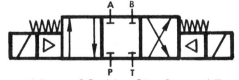

Closed Center, 3-Position, Pilot-Operated Type

FIGURE 1-4. Graphic Symbols for Air Valves

FIG. 1-5. Graphic Symbols for Hydraulic Valves

Action of Double Solenoid Air Valve. Figure 1-6. The illustrations on this page show the action of a 2-position double solenoid valve in operating a standard cylinder, air or oil. A 2-position valve is said to require a "momentary" electrical impulse for its operation. Once the valve spool has been shifted by the solenoid, it will remain in that position, even though the solenoid is de-energized, until the opposite solenoid is energized. Most valves will shift reliably on a signal duration as short as 1/10th second.

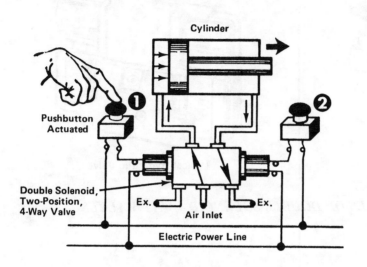

A. Cylinder extends when electric pushbutton on the left is pressed.*

Part A, Figure 1-6. When the left pushbutton, 1, is momentarily pressed, the valve spool is shifted to its opposite position, directing inlet air to the back side of the cylinder piston, causing it to move forward. It will continue to travel until it stalls against the work or against its front end cap, even though the button has been released.

Part B, Figure 1-6. Pressing the pushbutton on the right shifts the valve spool back to its original position which directs air flow into the rod end of the cylinder. The piston retracts until reaching stall against its rear end cap.

Reversal can be made to take place at any point in the piston stroke while the piston is traveling. But since the valve has only two working positions, there is no electrical means by which the piston can be stopped at any intermediate point in its travel.

Design Note: All spool-type 4-way valves should preferably be mounted with spool in a horizontal plane to avoid the possibility of self-shift due to excessive air flow or vibration.

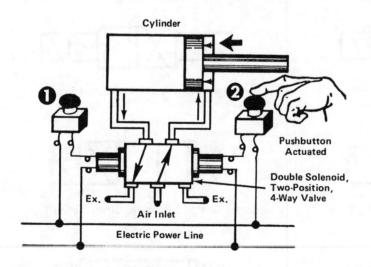

B. Cylinder retracts when electric pushbutton on the right is pressed.*

FIGURE 1-6. Pushbutton control of a cylinder with a 2-position double solenoid valve.

*Some brands of double solenoid valves may have reverse action: energizing left solenoid may cause cylinder to retract.

Action of a 3-Position, Double Solenoid Valve. To understand the action of a 3-position valve in controlling a double-acting hydraulic cylinder, please refer again to Figure 1-6.

Electrical connections are the same whether for a 2-position or a 3-position valve, but the internal action is different on the two types, and the overall electrical control circuit must be designed differently. The 3-position valve has a spring centered neutral position for its spool, and this center spool position is used to stop a hydraulic cylinder at any intermediate position between the two extremes of its piston travel. Because of the centering springs, it is necessary to hold current on one solenoid or the other to keep the spool in one of its side positions to keep the cylinder moving. Therefore, a 3-position valve is said to require a "maintained" electrical signal for its operation; any time both solenoids are de-energized the valve spool will spring to center and stop the cylinder.

Note: Some brands of air or hydraulic solenoid valves will have one coil burn out if both coils are energized at the same time, and if this condition is maintained very long or repeated often. This includes those valves which have the two solenoids yoked to opposite ends of the same spool. When using valves of this kind the electrical circuit should be designed to make it impossible to have current on both solenoids at the same time. An interlocking circuit through the pushbuttons can be used.

Directional Control Valves — 3-Way, Single Solenoid . . .

This type is used principally to control direction on single-acting air cylinders; sometimes, but not often, used to control single-acting hydraulic cylinders on special applications. Also, sometimes used for control of vacuum.

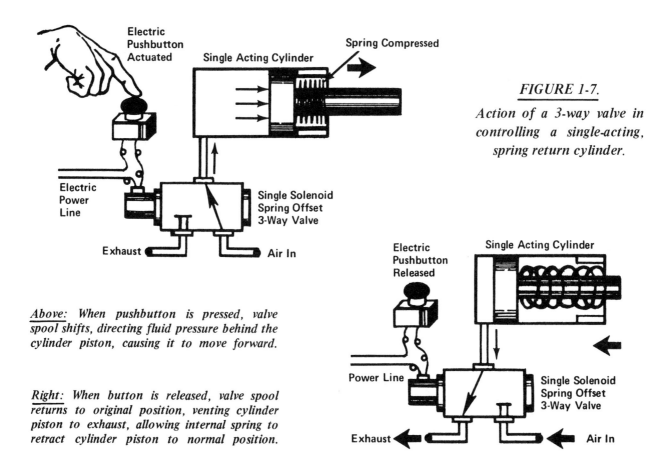

FIGURE 1-7.

Action of a 3-way valve in controlling a single-acting, spring return cylinder.

Above: When pushbutton is pressed, valve spool shifts, directing fluid pressure behind the cylinder piston, causing it to move forward.

Right: When button is released, valve spool returns to original position, venting cylinder piston to exhaust, allowing internal spring to retract cylinder piston to normal position.

12

Spool-type 3-way valves are usually similar in appearance and construction to 4-way valves of the same brand, but may be shorter in length. From most manufacturers they are available only in single solenoid models, with either a N.O. (normally open) or N.C. (normally closed) configuration. A few manufacturers may offer them in 2-position and 3-position double solenoid models. However, most applications for 3-way valves do not require anything more elaborate than single solenoid action.

When 3-way action is needed from a spool valve the most common arrangement is to use a standard 4-way spool valve and install a plug in the cylinder port which is not used. One advantage is that by choosing the correct cylinder port to use, the 4-way valve can be made into either a N.O. or N.C. 3-way valve. However, before plugging any port on a 4-way valve, the valve data sheet or the valve manufacturer should be consulted. Some brands will not stand full pressure on the tank port, or may have packing unseated or leak if certain ports are plugged.

Two-Way Solenoid Valves . . .

Figure 1-8. Two-way solenoid valves are classed as "directional" valves although their action is only to open and close by solenoid motivation. They are used to start and stop the flow of fluids – air, oil, water, etc. Solenoid action permits them to be controlled from a remote location, or allows them to be wired into an automatic cycle with other electrically operated equipment. They can also be used in groups of 2, 3, or 4 to give a greater number of valving functions for controlling a cylinder than are possible with one 3-way or 4-way valve.

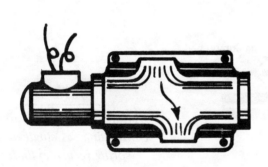

Part A. Spool-Type 2-Way valve.

May be mounted in any position. They can usually be operated with full pressure on either or both ports. Some models may have an external drain port on the end cap to drain spool leakage to tank.

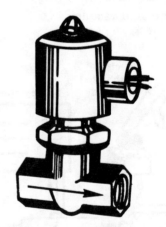

Part B. Poppet-Type 2-Way Valve.

Some models must be mounted vertically as shown. Pressure should be connected only to the inlet port.

FIGURE 1-8. Two-way valves can be constructed with either sliding spool or poppet action.

Poppet action and sliding spool action are two methods of construction most often used for directional control valves. The illustrations above are examples of the general appearance of each type. Poppet construction is more popular for 2-way valves, and two poppets yoked together are used for 3-way action. Since 4 poppets, yoked together, would be required to obtain 4-way action, spool-type construction is more popular for both air and hydraulic 4-way valves.

Part A, Figure 1-8. 2-Way Spool Valves. Most manufacturers offer 2-way valves only with single-solenoid action; double solenoid 2-way valves are very rare.

There is no practical use for a center neutral position on a common shut-off valve; it is either open or closed, or partially closed for metering.

Part B, Figure 1-8. Solenoid 2-Way Poppet Valve. Mounting requirements may vary with brand and nature of the valve. Some solenoid poppet valves are constructed so they can be mounted in any position; others must be mounted vertically, with solenoid up, to function properly or at all. The weight of the poppet is used to close the orifice after the coil is de-energized. If no specific mounting information is available, the best practice is to mount a valve of this type with solenoid up.

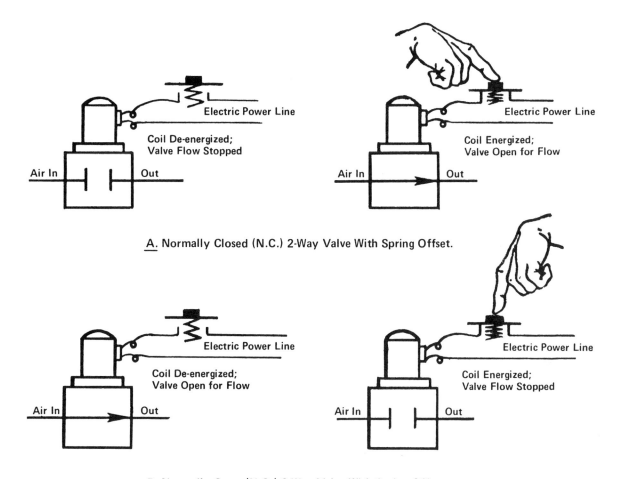

A. Normally Closed (N.C.) 2-Way Valve With Spring Offset.

B. Normally Open (N.O.) 2-Way Valve With Spring Offset.

FIGURE 1-9. Examples of the action of 2-way solenoid valves of the N.O. (normally open) and N.C. (normally closed) types.

Action of 2-Way Solenoid Valves. Figure 1-9. Two-way valves may be either N. C. (normally closed) or N.O. (normally open). This nomenclature refers to the state of its flow passage when its solenoid is de-energized.

Part A of this figure shows that a N.C. valve, when its solenoid is de-energized, has its flow passage blocked. When its solenoid is energized, the flow passage opens, allowing flow entering the inlet to flow through to the outlet. Ports will be marked or the flow direction will be indicated by a flow arrow on the valve body.

Part B of Figure 1-9 shows that a N.O. valve, when de-energized, will pass fluid flow in the direction of its flow arrow, and will close when its solenoid is energized.

Important Note: When selecting a 2-way poppet valve for a given application be sure you understand its flow characteristics. If you must have unrestricted flow in both directions when the valve is open, be sure to choose a suitable brand and model. There are important variations between brands and between different models in the same brand. Some valves will permit reverse flow even when closed to flow in the forward direction (similar to check valve action). Some will not pass flow at all, or with severe restriction, in the reverse direction even when open to flow in the forward direction. Some may have large external connections, but the internal orifice may be much smaller.

Choice of N.O. or N.C. valve action depends on the fluid action desired when the valve is energized. Sometimes, either action could be used if tied in with the proper electrical contacts of a switch or relay, and the choice should be made on the basis of "fail-safe" operation; that is, to put the circuit in a safe state if there should be an electrical failure. On most applications a N.C. model would be preferred because it would close, cutting off the fluid flow if there should be a failure in the control current or if a solenoid coil should burn out. A notable exception is relief valve venting (for pump unloading) by means of a 2-way solenoid valve. In this case a N.O. model would ordinarily be preferred. In case of a control current failure the pump would revert to its unloaded condition.

The best valve type can also be selected on the basis of the length of its ON and OFF periods. Select the type which requires energization over the shorter period of time. See Page 99.

Poppet-Type 3-Way Valves . . .

Figure 1-8. This figure can also be used to illustrate the general appearance of a 3-way poppet valve which has both poppets operated by one solenoid. There will be three main ports, and electrical circuitry will be as described for 3-way spool-type valves. See Figure 1-7. Larger size 3-way valves can have a N.O. and a N.C. poppet each operated by a separate solenoid. On these valves, the solenoids are wired so one solenoid becomes energized during the time the other solenoid is de-energized.

Directional Control Valves — 5-Way . . .

These are sometimes used on compressed air service but seldom on hydraulics. Their appearance is usually identical to that of a 4-way valve of the same brand and size. They have two inlet ports (instead of one), two outlet (cylinder) ports, and one exhaust port (instead of two). Their most common application is to operate a double-acting air cylinder from a different pressure level in each direction. With some brands, a standard 4-way valve can be used for 5-way service by using the original exhaust ports for air inlets and the original inlet port for a common exhaust. Five-way valves are described in more detail in the Womack books "Industrial Fluid Power — Volumes 1 and 2". See book listings inside rear cover.

Orienting Cylinder Direction of Movement With Valve Position . . .

If, after making an installation, the cylinder piston rod moves in the wrong direction in response to a given electrical signal, its motion can be re-oriented in relation to the electrical circuit as follows:

On double solenoid valves interchange fluid connections either at the valve ports or at the cylinder ports, or, interchange wiring between the two solenoid coils.

On single solenoid valves interchange fluid connections either at the valve or at the cylinder ports.

On 3-way valves operating a single acting cylinder, the normal porting of the valve must be changed. If a N.O. type, change to N.C., etc. When using a 4-way valve for 3-way service, this is accomplished by connecting cylinder line to opposite cylinder port on the valve and plugging the original cylinder port.

INPUT SWITCHING DEVICES (SENSORS)

It is beyond the scope of this book to give a complete and comprehensive description of the many switching components which are available for setting up an automatic cycle. Our descriptions are limited to those more commonly used. Appearance of components will vary from the sketches shown here, according to brand and model. Before selecting components, manufacturers catalogs should be studied for electrical specifications, choice of options, and suitability for the application. For example, on a limit switch there may be several dozen options or special features such as choice of enclosure, type or position of actuator, electrical rating, to name a few.

Definition of a Sensor . . .

The term "sensor" as used in this book includes any device which can produce an electrical switching signal in response to some action either in the fluid circuit or in the mechanical structure. Three distinct classes of sensors are commonly used:

(1). Switches of many kinds which deliver a switching signal when actuated by a moving part on a cylinder or a cam mounted on another part of the machine. Various kinds of limit switches fall into this category.

(2). Pressure switches of various kinds deliver a switching signal in response to a rise or fall of pressure in the fluid. Most of them are adjustable, and can be pre-set to trip at a given pressure in the fluid.

(3). Manually operated switches for an operator, such as pushbuttons, jog buttons, toggle switches, rotary and selector switches of many kinds.

Finally, there are numerous devices of a miscellaneous nature which can produce switching signals. These include photoelectric sensors, proximity switches, acoustic or ultrasonic sensors, heat sensors, electric timers, electric counters, etc., some of which are illustrated later in this chapter.

Duty Rating of Switches and Other Sensors . . .

Switches are the components most likely to fail first on an electrically controlled machine. Therefore, it is important to select them wisely according to the duty expected from them. Low priced, miniature, sub-miniature, non-enclosed, or light-duty switches should be used only on applications where operation will be infrequent, where they cannot be invaded by water, oil, heat, or other environmental conditions, or where cost is a more important factor than reliability. Good switches cost more but on most applications will more than pay for themselves with their longer life and greater reliability. If an electrical breakdown would be costly in terms of lost time or production, heavy-duty industrial limit switches should be used. Your electrical distributor can offer sound advice on the quality of switches which should be purchased according to the duty and the life expectancy required.

But even switches of high quality will not give good service unless properly mounted, and actuated with properly designed cams. Some of the main points to be considered are:

(1). Machine cams which actuate limit switches should be designed so they contact the switch roller at the proper angle. For high speed actuation their leading edge should be contoured to give uniform acceleration to the switch arm. Cams which can override the switch arm must be designed so the switch arm cannot snap off unrestricted after passing the trailing edge. Details of proper cam design are covered in Chapter 6.

(2). It almost goes without saying that a switch should be mounted so it will be protected from physical damage if a cylinder should get out of control and override it.

(3). Switches should not be operated beyond the normal recommended travel of the actuator arm. On some switches this could cause internal stress and a shorter switch life.

Standard Limit Switches, Figure 1-10 . . .

Limit switch types are not limited to those shown in Figure 1-10. A complete catalog of electrical switches should be consulted to select the best type for a given application.

Part A, Figure 1-10. The basic snap-action switch is available with many different actuators, and is relatively inexpensive. It is intended for light-duty service in a protected environment. Although the switch contacts are enclosed, they are not sealed against entry of water and oil, and the electrical terminals are exposed. For fluid power the light-duty basic switch is useful on experimental or temporary set-ups but should, if possible, be avoided on industrial and permanent, heavy-duty installations.

A. Basic light-duty switch, non-enclosed, with roller actuator.

C. Light-duty switch in protective housing. Roller actuator illustrated.

D. Heavy-duty industrial type limit switch illustrated with roller arm actuator.

B. Light-duty switch in protective housing. Pin actuator illustrated.

FIGURE 1-10. Examples of limit switches having standard action and with spring returned contacts.

Parts B and C, Figure 1-10. The light-duty basic switch element is supplied with choice of several actuators in water and oil-tight enclosures. The electric terminals as well as the contacts are completely protected. This makes it environmentally suitable for most fluid power installations. The classification of "light-duty" for these switches does not infer they are inferior in quality. They are specifically designed for a good balance between cost and contact service. Their best application is on installations subject to a moderate number of switching cycles, and where an occasional failure and replacement of a switch is not a major problem. Small size is also a factor in their favor.

Part D, Figure 1-10. Heavy-duty industrial limit switches should be used on machines where the utmost in reliability is important; where a switch failure would be costly in terms of lost production. Industrial switches are more expensive. They are larger and may present a mounting problem if space is limited. A designer must weigh advantages against disadvantages in selecting switches most suitable for a particular machine in a particular type of service. Plug-in switches are available. They can be quickly replaced by removing only two screws.

CAUTION! Limit switches should always be mounted in such a way that they cannot be damaged if the actuating cam should accidentally overrun them. This could happen if a solenoid coil should burn out or if control current should fail. Switch mounting brackets should be designed to allow a position adjustment in switch mounting.

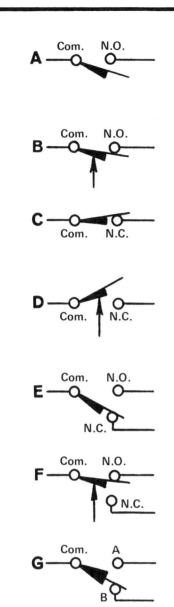

A. SPST (single pole, single throw) N.O. (normally open) set of contacts, shown here in their "normal", unactuated state.

B.* Same contacts as in Part A drawn in their actuated state. The side arrow is a reminder that they are physically held actuated by a cam before the start of a cycle or during a standby period.

C. SPST (single pole, single throw) N.C (normally closed) set of contacts shown here in their normal, unactuated state.

D.* Same contacts as Part C but drawn in their actuated state. The side arow is a reminder that they are being physically held open by a cam before the start of a cycle or during a standby period.

E. SPDT (single pole, double throw) set of contacts. Sometimes called "transfer" contacts. Placement of the solid triangle on the switch arm indicates which is the N.O. and which the N.C. circuit. It also indicates the contacts are in their "normal" state.

F.* Same contacts as Part E but drawn in their actuated state. The side arrow is a reminder that the contacts are being physically held in an actuated (abnormal) state.

G. SPDT contacts on a maintained type (no return spring) switch as in Figure 1-17, Part B. A solid triangle on both sides of the switch arm indicates it must be actuated in both directions. There is no N.O. or N.C. terminal markings because the switch has no "normal" state.

Note: Abbreviations next to contacts, N.O., N.C., and Com., indicate normally open, normally closed, and common respectively.

*Side arrows are not standard JIC markings but are used in this book as aids to quickly identify switches which are held actuated.

FIGURE 1-11. Contact Arrangements for Limit Switch Sensors.

Limit Switch Contacts and Terminology . . .

Figure 1-11. These diagrams show JIC electrical symbols for ladder diagrams. A more complete list of symbols is on Page 245. When correctly drawn, symbols give important information on switch type and action. A clue is the solid triangle drawn on the switch arm. The operating cam works against this triangle to force the switch contacts closed or open. Contacts return to their normal state by spring force when cam force is removed. Switches in Figure 1-11 are drawn in their "normal" (unactuated) state except where a vertical arrow is shown touching the triangle on the switch arm. The arrow indicates the contacts are drawn in their actuated state, being physically held there by the operating cam. See explanation on Part B, Figure 1-11. Abbreviations N.O. (normally open) and N.C. (normally closed),

Double Pole limit switches are not recommended and are not often used, but they are available. This is a switch with two separate sets of contacts, operated by the same arm, for operation of two independent circuits.

Switch contacts having a return spring (and most of them do) are said to be in their "normal" state when not actuated. If a cylinder, for example, should return to home position and "stand" on a limit switch, the switch contacts should be drawn in their actuated state with an arrow holding the switch arm in the actuated position. See Examples B, D, and F on Figure 1-11. On the next cycle, as soon as the cylinder has moved forward a short distance, these contacts will return to their normal, unactuated state. For example, in Part A of Figure 1-11, the contacts have N.O. action and are shown open. But in Part B of the same figure, the contacts are shown closed because they are physically held in this state. They will resume their normal state when the cylinder has moved a short distance.

Limit switches which do not have a return spring stay in the last position to which they were actuated. See Part G of Figure 1-11. The double triangle on the arm shows that the switch must be actuated in both directions by cams. On a ladder diagram they should be shown in the state they will be in at the end of a cycle.

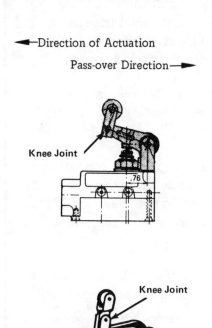

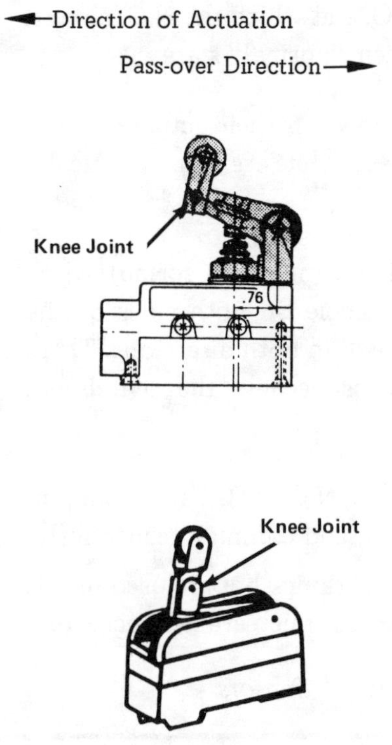

←Direction of Actuation

Pass-over Direction→

Knee Joint

.76

Knee Joint

FIGURE 1-12.

Standard limit switches fitted with 1-way actuator.

Limit Switch With One-Way Roller Actuator . . .

Figure 1-12. Examples of a standard switch fitted with a 1-way roller actuator. The actuator has a "knee joint" which folds out of the way of a machine cam approaching from the left, without actuating the switch contacts. But when a cam approaches from the right, the "knee joint" becomes stiff and the switch contacts are actuated.

This one-way action is useful on switches to be actuated by a passing cam during the stroke of a cylinder. An impulse can be produced which is proportional to the length and speed of the passing cam. The returning cam can pass over the switch without producing a second, and unwanted, switching signal. See more on Page 122.

Switches with "knee action" roller should not be used at cam speeds over 50 feet per minute. See recommendations in Chapter 6 on cam shape and recommended speeds.

Where cam approach speed exceeds 50 feet per minute, other forms of 1-way switch action are available. A standard switch is fitted either with a flattened roller rotationally spring loaded, or with an actuator with built-in ratchet. Either of these switches will actuate the contacts in only one direction of cam approach. Or, a standard switch actuator can be used by attaching a hinged and spring loaded dog to a machine member. In one direction of cam approach the dog lifts out of the way without actuating the switch contacts.

Impulse Limit Switch . . .

Figure 1-14. The 1-way impulse limit switch shown on the next page is a special switch for simplifying certain difficult circuit problems. Where applicable, it can eliminate holding relays and associated wiring. It is subject to certain limitations and can only be used in circuits designed for it.

Switch action is as follows: A switching signal (either make or break, or both), is produced only while the plunger is traveling inward. The signal cuts off and contacts return to their normal state when full plunger travel position is reached. Contacts do not actuate again while the plunger is returning by spring force to its extended position. Usually has one set of SPDT contacts.

Maximum actuation speed, about 50 ft/min. Must be accurately positioned to within 1/32". The traveling mechanism must carry the plunger to full depth to cut off the switching impulse but must not carry it far enough to damage the switch or other mechanism.

Most of these switches have disappeared from the market, but one model may still be available from Microswitch.

Pressure Switches . . .

Figures 1-15 and 1-15A. A pressure switch can be teed into a fluid line carrying air, hydraulic oil, water, or vacuum, etc. Its working element or "movement" responds to a rise or fall of pressure to close or open a set of electrical contacts when a desired level of pressure has been reached.

Pressure switches can be purchased, factory adjusted, to work at a specified pressure. However, most of them are adjustable by the user, at least over a limited range.

The bourdon tube movement of Figure 1-15 is probably the most popular one for mid-range hydraulic pressures, 500 to 3000 PSI. It is a curled tube of steel, closed at one end, into which fluid pressure is introduced. Uncurling of the tube is proportional to pressure. The tube movement is linked to a set of electrical contacts. Bourdon tube movements using a brass or bronze tube are commonly used for compressed air.

The piston movement of Figure 1-15A is used more for higher pressures, above 3000 PSI. It is a simple movement: pressure is introduced to a spring loaded piston. Piston travel is proportional to pressure. The movement is linked to electrical contacts.

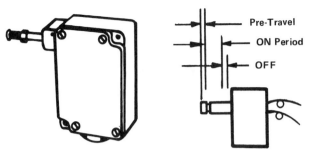

Enclosed Impulse Switch   Action of Impulse Switch

FIGURE 1-14.

Impulse-Type Limit Switch.

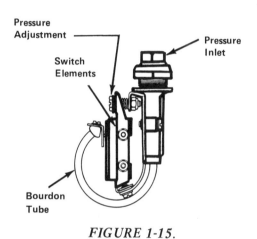

FIGURE 1-15.

Bourdon Tube Pressure Switch.

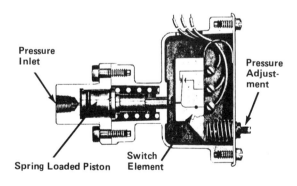

FIGURE 1-15A.

Piston Type Pressure Switch.

For information on selection of pressure switches, refer to Page 253 in the Appendix.

A copper or bronze bellows movement is quite accurate and is widely used for vacuum up to 200 PSI air, oil, or water. A steel bourdon tube movement is used only for oil, and usually in the range of 500 to 3000 PSI. Stainless steel bourdon tubes are preferred for pressures over 3000 PSI and must be used on high pressure gauges for water service. Although bourdon tube gauges are built for hydraulic service up to 10,000 PSI, piston movements are usually preferred for pressures over 3000 PSI and are considered safer than bourdon tubes. See Page 253 for more information.

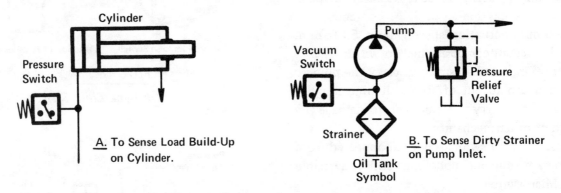

FIGURE 1-16. Examples of pressure switch applications.

Figure 1-16. Pressure switches may be installed in various parts of a fluid system to produce an electrical switching signal in response to the rise or fall of pressure in a fluid line. One of the more useful applications is shown in Part A of Figure 1-16. The pressure switch, of suitable range, is teed into a cylinder line to give a switching signal when load being moved by the cylinder has caused fluid pressure behind the piston to rise to the adjustment set on the pressure switch. The pressure switch signal can be used instead of a limit switch signal to start another action, for example, retraction of the same cylinder or starting another cylinder forward. The secondary action starts when a desired "tonnage" has been produced against the load.

In Part B of Figure 1-16, a vacuum switch is teed into the inlet (suction) side of a hydraulic pump. Its contacts can be connected to an electric warning signal to show when the pump inlet vacuum has risen to a dangerous level, or it can be wired to the system motor starter to shut the system down.

Terminology. Switching contacts in a pressure switch are sometimes called "make-on-rise" or "break-on-rise". These terms describe switch action as fluid pressure increases. Comparing this terminology with that of limit switches, "make-on-rise" is equivalent to N.O. (normally open), and "break-on-rise" is equivalent to N.C. (normally closed).

Toggle-Type Switches . . .

Toggle action, as applied to switches, can be described as an over-center snap action that rapidly snaps a set of contacts open or closed. It is further defined as having no return spring; the contacts must be mechanically actuated in both directions. A toggle switch does not have a "normal" state to which the contacts return by spring force after external actuating force has been removed.

Several terms are used to describe this kind of switch action: "maintained" and "flip-flop" are terms frequently used.

Figure 1-17. Several types of "toggle" or "maintained" action switches are available for electrical control of fluid power. Part A of Figure 1-17 shows a miniature switch designed for finger operation,

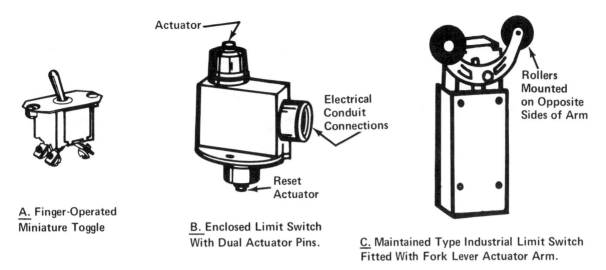

Actuator

Electrical
Conduit
Connections

Rollers
Mounted
on Opposite
Sides of Arm

Reset
Actuator

A. Finger-Operated
Miniature Toggle

B. Enclosed Limit Switch
With Dual Actuator Pins.

C. Maintained Type Industrial Limit Switch
Fitted With Fork Lever Actuator Arm.

FIGURE 1-17. Examples of switches having "maintained" or "toggle-type" action.

usually.to be mounted on a control panel. It can also be mounted on a machine for actuation by a moving cam, subject to certain operating limitations described later, and must be protected against overrun by a cylinder. Although it can be used as a cam-actuated switch, for such applications it should be restricted to light-duty and experimental use because it is not sufficiently rugged to stand up long on normal applications.

True toggle switches, with their over-center action, are necessarily limited to two working positions. Similar switches are available having a center neutral, and these usually have either double toggle action or simply a 3-position detent.

Part B, Figure 1-17. This sketch shows a maintained-type switch mounted in a protective enclosure. Two stems, one on top, the other on the bottom, toggle the contacts from one position to the other. There is no internal return spring. The contacts remain in the last position to which they were toggled until being shifted to the other position by the opposite stem.

Part C, Figure 1-17. This is a heavy-duty industrial limit switch fitted with a "fork lever" actuator arm. The basic switch to which this arm is fitted must have a maintained, or toggle, action with no return spring. There are several variations of this switch. The version often used in fluid power has two rollers, one mounted on either side of the fork lever. Each roller can then be actuated by a different cam on the machine. This variation is known as an "offset" type of fork lever. An alternative lever is available in which both rollers are mounted on the same side of the fork. This variation can be used on applications where both rollers are to be actuated by the same moving cam. See diagrams in Chapter 3.

Foot Operated Switches . . .

Figure 1-18. Part A of this figure shows a light-duty foot switch which can be actuated by an operator's foot, knee, hand, elbow, or arm. It is available with choice of several operating arrangements: (1), foot actuation with spring return, and with either N.O., N.C., or SPDT contacts; (2), with pedal hinged at the center, with centering springs or center detent, and with two separate sets of contacts for toe (forward) or heel (backward) actuation for switching two separate circuits with one pedal; (3), two sets of contacts at different depths of pedal travel; the first pedal movement actuates the first set, then as the pedal is pressed further, the second set is also actuated. Light-duty switches of this general type are usually not sealed; they are primarily for portable use and can be moved by the

<u>A.</u> Light-Duty Foot Switch in Open-Type Housing.   <u>B.</u> Light-Duty Switch Element Enclosed in Watertight Housing.   <u>C.</u> Heavy-Duty Industrial Foot Switch With Toe Guard & Latch.

FIGURE 1-18. *Examples of foot-operated switches.*

operator to the most convenient location for operation. They are connected with rubber covered electrical cable to the main control box.

Part B, Figure 1-18. This sketch illustrates one brand of light-duty switch ememt enclosed in a ruggedly constructed iron housing sealed against entry of dirt, water, and oil. Available with or without a guard to protect against accidental actuation by a falling object. Enclosed switches usually have an electrical connection sealed for permanent installation, but can be adapted for portable use by using a waterproof cable properly sealed at the conduit opening.

Part C, Figure 1-18 illustrates a heavy-duty model foot switch having a rugged frame, usually cast iron, to resist considerable physical abuse. Switching elements have a high amperage rating and are completely sealed against entry of oil, water, and dirt. These switches are available with or without a guard and with or without a latch. On latching models, when the pedal is first depressed, it latches down. A second foot pressure unlocks the latch and allows the pedal to return to its original position.

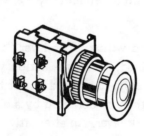  

<u>A.</u> Industrial Pushbutton for Panel Mounting.   <u>B.</u> Momentary Pushbutton in Enclosure.   <u>C.</u> Momentary or Maintained Pushbutton in Enclosure.

FIGURE 1-19. *Examples of electrical pushbuttons.*

Electrical Pushbuttons . . .

Figure 1-19, Part A illustrates an industrial type momentary pushbutton designed for mounting in a control console. A stack-up of two contact blocks, each with two sets of contacts, is shown. This gives a total of four independent sets of contacts, choice of N.O. or N.C. To get SPDT action, one set of N.O. and one set of N.C. contacts can be combined. Any reasonable number of sections can be stacked together, although the required operating force increases with the number of sections stacked.

In fluid power control, except on highly involved circuitry, more than one section is seldom required. Push knobs are available in several colors for easy identification. Some brands can be purchased with lighted buttons. A choice of knobs is also available from small-diameter miniature knobs to large diameter mushroom knobs. A further choice is with key lock to prevent unauthorized tampering.

Part B, Figure 1-19 shows some enclosures for pushbuttons which are not part of the control console, for mounting pushbuttons separately. The buttons shown in Part A can be mounted in enclosures designed for one to four or more buttons.

Part C, Figure 1-19 shows pushbuttons in pairs, available in two types of action: momentary buttons, each one with spring return for functions like "Forward - Reverse". "Up - Down", "Start- Stop", and others. Also pairs of maintained buttons which are mechanically interlocked so that when one button is pressed down it locks down and the opposite button pops up. Electric circuitry can sometimes be simplified by using maintained instead of momentary pushbuttons. However, momentary pushbuttons have this important advantage: control can be exercised from several locations.

Rotary Selector Switches . . .

Figure 1-20. For electrical control consoles this type of rotary switch is normally used. It is available in 2-position and 3-position models and with any reasonable number of contact sets by stacking sections on the basic switch mechanism. The illustration shows a 3-section stack. There is a choice of 2-position with or without spring return, 3-position with spring centering or center detent. Also available with key lock.

If three positions are not sufficient, rotary switches used in the electronic industry may be available with up to 25 or more rotary positions.

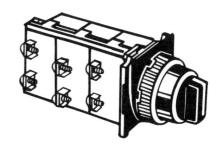

FIGURE 1-20. Industrial rotary switch.

Indicator Lamps . . .

An indicator lamp permanently wired across each solenoid valve coil will provide a troubleshooter with a quick means of pinpointing trouble if there is an electrical breakdown. If mounted on an operator's panel they should be mounted in order of their actuation. Since they are not a functional part of the electrical circuit, their addition is left to the option of the designer.

On spring return and spring centered solenoid valves, the lamps can be wired directly across each solenoid coil. For addition to momentary type 2-position valves, pilot lamps can be operated from contacts on holding relays to indicate the solenoid which was last energized.

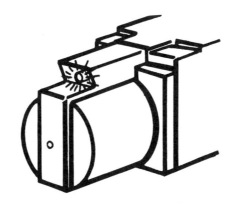

B. Lamp on Solenoid Coil.

A. Panel Mounted Lamp.

FIGURE 1-21. Indicator lamps.

Most hydraulic valve manufacturers can supply solenoid valves with built-in indicator lamps. This adds a little to the valve cost but is quite valuable as a troubleshooting aid to check the electrical circuit.

OTHER ELECTRICAL COMPONENTS

This section illustrates some of the many other electrical switching devices available for control of fluid power. While components of different brands may vary, sometimes widely, in physical appearance from the ones shown, they may still have identical electrical action.

Control Relay . . .

A relay consists of an electromagnet with a moving armature. One or more sets of electrical contacts are actuated by closure of the armature as the relay coil is energized. These contacts are said to be in their "normal" state when the coil is de-energized, and in their actuated state when the coil is energized.

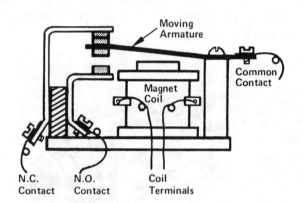

FIGURE 1-22A. Electrical relay shown with coil de-energized.

FIGURE 1-22B. Same relay with coil energized. Contacts have changed position.

Types of Relay Contacts. Industrial relays having heavy-duty contacts are usually available with only two types of contacts: N.O. (normally open) and N.C. (normally closed). Several sets of either type can be mounted on the same structure and operated with a single coil.

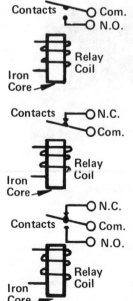

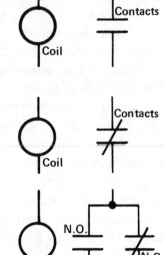

Normally Open (N.O.) Contacts. When the relay coil is energized the contacts close. Picture symbol of relay is shown to the left, standard JIC schematic symbol to the right. The circle is the coil magnet and a set of parallel bars represents a set of N.O. contacts.

Normally Closed (N.C.) Contacts. When the relay coil is energized, the contacts open. Standard JIC symbol for diagrams is shown to the right, with a circle for the coil magnet and a set of parallel bars with a slash representing a set of N.C. contacts.

Transfer Type Contacts. Transfer type contacts have single pole, double throw action. While available on some relays, on an industrial relay they are constructed by combining a N.O. set with a N.C. set of contacts as shown in the diagram to the right.

Relay Applications . . .

A designer should use good judgement in selecting relays for a control circuit, according to the duty expected of them. The sharp impact of the relay armature tends to be destructive, so any relay will have a definite life expectancy. Light-duty relays are low in cost and may be a good choice for experimental circuitry, on machines which are operated occasionally, or where very low currents are to be handled. But on industrial machines operating on a high duty cycle and where long, trouble-free life is demanded, heavy-duty industrial relays should be used. Their first cost is higher but they will be much cheaper in the long run because service problems will be reduced.

Plug-in relays are useful on compact console construction and they are sealed against entry of oil, water, and dirt. They should give good service on low-current applications.

"Contactor" is another name for relay. In common usage a contactor is considered to be primarily a power handling relay for switching high current. A "relay" is considered to be a control device operating at a low current level and used for logic functions.

It almost goes without saying that a designer in ordering relays must specify the number of contact sets and their type, that is, N.O. or N.C. He must specify coil voltage and frequency (Hz) if for A-C service. He must be sure the contact ratings will safely handle the circuit voltage and current.

Figure 1-23. The four application sketches shown here and on the next page show some of the important uses of relays on fluid power machines. Usually at least one, and sometimes many, relays are essential in the logic circuit of most electrically operated machines.

Figure 1-23A. Power Handling. Contactors, with their heavier contacts, are normally used instead of relays for switching high current loads. The contactor coil operates at a relatively low power level and can be controlled with small limit switches and pushbuttons. Assemblies of several sets of contacts can be obtained on each contactor to switch single phase or 3-phase loads at the same or a different voltage than used on the contactor coil.

Examples of contactors on 3-phase loads are magnetic motor starters for electric motors driving air compressors, hydraulic pumps, or hydraulic power units.

Electric immersion heater elements are controlled by thermal switches through contactors. Heaters may be installed under the oil level of hydraulic tanks for overnight protection in cold climates.

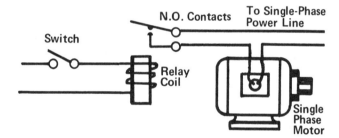

A. Relay Operating a Single-Phase Device.

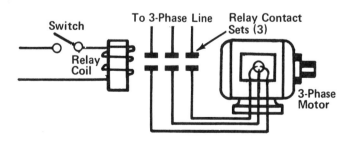

B. Relay Operating a 3-Phase Device.

FIGURE 1-23A.

As power handling devices, relays and contactors can switch high power single-phase or 3-phase loads.

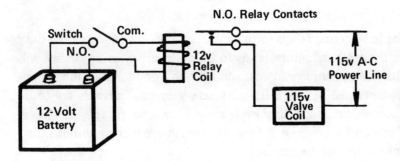

FIGURE 1-23B. A relay or contactor can be used to interface from one type of power to another.

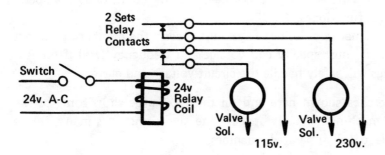

FIGURE 1-23C. Several independent power circuits can be simultaneously switched with relays.

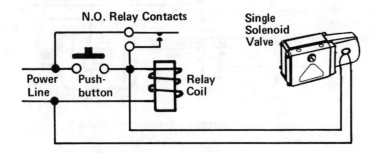

FIGURE 1-23D. Current can be maintained on spring returned or spring centered solenoid valves.

Figure 1-23B. Transition. Relays or contactors can be used as intermediary devices for coupling two circuits which operate at different voltage or frequency level, between D-C and A-C circuits, or between single-phase and 3-phase. They couple the two circuits together; one circuit can cause the other to operate, but the two circuits are kept electrically isolated. In this sense a relay is acting as an "interface" device. An interface device can be defined as a coupling between two dissimilar kinds of circuits.

Figure 1-23C. Isolation. Relays are not only used to isolate a coil circuit from a contact circuit, but may be used to isolate and switch loads of different characteristics. As illustrated here, two loads, one operating at 115 volts, the other at 230 volts are simultaneously switched with one relay. This relay may obtain its coil voltage from either of these two sources or from an entirely different source.

Figure 1-23D. Electrical Lock-In. An important use of a relay in control circuits is to hold current on a fluid power solenoid valve after the valve coil has been energized momentarily from a pushbutton or other source. To release the relay and solenoid valve, the power source to the relay coil must be momentarily interrupted. Details are given in the following description.

Holding Relay Principle . . .

Any relay or contactor becomes a "holding relay" when wired through its own contacts in such a way that the armature will lock closed electrically after its coil has been momentarily energized. The locking or "hold-in" action is obtained by holding current on the coil and not by mechanical latching action as is the case with certain special relays which have a mechanism to lock the armature closed. In that case, the latch can be opened only by energizing a second coil. These are not classed as holding relays but as "latching relays". They serve many useful functions in circuits designed for them.

On electrical ladder diagrams (schematics), holding relays are one form of control relay and are designated as 1-CR, 2-CR, 3-CR, etc. on JIC electrical diagrams. Contacts operated by their coils carry the same designations. This will be illustrated by circuits later in this book.

The lock-in action of a holding relay is one of the most important principles to understand and use when designing control circuits. It is especially useful for controlling spring return and spring centered solenoid valves, both air and hydraulic, from momentary signals derived from pushbuttons. It is widely used in magnetic motor starters of 3 HP and over because it will permit a motor to be tied into microprocessor control and to be started and stopped remotely from one or more locations.

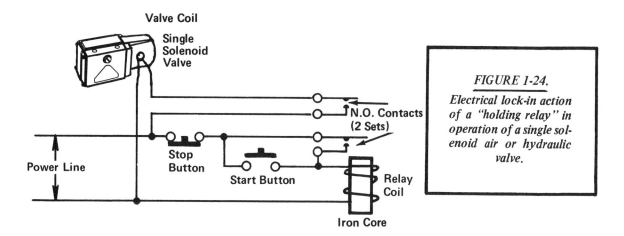

FIGURE 1-24.
Electrical lock-in action of a "holding relay" in operation of a single solenoid air or hydraulic valve.

Figure 1-24. Holding relay action is shown pictorially in this diagram. The same circuit will be shown in standard graphic symbols later.

The purpose of using a control relay as a "holding relay" to control a spring return solenoid valve is so the valve solenoid, after being briefly energized with an impulse from a pushbutton, can be kept energized indefinitely. Circuit action in Figure 1-24 is as follows:

When the "Start" button is momentarily pressed, the relay coil becomes energized and both sets of its contacts close. The lower set has been wired as a holding circuit. They are in parallel with the pushbutton, and when closed they by-pass around the pushbutton to keep the relay coil energized even though the pushbutton has been released. The solenoid valve receives current through the upper set of contacts on the relay, and as long as the relay holds in, the valve coil remains energized.

To release the relay coil (and valve solenoid), the "holding" circuit must be momentarily broken by pressing the "Stop" pushbutton. The relay "drops out" and the valve solenoid becomes de-energized.

Electric Timers . . .

Figure 1-25. May be used in a fluid power control system to delay any action such as start-up of a cylinder, or to establish a "dwell" period at one end of a cylinder travel before it reverses. Many kinds of timers are available, some motor driven, some solid state. Timer delay can range from a fraction of a second to many hours, or even days.

A re-set timer is one which starts timing from zero reference when energized. At the end of the set

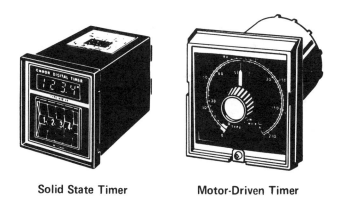

Solid State Timer   Motor-Driven Timer

FIGURE 1-25. Examples of electric timers.

28

time period its contacts transfer to their other state. When the coil is de-energized, the contacts re-set to their original state. On some timers the contacts remain actuated at the end of the time period and they must be re-set to their original state by another electrical signal.

A timer may have any number of contact sets but one set of N.O. and one set of N.C. contacts are all that are usually required.

The time setting adjustment is usually made with a knob in the case of a motor driven timer and with pushbuttons on a solid state timer. Elapsed time as well as the time setting are displayed on the timer face.

Photoelectric Sensors . . .

Figure 1-26. A photoelectric sensor will give a switching signal when a pre-set level of light is received. It is used to detect the presence of moving objects such as the presence or absence of objects on a conveyor belt, a break in a moving roll of material, lack of fluid or incorrect fluid level in a bottle filling operation, detection of objects of a certain color, etc. The switching signal produced by a moving object can be connected into an electric control circuit to stop the operation or to provide a corrective action. The three common arrangements for photoelectric sensing are:

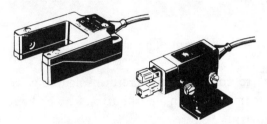  

Grooved Head Type for Mark Sensing and Positioning.

Separate Type for Use With Focusable Light Beam.

Focusable, Self-Contained Type for Reflection Sensing.

FIGURE 1-26. Examples of photoelectric sensors.

(1). Separate Type. A light beam at one location focused on and shining into a photoelectric receiver at another location. An object moving between the light source and the receiver will interrupt the light beam and trip the receiver.

(2). Retroreflective Type. The sensor contains both the light source and the photo receiver. A mirror is placed at another location behind the moving objects. Normally, the light source will be reflected by the mirror back into the sensor. An object moving between the mirror and the sensor will interrupt the light beam and produce a switching signal.

(3). Diffuse Reflection Type. The sensor contains both the light source and the photo pickup. Normally the light beam is shining out into space and is not reflected back. An object moving through the light beam will cause some of the light to be reflected back to the sensor and this will produce a switching signal.

Proximity Sensors . . .

Figure 1-27. A proximity sensor will give a switching signal when objects pass close to it, within its rated sensing distance. There are several ways of producing a switching signal including magnetic fields, accoustical (ultrasonic) reflection, high frequency inductive interference, and high frequency capacitative interference, heat sensing, among others.

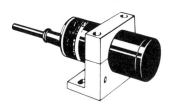

Electrostatic Capacitative Type for Non-Metals.

Heavy Duty, High Frequency Inductive Type.

Miniature, Pass-Through Inductive Type Sensor.

FIGURE 1-27. Examples of proximity sensors.

(1). In the high frequency inductive method, the moving object passes through a high frequency radiation field produced by the sensor, changing the circuit inductance and de-tuning an oscillator. The rise in oscillator current operates a mechanical or solid state relay to produce a switching signal. This method works best with metallic objects.

(2). In the electrostatic capacitive method the objects move through an electrostatic field produced by the sensor. The change in circuit capacitance produces a switching signal. This method is effective for both metallic and non-metallic objects.

Counters . . .

Counters can be used on fluid power applications for counting the number of parts processed, the number of cycles which have been made, etc. Refer to Chapter 7 for additional information.

FIGURE 1-28.

A typical solid state counter.

Figure 1-28. The electromagnetic counters previously used have largely been superceded by solid state counters which can count faster and to higher counts. Electromagnetic counters used pawls, ratchet wheels, pinions, and had a magnetic coil. Counting action was mechanical, and even with high speed models, the maximum reliable speed was limited to less than 20 counts per second. The life expectancy was also limited because of mechanical wear. Solid state counters can count 1000 impulses pre second or more. For extremely high count numbers two or more counters can be pyramided so when the first one reaches its maximum count, the next one is started. They have an almost infinite life because no mechanical parts are involved.

There are several kinds of counters: (1), the pre-set type in which the contacts actuate and deliver a switching signal when the pre-set count has been reached; (2), addition counters which count from zero upward; (3), subtraction counters which count from the pre-set count toward zero; (4), reversible counters which can count either upward or downward; (5), totalizing counters which simply count and show a display but do not have a contact output; (6), readout counters in which the output signal is related to the count value.

Solid state counters have various means of re-setting to starting value: (1), power re-set in which re-set occurs when power is interrupted; (2), external re-set in which an external electrical signal is applied to re-set terminals on the counter; (3), self re-set in which the counter re-sets itself when the desired count has been reached; (4), manual re-set in which a re-set button on the counter can be actuated by an operator.

CHAPTER 2

How to Draw and Read Electrical Diagrams

In this book we are showing a fluid circuit alongside the electrical circuit to control it. Since many of the fluid circuits have been described in detail in the Womack textbooks Volumes 1 or 2 "Industrial Fluid Power", fluid circuit descriptions are brief with most of the description devoted to the electrical circuit. The reader can find complete descriptions of fluid circuits in the textbooks. See inside back cover for textbook listings.

SCHEMATIC DIAGRAMS

Definition of a Schematic Diagram . . .

JIC schematic diagrams are covered in this chapter. Programming diagrams for solid state programmable controllers are covered in Chapter 10.

A schematic diagram shows function only, without regard to size or appearance of components, the placement of parts, or routing of wiring. Its purpose is to show electrical connections which must be completed between components for proper system functioning, and to provide information for analysis, servicing, and for a permanent record of the system. It is the basic and most important of all diagrams.

JIC electrical systems are "hard wired". Components are connected with wires, and often the wires are bundled into "harnesses" and tied together. The more popular electrical symbols used for diagrams are shown in this chapter. A more complete list of symbols is on Page 245 in the Appendix.

Electrical symbols have been standardized by the ASA (American Standards Association). They were selected for ease of drawing, clarity, and to provide a maximum of information consistent with simplicity. Since they do not show details of construction of components, they are timeless and nonproprietary; they are independent of variation in construction, size, and physical shape used by manufacturers now or in the future.

We believe when learning something new it should be learned correctly so it will not have to be "re-learned" later. Standard symbols should be learned and should be used on all diagrams, even practice diagrams. Not only are they standardized in the U.S.A., but are understood in most countries of the world. If you have been making electrical circuits by drawing little pictures of the components, now is the time to break this habit. Your symbols may be clear to you but will not communicate clearly to someone else. Picture diagrams do have a place to show physical details of component mounting and wire routes, but should be used only to supplement a schematic diagram.

Graphic Symbols Most Often Used on Electrical Schematic Diagrams . . .

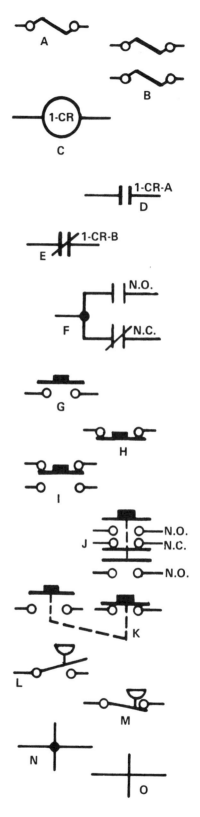

A. Load device. Most often used in fluid power electrical circuits to represent the coil of a single solenoid air or hydraulic valve.

B. Load device with two coils. The two symbols should be placed side by side to represent any double solenoid valve, either 2-position or 3-position type. Each of the coils should be marked with the same designation appearing on the fluid diagram, as Sol. A, Sol. B, etc.

C. Coil or winding, only, of a "control relay". Relay coils are designated as 1-CR, 2-CR, 3-CR, etc. Contacts operated by each coil are shown separately and similarly marked. See next paragraph.

D. Normally open (N.O.) relay contact set. Should carry same designation as coil which operates it. Example: several contact sets on Relay 1-CR should be marked: 1-CR-A, 1-CR-B, 1-CR-C, etc.

E. Normally closed (N.C.) relay contact set, marked as noted above.

F. Transfer set of contacts consisting of one N.O. and one N.C. set. These two sets when combined give SPDT action. See Page 25.

G. Contacts on a momentary type pushbutton, N.O. (normally open), spring return to open position.

H. Contacts on a momentary type pushbutton, N.C. (normally closed), spring return to closed position.

I. Momentary pushbutton contacts. Example shows one set N.O. and one set N.C. contacts operated by the same button. (SPDT).

J. Example of momentary pushbutton with two sets N.O. and one set N.C. contacts operated simultaneously with the same button.

K. Maintained pushbutton set. Always in pairs, mechanically interlocked. When one button is pressed, the other is released.

L. Pressure switch with N.O. (make on rise) contacts.

M. Pressure switch with N.C. (break on rise) contacts.

N. In this book we follow the accepted practice of using a dot to show each electrical junction.

O. Two wires crossing without a dot are not electrically connected.

FIGURE 2-1. Standard ASA graphic symbols for JIC electrical diagrams. See also Page 18 for limit switch symbols and Pages 245 and 246 for additional electrical symbols.

Layout of a Schematic Diagram . . .

Figure 2-2. This diagram which appears on Page 54 is representative of standard practice in drawing a schematic diagram for a JIC hard wired circuit. A vertical ladder format is used, and the diagram is read from left to right and from the top down. Circuits in previous editions of this book were drawn in horizontal ladder form but have been re-drawn to this more standard form. In Chapter 10, electrical diagrams for programmable controllers are also drawn in a vertical ladder format but with slightly different rules. This subject is covered starting on Page 174.

In this diagram, 1-PB and 2-PB are "Start" and "Stop" pushbuttons. Switches 1-LS and 2-LS are limit switches mounted on the machine. A side arrow on 1-LS shows that it is being held in its actuated state before the cycle starts. Sol. A and Sol. B are the two solenoid coils of a double solenoid 4-way valve. Two control relays 1-CR and 2-CR are used and their coils are drawn with circles. Contacts operated by 1-CR are marked 1-CR-A, 1-CR-B, and 1-CR-C, with 1-CR-A being N.C. and the others N.O. One contact operated by Relay 2-CR is marked 2-CR-A.

The object in drawing a ladder diagram is to show how each load device (valve solenoids, etc.) is energized by closure of all switch and relay contacts which precede

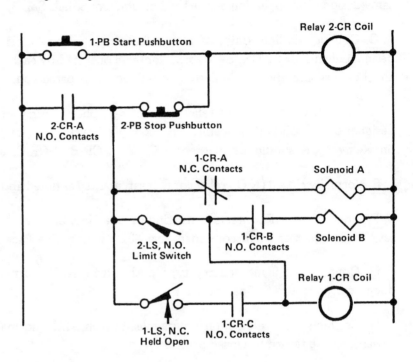

FIGURE 2-2. Example of a ladder-type schematic diagram.

it. These contacts must be drawn either N.O. or N.C. and must be joined either in series or parallel with other contacts on that rung. How they are joined is determined by circuit action.

Relays can be considered as tools for solving circuit problems which cannot be solved with switch contacts alone. Their primary function is to keep a spring centered or spring returned solenoid coil energized for the required length of time even though the switch which energized it has opened. When used this way it is called a "holding relay", and holding relay action is explained on Page 27.

General Rules for Drawing JIC Ladder-Type Schematic Diagrams . . .

(1). The two uprights should be spaced several inches apart on the drawing paper. These are the two power buses. The left upright represents the "hot" or ungrounded side of the power line and will be the black wire in the power cable. All switches must be connected to this bus. The right upright represents the grounded side of the power line and will be the white wire in the power service.

(2). As many rungs as necessary are hung between these uprights, starting with switches connected to the left bus and terminating in a relay or solenoid coil connected to the right bus. Rung construction should start at the top and work down.

(3). Insofar as possible the rungs should be drawn in the approximate order in which the electrical action takes place. This will make it easier for another person to understand the electrical action and may facilitate troubleshooting later.

(4). Relay coils are drawn with a circle and marked 1-CR, 2-CR, 3-CR, etc. Contacts operated by each coil can be located anywhere on the drawing and must be identified with the same symbol as the coil which operates them. Contacts operated by Coil 1-CR are marked 1-CR-A, 1-CR-B, 1-CR-C, etc. Make sure no two relay contacts or coils carry duplicate numbering. Many examples of diagram construction are shown throughout Chapters 3 through 9.

(5). There are many kinds of switches which can be used in electrical circuitry. In addition to those shown on Page 32, other kinds are shown in their proper graphic form on Pages 18, 245, and 246. Switch and relay contacts should be drawn in their "normal" or non-actuated state. An exception is a limit switch mechanically held actuated by a cam standing on it during standby condition or between cycles. Although not standard JIC practice, we use a side arrow to indicate the switch is being held in an actuated state (see Page 18). Limit switches should be identified with symbols 1-LS, 2-LS, 3-LS, etc. Note: LS is an abbreviation for "limit switch". Other kinds of switches should be identified with appropriate symbols such as 1-TR, 2-TR, for timing relays, 1-PS, 2-PS for pressure switches, etc.

(6). Where possible, show the means by which each limit switch is actuated. This can best be shown by drawing them on the fluid diagram in the proper relationship to the cylinder cams which actuate them and at the approximate position in the cylinder stroke. It may be helpful to mark switch terminals such as COM, N.O., and N.C., although if symbols are correctly drawn as shown on Page 18, these markings can be omitted.

(7). All components should be drawn on horizontal lines, although vertical lines can be used for connecting points on different rungs or different legs of the same rung.

(8). Finally, an all-important rule for a circuit designer: All switching of whatever nature, limit switches, pressure switch, relay contacts, timer and counter contacts, pushbuttons, selector switches, etc. must always be done in the "hot" side of the line. All load devices of whatever nature, relay coils, solenoid valve coils, pilot lights, counter and timer coils, warning devices, etc., must always be connected to the "ground" side of the line. Switches must never be connected directly to the ground line, nor load devices to the hot line. Exceptions to this rule, if any, will be rare.

OTHER TYPES OF DIAGRAMS

Picture Diagrams . . .

A picture diagram may be useful for instruction of non-technical people who have no reason to learn the art of reading a ladder schematic. It can be useful for explaining fluid or electrical flow or can be used to identify components for repair or replacement. It is more difficult and time consuming to draw, and is ordinarily not needed by technical people to convey information to other technical people. A student learning electrical control should memorize and use the standard symbols every time he draws a diagram. The symbols are the universal language of communication between technical people all over the western world. They have been chosen because they convey the maximum amount of information consistent with ease and speed of drawing them.

Examples of picture diagrams are shown earlier in this book. See Figure 1-2, Page 9 and Figures 1-6 and 1-7 on Pages 11 and 12. Later, in Chapter 3 these circuits are shown in standard graphic form.

Wiring Diagrams . . .

Figure 2-3. After a schematic has been developed, a wiring diagram can be made to show placement of each component on the chassis or in the control cabinet, and the routing of connecting wires. Components should be drawn in block or picture form with enough detail to be recognizable. Terminal locations and markings should also be shown. Each component should be drawn approximately to relative size and placed in its approximate position relative to other components.

A suggested procedure for working out a wiring diagram from the basic schematic is shown below. Components like relays, terminal blocks, timers, and counters should be mounted in an enclosed metal box for protection against oil and water. Pushbuttons and thermal re-set buttons are sometimes mounted in the same box, sometimes in separate enclosures or in the motor starter box. Limit switches are necessarily mounted where they can be actuated by the machine. Enclosed switches are recommended, wired through conduit to the main enclosure.

Terminal blocks should be provided for the inlet power wiring. Duplicate terminals as shown here are often provided to prevent having too many wires under one screw. Separate terminal blocks should be provided for wiring junctions of the control circuit. Individual terminal blocks should be installed adjacent to each component which has wire leads.

The schematic shown here for illustration is the cylinder reciprocation circuit of Figure 2-2, Page 33. Please refer to that figure for more circuit details.

To construct a wiring diagram, first mark up the schematic with a number assigned to terminal points of all components.

Next, draw connecting wires inside the box, following the desired routing path. Avoid making splices. Each component should be wired so it can be removed without cutting wires or unwrapping a wire bundle.

Wire colors and sizes can be added to a wiring diagram, a feature not usually practical on a schematic.

Terminal block connections can be numbered for clarity.

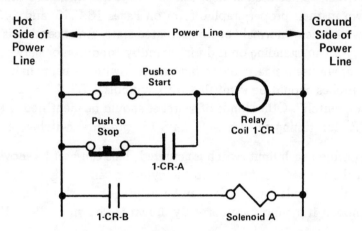

FIGURE 2-3A. Schematic diagram of Figure 2-2, Page 33, marked with reference numbers for development of the wiring diagram below.

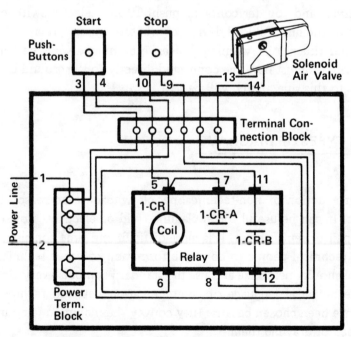

FIGURE 2-3B. This wiring diagram was constructed from the schematic diagram above.

Sequence Diagrams . . .

A sequence diagram is an auxiliary diagram which usually does not add information to that conveyed on the schematic, but it can aid the user in understanding circuit operation and to remember which components are actuated or energized at any given time during the cycle. For this purpose it can be of considerable value to a troubleshooter. It shows graphically, for a period of one complete cycle, the electrical state of each component.

We will not show a sequence diagram for every circuit in this book. However, we recommend that the student construct such a diagram for any circuit he finds difficult to visualize.

There are no official standards for drawing a sequence diagram. The sample diagram shown below and those shown in Chapter 4 illustrate the way we prefer to draw such a diagram, with a time base for one complete cycle, drawn on the horizontal axis. One horizontal line is added for every time there is an electrical action such as a switch being actuated, a relay closure, etc.

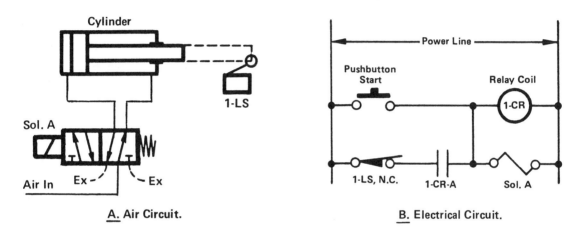

FIGURE 2-4. Reciprocation circuit, air and electrical, of Figure 3-3, Page 41 is used here to illustrate construction of a sequence diagram.

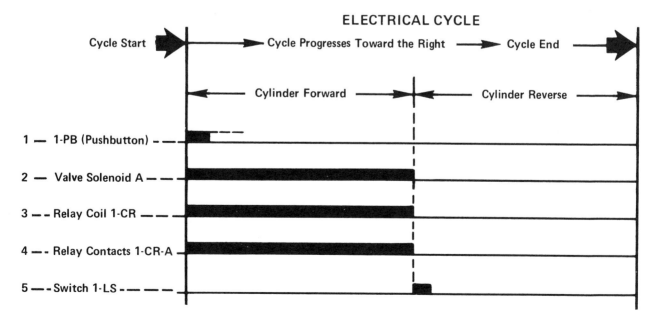

FIGURE 2-5. Sequence diagram constructed from schematic diagram above. See description next page.

Constructing a Sequence Diagram, Figures 2-4 and 2-5. The circuit chosen to illustrate construction of a sequence diagram is the one-cycle reciprocation circuit described in detail in the box on Page 41. The student can refer to that description while studying construction of the sequence diagram on the preceding page. Another example of sequence diagramming is on Page 73.

Each major electrical component is assigned a horizontal line. On this particular application these components consist of a pushbutton, a limit switch, a relay coil and its contacts, and a solenoid valve coil. The wide portion of each line shows the time period(s) during the cycle that each component is actuated or energized.

The start of a typical cycle is at the vertical line marked "Cycle Start". This is "time zero", and the action progresses toward the right until the end of a cycle at the vertical line marked "Cycle End". The time duration of one cycle (in seconds) depends on the speed of the cylinder.

Analysis of Sequence Diagram, Figure 2-5. To start a cycle the operator momentarily presses the pushbutton. The length of time the button is held down is unimportant except that it must be released sometime during the forward stroke of the cylinder, or, the cylinder will stop and hold at its forward stroke limit, being unable to start retraction until the button is released. Line 1 on the diagram shows that the button may be held down for a variable length of time. The schematic diagram could be amplified with components to disconnect the pushbutton immediately after the cylinder leaves home position, and to keep it de-activated when the cylinder returns to home position unless the pushbutton has been released in the meantime.

When the pushbutton is pressed, the relay coil and the valve solenoid immediately become energized as shown on Lines 2 and 3 on the diagram. Relay Contacts 1-CR-A close when the relay coil becomes energized (Line 4). This sets up a holding circuit through Switch 1-LS and Contacts 1-CR-A which keeps current on the relay coil and the valve solenoid even though the pushbutton has been released.

The cylinder travels forward, and at the end of its stroke actuates limit Switch 1-LS, shown on Line 5. When these switch contacts open, current is removed from the relay coil (provided the operator is not still holding the pushbutton down). Relay Contacts 1-CR-A open, removing current from the solenoid valve. Internal springs shift the solenoid valve spool to the cylinder retract position and the cylinder starts its return stroke. Switch 1-LS contacts close again as the cylinder backs off the switch, but the relay coil and valve solenoid do not become energized again because Contacts 1-CR-A are open at this time.

CHAPTER 3

Directional Control: Reciprocation of Cylinders

The direction in which a cylinder piston will move or in which a fluid motor will rotate can be controlled by the direction of flow to the device. Reversing the direction of flow will cause the device to reverse direction. There are several methods of reversing the flow but the one more common, and the one considered in this book is with the use of 4-way valves. Specifically, our study will be limited to control by solenoid 4-way valves.

The primary objective of electrical circuits in this and the following chapter is directional control. In this chapter, methods of reciprocating an air or hydraulic cylinder are covered. The circuits in the following chapter deal with methods of operating several cylinders in a programmed sequence. Some circuits in later chapters also deal with directional control, although their main objective may be a special function such as safety, interlock, dwell, etc.

RECIPROCATION OF CYLINDERS

A cylinder is said to "reciprocate" if its piston travels back and forth, being reversed automatically at each end of its stroke without operator attention. Automatic reversal can be achieved with solenoid controlled valves actuated in one of three ways: (1), with some type of limit switch placed at the desired point of reversal; (2), with a pressure switch; or (3), with an electric timer.

For circuit consideration we have classified reciprocating action into "1-cycle" and "continuous". These classifications may be defined as follows:

One-Cycle Reciprocation. When started by an operator, a cylinder makes a forward stroke, automatically reverses, travels to home position and stops; it makes one complete cycle. The cycle can be initiated by an operator pressing a momentary pushbutton, stepping on a foot switch, throwing a toggle-type switch, or by any other switching action. One-cycle reciprocation is used on machines where an operator sets the "work pace". The machine stops after one cycle, then waits for the operator to re-load and start another cycle.

Continuous Reciprocation. This kind of reciprocation can be used where the machine sets the "work pace". Loading and unloading, if required, can be done either by an operator at some point in the cycle without interrupting the cycle or stopping the machine, or can be done with automatic loading circuits built into the machine and programmed into its cycle, feeding from a bin, hopper, weighing scale, roll of material, a tank, or a vibratory feeder. The machine, when initially started by an operator, runs continuously and repetitively for an indefinite time until stopped by an operator, a counter, or by a safety device signalling a malfunction.

ONE-CYCLE RECIPROCATION OF AIR CYLINDERS

In our experience we have noticed that nearly every electrical circuit for controlling reciprocating cylinders can better use a momentary electrical signal for starting the cycle. A momentary pushbutton provides such a signal and is shown as the starting device in most of the circuits in this section.

Sometimes, however, if the starting signal comes from another machine, from a tape or card reader, or from a toggle-type switch, it will be a maintained rather than a momentary signal. In this case the electrical circuit must be designed to break the starting signal at some place in the cycle. Before another cycle can be started, the maintained starting signal must be momentarily interrupted. Or, the maintained starting signal can be converted to a short duration impulse with a relay or timer. Several means are covered in Chapter 6 for converting a continuous signal into an impulse.

If indeed the starting signal is momentary, we have found that the simplest electrical circuit can usually be worked out by using solenoid valves of the double solenoid, 2-position type. These will respond to momentary signals and the spool will remain in shifted position after the signal has been removed. Single solenoid valves can be used with equal effectiveness but a holding relay may be necessary to keep the valve spool shifted after the starting signal has been removed. We have shown several circuits using both types of valves.

Graphic Symbols for 4-Way Solenoid Air Valves on Schematic Diagrams

(See Pages 8 and 10 for additional information on air valve symbols)

Two-Position, Double Solenoid,
Dual Exhaust Valve.

Two-Position, Double Solenoid,
Single Exhaust Valve.

Two-Position, Single Solenoid,
Dual Exhaust Valve.

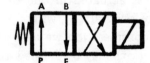

Two-Position, Single Solenoid,
Single Exhaust Valve.

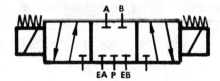

Three-Position, Double Solenoid,
Closed Center, Dual Exhaust Valve.

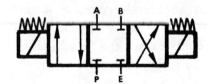

Three-Position, Double Solenoid,
Closed Center, Single Exhaust Valve.

Most solenoid air valves are constructed with dual exhaust ports, and are shown this way on diagrams in this book. Some valves intended for subplate mounting may have one exhaust port serving both cylinder ports.

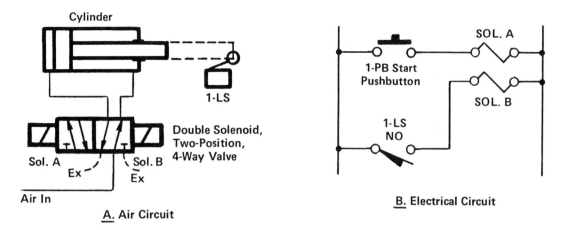

A. Air Circuit

B. Electrical Circuit

FIGURE 3-1. A pushbutton starts the cylinder forward; retraction is automatic when the cylinder actuates a limit switch.

Pushbutton Start, Limit Switch Return. Figure 3-1. Momentarily pressing the pushbutton energizes valve Solenoid A, starting the cylinder forward. When 1-LS is actuated, valve Solenoid B becomes energized, causing the cylinder to return to home position. The pushbutton, if not released before Switch 1-LS is actuated, will cause both solenoids to be energized at the same time. On some valves this could cause one of them to burn out. See Page 149 for pushbutton interlocking circuits.

If either solenoid of the double solenoid air valve is energized momentarily, the valve spool shifts and stays in that position until the opposite solenoid is energized. Mount the limit switch so it cannot be damaged if the cylinder should accidentally over-travel. Wiring to 1-LS is to COM and N.O. terminals.

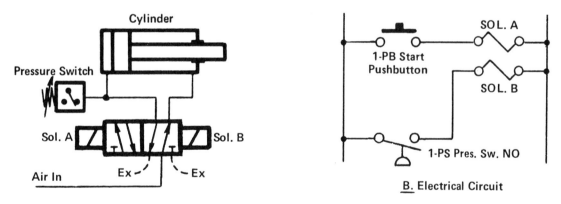

B. Electrical Circuit

FIGURE 3-2. A pushbutton starts the cylinder forward; retraction is automatic when load resistance builds up to the adjusted trip setting of the pressure switch.

Figure 3-2. Pushbutton Start, Pressure Switch Return. Retraction is automatic, even before reaching the end of the stroke if pressure behind the piston rises high enough to trip the pressure switch. This circuit is said to be "load sensitive". If air pressure does not build up to the pressure switch setting during the stroke, reversal takes place when the piston stalls against the cylinder forward end cap. Pressure switch reversal is used if work pieces vary in thickness and each one requires full force.

The pressure switch contacts must be N.O. or "make-on-rise". They must close when pressure in the cylinder has reached a pre-set maximum as determined by load requirements. They must be adjustable and set for no higher than 90% of the minimum available line pressure. A speed control for forward cylinder movement must be installed as described on Page 64.

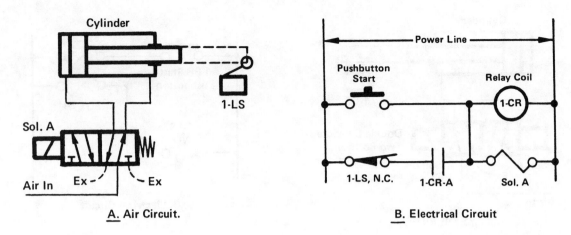

A. Air Circuit.   B. Electrical Circuit

FIGURE 3-3. Single solenoid valve kept energized with a holding relay.

Figure 3-3. A single solenoid air valve can be used in place of a more expensive double solenoid valve, but a holding relay, 1-CR, must be added to the electrical circuit.

Although the electrical circuit is more complicated than the simple electrical circuit of Figure 3-2, this arrangement has a very real advantage in being more reliable against accidental self-shift of the valve spool under conditions of high vibration, unfavorable mounting position, or excessive air flow.

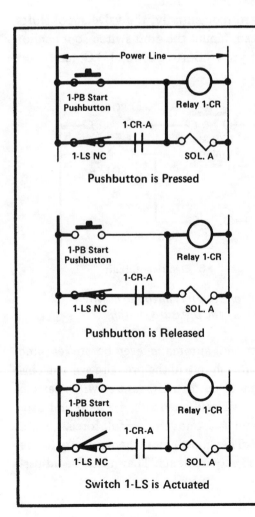

ANALYSIS OF ELECTRICAL CIRCUIT, FIGURE 3-3.

These three diagrams are reproductions of the electrical circuit Part B, Figure 3-3 above, showing current flow at the three significant points in the cycle. See further explanation on opposite page.

The first diagram shows current flow when the pushbutton is pressed. Current flows from the "Hot" side of the power line, through the pushbutton, to energize relay Coil 1-CR and valve Solenoid A. Relay Contacts 1-CR-A close when the relay coil is energized. This sets up a "holding" circuit, starting from the "Hot" line, through normally closed contacts of limit Switch 1-LS, through 1-CR-A, to the relay coil and valve solenoid. The solenoid valve shifts, starting the cylinder in forward motion.

The second diagram shows current flow after the operator has released the pushbutton. The relay coil and valve solenoid continue to be energized through the holding circuit, and the cylinder continues to travel forward.

The third diagram shows current flow when the cylinder has reached and actuated limit Switch 1-LS, causing the contacts on this switch to open. The holding circuit set up in the first diagram is broken, and current is removed from the relay coil and valve solenoid provided the operator is not still holding the pushbutton closed. The valve spool returns by spring action to its original state, causing the cylinder to start retracting. It travels to a stall at home position and the cycle is ended.

41

The valve spool is always held firmly in position against spool drift: by the solenoid in one direction and by the return spring in the other direction. Initial cost of the components is about the same as for Figure 3-2, but wiring cost may be higher and the circuit more difficult to troubleshoot.

The method of circuit analysis shown in the box for Figure 3-3 is recommended to the student for applying to all circuits in this book as a means of clearly understanding them, and to all circuit designers as a means of verifying new schematics drawn for any application. Errors or fallacies in a schematic are readily discovered by going through this kind of analysis step by step.

Several copies of the schematic can be made on an office copy machine. Then, one copy should be marked with a colored pencil (heavy black lines are used in these diagrams) to show current flow at each significant point of change in the cycle, such as a pushbutton being pressed, a limit switch actuated, a relay or valve solenoid becoming energized or de-energized. Three diagrams are sufficient for the simple circuit of Figure 3-3, but more may be required on more complicated schematics.

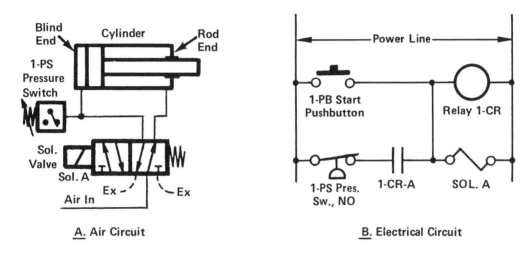

FIGURE 3-4. Single solenoid valve and holding relay; automatic retraction when pressure behind cylinder piston rises to a pre-set level.

Figure 3-4. This "load sensitive" circuit has a similar action to Figure 3-2, but uses a single solenoid valve with a holding relay to replace the double solenoid valve of the other circuit.

When load resistance causes air pressure behind the cylinder piston to trip the pressure switch, the N.C. contacts on this switch release the holding relay and solenoid valve, causing the cylinder to retract. Holding relay action is the same as described for the previous circuit, Figure 3-3. The pressure switch may be teed anywhere in the line connecting the blind end of the cylinder to the valve.

CONTINUOUS RECIPROCATION OF AIR CYLINDERS

A cylinder when once started into continuous reciprocation will continue to travel back and forth indefinitely until stopped by operator action, by a safety device, or by a counter.

The cylinder can be started and stopped, (1), by electrical action; or (2), by shut-off valving in the air line. If stopped by electrical action it will continue to travel until it reaches one end or the other of its stroke. If stopped by shutting off the air, it can be made to stop anywhere in its stroke by careful manipulation of the shut-off valve.

Refinements can be added for special control purposes. Some are illustrated in these circuits. They may include 1-cycle action or jog for use during set-up, panic controls for emergency stopping, and stopping at a pre-determined position. Safety circuits are covered in Chapter 8.

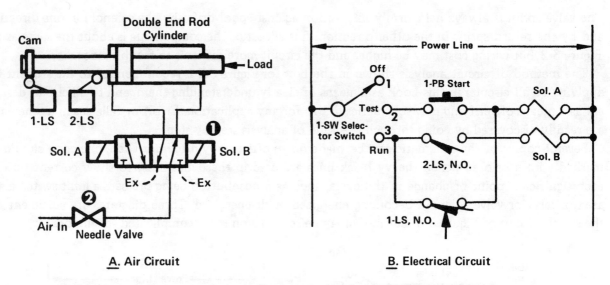

A. Air Circuit **B. Electrical Circuit**

FIGURE 3-5. Continuous reciprocation of air cylinder between two limit switches. Selector switch permits 1-cycle operation for set-up.

Figure 3-5. Several optional features are illustrated in this figure. A 3-position rotary selector switch, 1-SW exercises the main control. The pushbutton is an auxiliary control, used only during set-up to get 1-cycle action from the cylinder. The cylinder, when once started, reciprocates between limits established by locations of 1-LS and 2-LS which may or may not be at extreme ends of the cylinder stroke. Wiring to both these switches is to their COM and N.O. terminals.

Rotary Selector Switch 1-SW. Position 1 is OFF. If rotated to this position while the cylinder is in motion, the cylinder will continue to travel to the end of its stroke in the same direction before stopping. Position 2 of 1-SW is for set-up and testing. It gives 1-cycle reciprocation when the pushbutton is momentarily pressed. Position 3 is running position for continuous reciprocation.

Inching Control, Valve 2. By careful manipulation of needle Valve 2 installed in the incoming air line, the cylinder can be stopped at any position, or its speed can be reduced for set-up operations. This is not a desirable method of speed control during normal running because loads in forward and in reverse may be quite different. Flow control valves installed at the cylinder ports are better for this purpose.

Double-End-Rod Cylinder. The extra rod shown on the left end of this cylinder is optional. In this case it is used to carry a cam for operation of the two limit switches, and the rod on the right end is connected to the load. This feature adds extra expense and is desirable only on machines where there is no access to the front rod nor to any moving part of the machine for mounting limit switch cams, or where it is necessary to rigidly support the piston rod against side thrust from the load.

Figure 3-6. Pushbutton Control. See next page. Momentarily pressing the Start pushbutton will start the cylinder into reciprocation. It will continue to reciprocate until the Stop pushbutton is momentarily pressed. These buttons can be marked "Start" and "Stop".

The advantage of pushbutton control is that the cylinder can be started and stopped from any one of several remote locations by installing Start and Stop pushbuttons at all locations. The Start buttons should be wired in parallel and the Stop buttons wired in series. "Start" buttons have one set of N.O. contacts and Stop buttons have one set of N.C. contacts. A similar multiple control is shown for motor starters on Page 158.

A holding relay is a necessary part of this circuit. Its coil is shown as a circle marked 1-CR. One set of N.O. contacts is operated by the relay coil and is marked 1-CR-A.

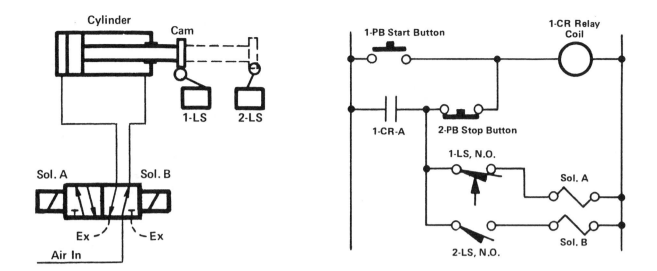

FIGURE 3-6. Continuous reciprocation of air cylinder between limit switches. Circuit features start/stop control with momentary pushbuttons, using 2-position, double solenoid, 4-way valve.

Limit switches 1-LS and 2-LS should be mounted at desired points of reversal, and these points may or may not be at the ends of the cylinder stroke. If they are not, and since the 4-way valve does not have a stop position, the cylinder cannot be stopped by a limit switch if control current is lost. If the switch is not positioned at the end of the cylinder stroke, the cylinder will override it and stall against its end cap. Therefore, if either switch is not at cylinder stall location, it must be protected to prevent the moving cam from getting behind it and damaging it when the next stroke is started. The cam length should be made long to prevent the switch actuating arm from dropping behind it.

Circuit Operation: When the "Start" button is momentarily pressed, relay Coil 1-CR becomes energized. The relay pulls in and locks in electrically by a holding circuit through the "Stop" button and Contacts 1-CR-A, and it will remain locked in even though the "Start" button is released. Electrical power to the rest of the circuit also comes through relay Contacts 1-CR-A, so when these contacts close, Solenoid A becomes energized and starts the cylinder forward. It continues to reciprocate between the limit switch positions in the manner described for Figure 3-5. When the "Stop" button is pressed, the relay coil becomes de-energized and relay Contacts 1-CR-A open. This removes current from the entire circuit. However, the cylinder will continue to travel to stall in the direction it was traveling, and in so doing will override a limit switch which has not been located at the cylinder stall position. If the cylinder stops in an extended position, it will start retraction next time the "Start" button is pressed.

Override and Panic Controls. Several refinements can be added to the basic electrical circuit shown above. These include additional pushbuttons to enable the operator to start the reciprocation in a desired direction, to reverse cylinder direction in the middle of a stroke, or a panic button to instantly reverse the cylinder while killing the electrical circuit against further reciprocation. Details of these refinements are included in later chapters. See Pages 146 and 147.

Flow control valves can be added to each cylinder port to limit cylinder speed. Throttle valving can be added in the air inlet for stopping the cylinder in mid-stroke or to reduce speed during initial set-up and testing of the machine.

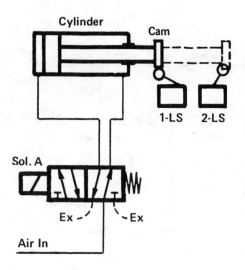

A. Air Circuit.

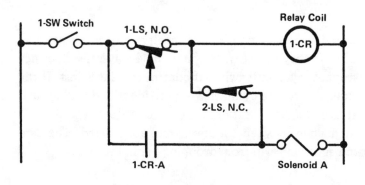

B. Electrical Circuit.

FIGURE 3-7. An air cylinder will reciprocate between two limit switches, and returns to a desired starting position when control current is switched off.

Figure 3-7. Reciprocation is started and stopped with a toggle-type or rotary-type selector switch, 1-SW. When this switch is opened, the cylinder cannot stop immediately; it will continue to travel until it reaches its fully retracted position, no matter in which direction it may have been traveling. This action may be desirable in some machines, to be able to start always from a known position and in a predetermined direction. To obtain the action described, a single solenoid 4-way valve is used, controlled with a holding relay.

Limit Switches 1-LS and 2-LS are positioned to limit cylinder travel during reciprocation, and to reverse it when these limits have been reached. Wiring to 1-LS is to its COM and N.O. terminals, but this switch has been drawn in a closed position because, while the cylinder is in home position, the switch contacts are physically held closed by a cam on the cylinder. After the first small forward movement of the cylinder, 1-LS returns to its N.O. state. Wiring to 2-LS is to its COM and N.C. terminals.

Circuit Operation. When Switch 1-LS is closed, Relay 1-CR and valve Solenoid A become energized and the cylinder starts forward. As the cylinder starts to move, Switch 1-LS opens but the relay coil and valve solenoid remain energized through 1-CR-A contacts and 2-LS limit switch. When Switch 2-LS is actuated, current is removed from the relay coil, and when its contacts open, current is also removed from the valve solenoid. The cylinder retracts and actuates Switch 1-LS. This energizes the relay coil and valve solenoid to start another cycle. When Switch 1-SW is opened, all current is removed from the circuit. The cylinder immediately starts to retract and eventually stalls at home position.

Figure 3-8. This circuit, like the preceding one at the top of this page, features immediate cylinder return to a reference or home position when current is switched off of its control circuit. The electrical circuit has been modified to use momentary pushbutton start/stop control rather than a toggle switch. This permits control from more than one remote location. Toggle Switch 1-SW of Figure 3-7 has been replaced with a pair of momentary start/stop pushbuttons and a holding relay, 2-CR.

Circuit Operation. When the "Start" button is momentarily pressed, Relay 2-CR coil is energized and locks closed electrically through the "Stop" button and 2-CR-A contacts. The other relay, 1-CR,

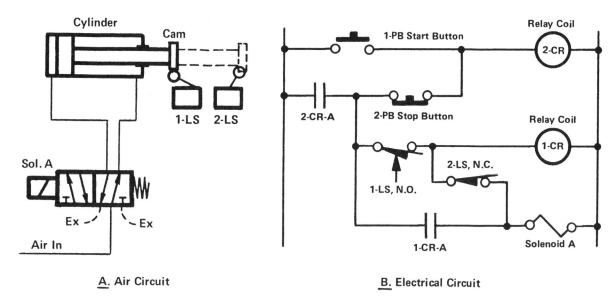

A. Air Circuit   B. Electrical Circuit

FIGURE 3-8. Air cylinder immediately returns to a reference position when control current is switched off. The preceding circuit was adapted here for pushbutton control.

now becomes energized through 1-LS switch and 2-CR-A relay contacts. This relay also locks in electrically through 2-LS and 1-CR-A contacts. Valve Solenoid A, now being in an energized condition, causes the cylinder to advance. When Switch 2-LS is actuated, 1-CR relay drops out. Its contacts, 1-CR-A, open and remove current from valve Solenoid A. The cylinder retracts and actuates Switch 1-LS at home position which starts another cycle. When the "Stop" button is pressed momentarily, Relay 2-CR drops out, removing all current from the circuit. The cylinder immediately starts to retract (if it happens to be extended at the time), and eventually stalls at home position.

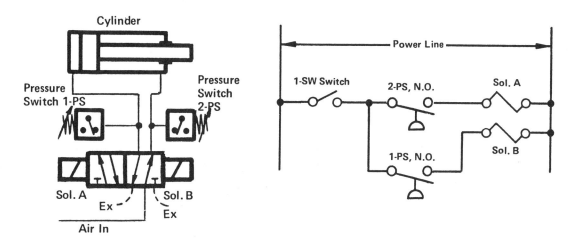

FIGURE 3-9. A pressure switch can be substituted for a standard limit switch in any circuit shown. Start/stop control in this circuit is by toggle Switch 1-SW.

Figure 3-9. Pressure Switch Reciprocation. The action of a pressure switch is identical to that of a standard limit switch as far as the electrical circuit is concerned, and a pressure switch can be substituted for a standard limit in any circuit in this section. One example is shown here. It is the pressure switch counterpart of the limit switch circuit of Figure 3-5.

Flow control valves are used in most air circuits, although not shown here. To prevent premature tripping of the pressure switch they must be installed as described on Page 64.

A limit switch is preferred for most applications because a pressure switch can use only about 90% of the available air pressure before retracting the cylinder. But a pressure switch must be used if retraction must take place, not at a certain stroke position, but when a desired force has been reached.

Electrical Circuit Action. Pressure switches are usually adjustable over a certain range. Each switch in this circuit has one set of N.O. or "make-on-rise" contacts. When action is started by closing 1-SW, reciprocation will continue indefinitely until 1-SW is opened. The cylinder continues to travel in the same direction until it stalls against its end cap or the load.

A variation of circuitry is to use a pressure switch at one end of the stroke and a limit switch at the other end. Be sure to set the pressure switch no higher than 90% of the minimum available line pressure.

Fork Lever Limit Switches. Figure 3-10. Refer to Page 22 for description of this switch. Action is like that of a toggle switch; a pair of cams on the moving mechanism mechanically actuate the contacts in both directions, and they remain in the state to which they were last actuated.

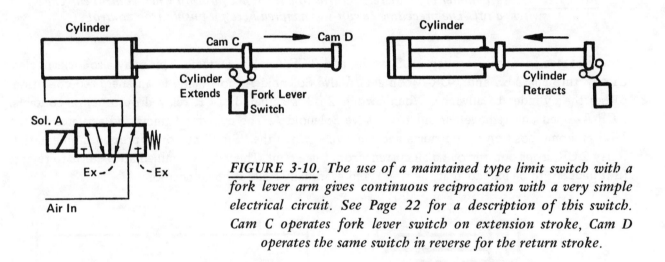

FIGURE 3-10. The use of a maintained type limit switch with a fork lever arm gives continuous reciprocation with a very simple electrical circuit. See Page 22 for a description of this switch. Cam C operates fork lever switch on extension stroke, Cam D operates the same switch in reverse for the return stroke.

Note that for applications described here, the fork lever should have offset rollers; each cam on the cylinder works against only one roller. To simplify these illustrations, the actuating cams are shown on the cylinder piston rod, but in practice they must be mounted to a moving part of the machine which cannot rotate, and each cam must be accurately aligned with the roller it actuates. The use of this type switch gives reliable operation with simple electric wiring, with the least number of components, and permits the use of the least expensive 4-way solenoid valve type — the single solenoid valve. However, fork lever switches have some circuit disadvantages, as pointed out on Page 59.

Control Circuits Using Fork Lever Limit Switches. Figure 3-11. Part A of this figure shows that circuitry can be extremely simple. Reciprocating action can be started and stopped with operator's Switch 1-SW, and this can be a rotary selector or toggle switch.

If the fork lever limit switch is wired to de-energize valve Solenoid A as the cylinder reaches maximum extension, the cylinder will always return to fully retracted position when 1-SW is switched off. If wired the other way, the cylinder will always move to its fully extended position when 1-SW is switched off. Returning to a predetermined reference position for starting the next cycle is an impor-

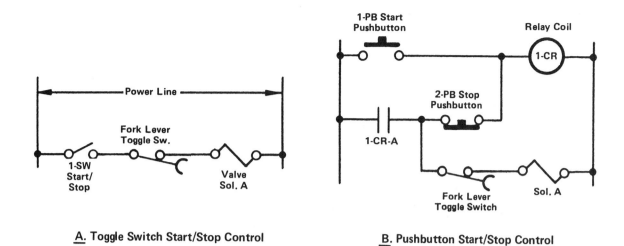

A. Toggle Switch Start/Stop Control

B. Pushbutton Start/Stop Control

FIGURE 3-11. Choice of two electrical control arrangements for operation of fork lever limit switch air circuit of Figure 3-10.

tant requirement in some reciprocation applications.

An alternate circuit is shown in Part B, with a pair of momentary pushbuttons and a holding relay to replace finger-operated switch, 1-SW. The action of this holding relay circuit has already been explained. It permits start/stop control from two or more remote locations.

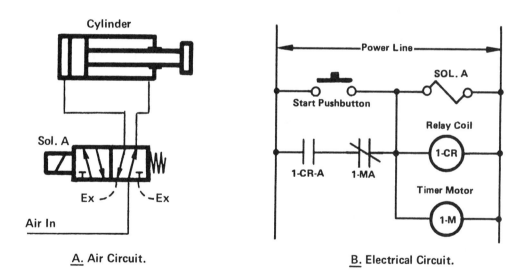

A. Air Circuit.

B. Electrical Circuit.

FIGURE 3-12. Cylinder reciprocation with electric timer. Useful also as a dwell circuit.

Reciprocation With Electric Timer. Figure 3-12. A re-set electric timer is used with time delay set for slightly longer than the time for the cylinder to make its forward stroke. When the pushbutton is momentarily pressed, holding Relay 1-CR becomes energized and locks in through 1-M-A and 1-CR-A contacts. The relay maintains current on valve Solenoid A and timer Motor 1-M during the forward stroke of the cylinder. When the cylinder reaches full forward position it stalls and remains stalled until timing is completed. When timer Contacts 1-M-A open, breaking the holding circuit to the relay coil, valve Solenoid A becomes de-energized and the cylinder retracts.

This can be used as a cylinder dwell circuit in place of the circuit on Page 126, and is useful when there is no available space for mounting a limit switch at the forward end of the cylinder stroke.

ONE-CYCLE RECIPROCATION – HYDRAULIC CYLINDERS

Before going into details of electrical control circuits for hydraulic cylinders we need to review several requirements which must be considered before a workable electric circuit can be designed. Some of the reciprocation circuits shown on preceding pages for air cylinders could possibly be used for hydraulic cylinders, but most hydraulic circuits have additional requirements which prevent the simple electric circuits for air cylinders from being practical. Such requirements as the following:

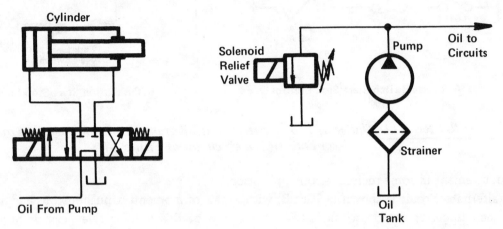

A. Tandem center 4-way valves are easy and conve-nient for unloading pump in low power systems.

B. Solenoid vent unloading gives less shock and is preferred especially on high powered systems.

FIGURE 3-13. These two methods of pump unloading are often used on electrically controlled systems operating from a fixed displacement hydraulic pump.

(1). Figure 3-13. Pump Unloading. Unlike an air system where the cylinder is allowed simply to stall against a positive stop with full air pressure behind its piston, most hydraulic cylinders must have a stop position in the valving. Those operating from a fixed displacement pump must include a provision in both the electrical and fluid circuits for unloading the pump while the cylinder is stopped. In the majority of such systems, unloading is through a tandem center or open center 4-way valve (Part A of figure), or by solenoid venting of a pilot-operated relief valve in the pump line (Part B). Examples of each method are shown in circuits on the following pages. See Page 99 for solenoid vent unloading.

(2). Figure 3-14. Locked Cylinder Ports. Also unlike an air system where the cylinder is held securely against a positive stop with full pressure against its piston, most hydraulic systems must block the cylinder ports while the cylinder is stopped, to prevent drift, or to prevent spring-back by the load. The ports can be blocked either by using 4-way valves with blocked cylinder ports (Part A of figure), or by installing a single or double pilot-operated check valve in one or both cylinder lines (Part B). A double pilot-operated check valve as shown in this figure is called a "lock valve".

Figure 3-15. Simple One-Cycle Reciprocation for Hydraulic Cylinder. A 3-position, double solenoid valve provides pump unloading as well as an oil lock on cylinder ports when both solenoids are de-en-ergized, and the valve spool moves to center position by spring force.

The 4-way valve must have current maintained on one or the other solenoids to keep its spool shifted and to keep the cylinder in motion. One or more holding relays are nearly always required when operating a spring centered or spring return valve from a momentary starting signal as from a

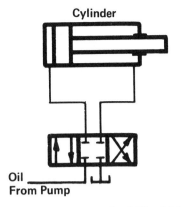

<u>A</u>. Closed Ports on the 4-Way Valve.

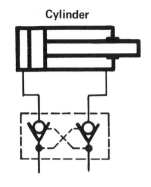

<u>B</u>. Lock Valve in the Cylinder Lines.

FIGURE 3-14. Two circuits for locking a hydraulic cylinder against drift.

pushbutton. Since holding relays are so important in an electrical circuit, the student may want to be sure he understands their operation by reviewing them on Page 27.

Figure 3-15, Part A. Hydraulic Circuit. Oil is supplied from a pumping system not shown in this diagram. Limit Switches 1-LS and 2-LS are appropriately placed at the desired ends of the cylinder stroke. Switch 2-LS automatically reverses the cylinder, and 1-LS automatically de-energizes the circuit by unloading the pump when the cylinder has returned to home position.

Figure 3-15, Part B. Electrical Circuit. Wiring to 1-LS and 2-LS is to their COM and N.C. terminals. Switch 1-LS, although normally closed, is shown in its open position because at that location it is being physically held open by a cam on the machine. On the diagram, the holding relay coil 1-CR is indicated with a circle. This coil operates two sets of contacts marked 1-CR-A and 1-CR-B. One set is normally open, the other is normally closed. See Pages 25 and 245 for review of contact symbols.

Operation of Electrical Circuit. When the pushbutton is pressed, relay Coil 1-CR and valve Solenoid A become energized. The relay coil is locked in electrically through Contacts 1-CR-A and 2-LS. The cyl-

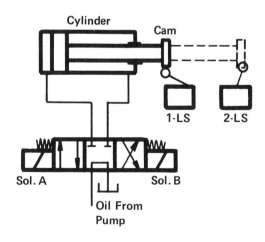

<u>A</u>. Hydraulic Circuit.

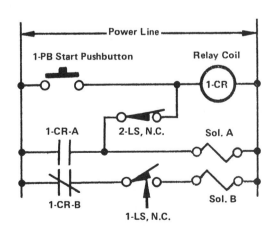

<u>B</u>. Electrical Circuit.

FIGURE 3-15. One-cycle reciprocation of a hydraulic cylinder. Pushbutton start, tandem center valve pump unloading.

inder moves forward until it actuates 2-LS. This drops out the holding relay and de-energizes Solenoid A. Relay Contacts 1-CR-B are now closed again, and since 1-LS was already closed, Solenoid B becomes energized. The cylinder returns to home position, actuating 1-LS as it reaches home position. Solenoid B now becomes de-energized, the valve spool centers by spring force, the cylinder stops, and the incoming oil supply is in an unloaded condition, flowing freely to tank through the tandem center valve.

This same circuit can be altered for cylinder reversal when a pre-set force has been reached. Limit Switch 2-LS must be replaced with a pressure switch of suitable adjustment range, and having one set of N.C (break-on-rise) contacts.

UNLOADING ON HIGH POWER HYDRAULIC SYSTEMS

The circuit just shown, Figure 3-15, using a tandem center 4-way valve for unloading the oil supply is simple and easy to use, and works well on low power hydraulic systems of, say, 25 HP or less. But on higher power systems, unloading through a tandem center valve may not work well. For one thing, too much heat may be generated in the oil by high oil flow through center-position resistance, and, momentary shock waves of high intensity may be produced during spool shift, and these shocks (or spikes) can cause major damage to components and to the plumbing.

(1). Heat Generation. Most solenoid 4-way valves used on high power systems are of the pilot-operated type. If shifting pressure is tapped off the pump line supplying the valve inlet, this line must not be unloaded to a pressure less than 100 PSI. This much pressure is required for pilot pressure on a 4-way valve with tandem or open center spool. An inlet or outlet restrictor must be placed in the oil flow to hold back 100 PSI, and at high oil flow this pressure loss can produce quite a bit of heat. Students who are not familiar with the methods of supplying pilot pressure to solenoid controlled, pilot-operated valves with tandem center spool can refer to "Industrial Fluid Power — Volume 2".

Power waste and heat generation can be minimized by using the solenoid vent pump unloading illustrated on the next page. Further description is on Pages 99 and 100.

(2). Shock Generation. When using a tandem center valve spool, a severe shock may be produced during spool shift between center and a side position. This can occur on any system using any 4-way valve which has closed-port crossover between side and center positions, but may be unimportant on low power systems. At high pressure and/or high flow in a large system the shock can be destructive. It is caused by momentary deadheading of the pump flow as the spool crosses between ports. The solenoid vent method of unloading, if properly applied, can almost entirely eliminate this kind of shock.

Note: Although solenoid vent unloading will eliminate shock when a reciprocation system is first started or stopped, it may not eliminate shock during quick reversal unless the circuit includes some means of momentarily unloading the pump during spool travel. It will not eliminate shock caused by oil decompression or by stress relief in machine members.

Figure 3-16. This circuit features solenoid vent pump unloading, lock valves, and the less expensive single solenoid 4-way directional valve.

The symbol shown for Valve 1 in the hydraulic circuit indicates a pilot-operated relief valve with a solenoid operator mounted on the valve structure. This composite valve is described on Page 98. Instead of a composite valve, a standard pilot-operated relief valve can be used as shown in other circuits such as those on Pages 99 and 100.

Solenoid B, mounted on the composite relief valve, when de-energized as shown on the drawing, causes the relief valve to open to by-pass the pump oil to tank at little more than 25 PSI. When Solenoid B is energized, pump pressure is allowed to build up to, but not to exceed, the knob setting on Valve 1.

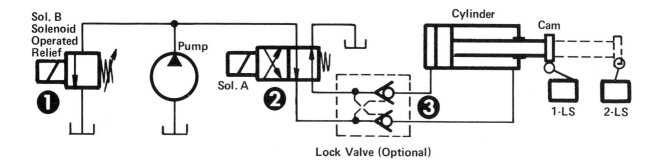

A. Hydraulic Circuit.

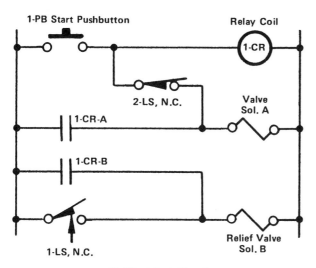

B. Electrical Circuit.

FIGURE 3-16.

A high power one-cycle reciprocation circuit to illustrate solenoid vent pump unloading, a lock valve to hold cylinder against drift, and the use of a single solenoid 4-way valve with a momentary pushbutton for starting.

In the electrical circuit, Part B, the starting actuator is a momentary pushbutton. Since the 4-way valve is a spring returned type, a holding relay must be used to keep it shifted after the pushbutton has been released. Its coil is shown as a circular symbol marked 1-CR. It has two sets of N.O. contacts marked 1-CR-A and 1-CR-B. Wiring to limit Switches 1-LS and 2-LS is to their COM and N.C. terminals. Note that 1-LS is drawn with contacts open because the cylinder, in home position, is holding them open. As soon as the cylinder starts to move, 1-LS contacts will return to their normally closed state.

The use of a lock valve, Item 3, is optional, depending on whether necessary to lock the cylinder against drift while it is stopped.

Operation of the Electrical Circuit. When the pushbutton is momentarily pressed, relay Coil 1-CR and valve Solenoid A become energized. The relay locks in electrically through its own contacts 1-CR-A so that it remains closed even though the pushbutton has been released. The 4-way valve, Item 2, is now in its shifted position ready to start the cylinder forward. Relay Contacts 1-CR-B have closed, causing relief Solenoid B to become energized. This causes pump pressure to build up without shock, and the cylinder can accelerate smoothly to its normal speed.

At the end of its forward stroke, a cam on the cylinder actuates limit Switch 2-LS. This breaks the holding circuit on relay Coil 1-CR, and in turn opens relay Contacts 1-CR-A and 1-CR-B. Valve Solenoid A, being now de-energized, retracts the cylinder. Relief valve Solenoid B remains energized during the retraction stroke through 1-LS contacts. When home position has been reached, 1-LS is cammed open, Solenoid B is de-energized, hydraulic pressure drops to near zero, and the cylinder stops with the pump unloaded.

CONTINUOUS RECIPROCATION – HYDRAULIC CYLINDERS

If a hydraulic cylinder is scheduled to reciprocate without stopping for an extended period of time, say at least an hour, or perhaps all day, an easy arrangement is to use one of the circuits shown for reciprocation of an air cylinder, using hydraulic instead of air components, and simply starting and stopping the electric motor which drives the hydraulic pump. But if the cylinder must reciprocate for shorter periods, a dozen or so cycles then stop for a resting or unloading period, the driving electric motor should not be stopped. Instead, the pump should be unloaded between running periods by one of the methods shown on Page 82 and other preceding pages. This is especially true of larger motors of 50 HP or more. These motors may be difficult to start or may require special starting equipment.

The circuits in this section assume short running periods and have some provision for pump unloading included in the fluid and electrical circuits.

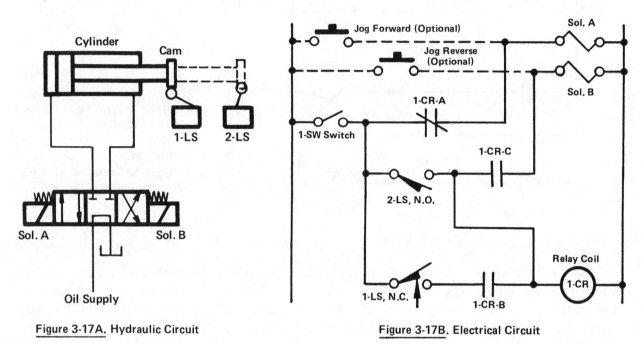

Figure 3-17A. Hydraulic Circuit

Figure 3-17B. Electrical Circuit

FIGURE 3-17. Simplest circuit for continuous reciprocation of a hydraulic cylinder in low power systems, using tandem center valve for pump unloading, and toggle switch start/stop control.

Figure 3-17. Tandem Center Valve With Toggle Switch Control. On low power systems, 25 HP or less, this is the simplest reciprocation circuit. A stripped down circuit is shown here; refinements can be added for special effects. These are considered later. Depending on the action wanted from the cylinder, certain characteristics of this circuit may not be desirable on some applications: when first started, the cylinder always starts in the extension direction no matter in which direction it was moving when stopped. And, when control current is switched off of both valve solenoids, the cylinder immediately stops without returning to a reference or home position.

Hydraulic Circuit. Figure 3-17A. The 4-way valve is a double solenoid, 3-position, tandem center model. In center neutral position of the valve spool, the cylinder is stopped with an oil lock on both ports and the pump is in an unloaded state. Limit Switches 1-LS and 2-LS are appropriately placed to define the limits of cylinder travel in both directions.

Figure 3-17B. Electrical Components. One holding relay is required; its coil is shown as a circular symbol marked 1-CR. Three sets of contacts operated by the coil are marked 1-CR-A and 1-CR-C which have normally open action, and 1-CR-B which has normally closed action. Switches 1-LS and 2-LS are standard limit switches. Wiring to 1-LS is to its COM and N.C. terminals. Its contacts are drawn open because they are held open by a cam on the cylinder when the cylinder has returned to home position. Wiring to 2-LS is to its COM and N.O. terminals.

Operation of the Electrical Circuit, Figure 3-17B. Closing the starting switch 1-SW energizes valve Solenoid A through closed relay Contacts 1-CR-A. The cylinder starts and travels until it actuates 2-LS. Relay Coil 1-CR now becomes energized and immediately locks itself in electrically through 1-CR-C contacts and 1-LS (which is closed at this time because the cylinder cam has released it). Relay Contacts 1-CR-A de-energize Solenoid A while Contacts 1-CR-B energize Solenoid B. The cylinder retracts while the relay remains locked in electrically. At home position, Switch 1-LS contacts are forced open by the cam. This releases the holding relay and the cylinder starts forward in the next cycle. When 1-SW is opened, all current is removed from the circuit; the solenoid valve spool centers; the cylinder stops immediately with the oil supply unloaded to tank. When 1-SW is next closed, the cylinder will always start in a forward direction regardless of its direction before it was stopped.

Jog Control. Figure 3-17B. Forward and reverse jogging buttons are shown on the electrical circuit; they are optional and are useful for inching the cylinder forward or backward during work set-up. Momentary pushbuttons are used and are wired ahead of the starting Switch 1-SW so the cylinder can be jogged without closing the starting switch. More information on jogging is on Page 142.

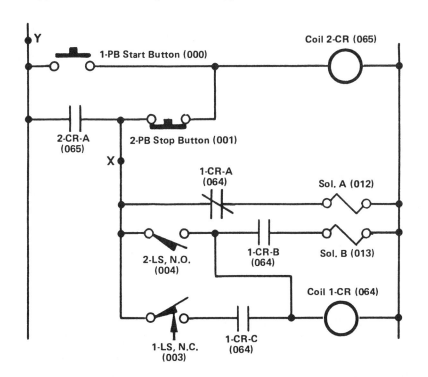

FIGURE 3-18.

Alternate electric circuit for control of tandem center valve in Figure 3-17 on preceeding page. Some users prefer pushbutton action. Pushbutton jogging may be added to this circuit by connecting pushbuttons from each valve solenoid coil to Point X or Y.

– Special Note –

The 3-digit number in parentheses under each component identification symbol are terminal number assignments for programmable controller ladder diagrams. This is one of the circuits used to demonstrate ladder diagrams in Chapter 10, Page 192.

Momentary Pushbutton Control. Figure 3-18. On some installations it may be preferable to have a set of momentary start/stop pushbuttons instead of 1-SW toggle switch of the preceding figure. A simple conversion is shown in this figure, in which the toggle switch is replaced by pushbuttons and a holding relay. The action of this circuit is basically the same as described for Figures 3-15 and 3-16. Pushbutton jogging can also be added as shown in Figure 3-17B.

For higher powered hydraulic systems, say of 25 HP or more, tandem center 4-way valves for pump unloading may become less desirable because of excessive heating and power loss through the valve while the spool is centered, and because of pressure shocks generated while the spool is shifting. For these higher powered systems the solenoid vent method of pump unloading can give less heating and less shifting shock. This method is described in Chapter 5, Page 99, and is also discussed in connection with cylinder reciprocation on Page 52.

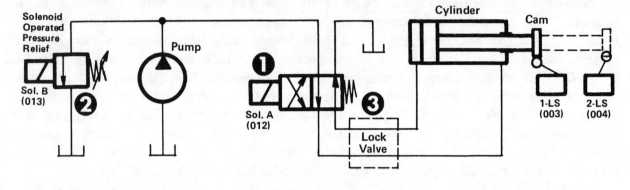

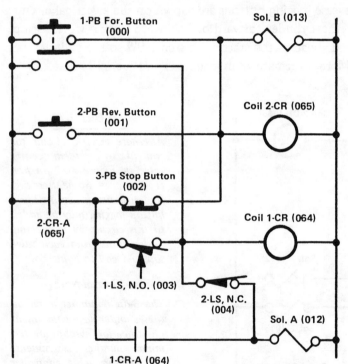

FIGURE 3-19A. Hydraulic Circuit (Above). Continuous reciprocation of a hydraulic cylinder featuring solenoid vent pump unloading, single solenoid 4-way control, and pushbutton operator control.

FIGURE 3-19B. Electrical Circuit. This is one possible control for the hydraulic circuit above. Note: the 3-digit codes under each component identification are terminal assignments for programmable controller operation. This circuit is used for demonstration in Chapter 10.

Figure 3-19. Single Solenoid Valve Reciprocation. Part A shows the use of a single solenoid valve for reciprocation of a cylinder. Even though the valve has only two valving positions, the cylinder can be stopped in mid-stroke by venting the pump relief valve, 2, by de-energizing Solenoid B which is on the valve structure. For valve description see Page 97, Figure 5-3. Note that this circuit does not provide an oil lock on cylinder ports, while the cylinder is stopped, unless a lock valve, 3, is added.

Electrical Circuit. Figure 3-19, Part B. Consists of two holding relays and three momentary pushbuttons for operator control. Limit Switch 1-LS, although its N.O. terminal is used, is held closed by a cam on the cylinder while at rest. After a short cylinder advance, 1-LS resumes its N.O. state.

Operation of the Electrical Circuit. Figure 3-19B. If the cylinder was completely retracted when last stopped, the 'Forward'' pushbutton can be used to start it into continuous reciprocation. If it was last stopped in mid-stroke, either the "Forward" or "Reverse" pushbuttons can be used. And, either button can be used in conjunction with the "Stop" button for jogging.

When the "Forward" button is pressed, two circuits are set up: Relay 2-CR coil and valve Solenoid B (relief vent) are energized from one set of button contacts. The relay is immediately locked in through the "Stop" button and its own contacts, 2-CR-A. The other set of button contacts energizes holding Relay 1-CR and valve Solenoid A. This circuit locks in electrically through 2-LS, 1-CR-A, and 2-CR-A contacts. The cylinder extends and actuates 2-LS. This breaks the holding circuit to Relay 1-CR but does not disturb the other relay holding circuit. Relay 1-CR and valve Solenoid A become de-energized and the cylinder retracts. At home position, 1-LS is pushed closed by the returning cylinder. Switch 1-LS re-energizes 1-CR and Solenoid A. This starts the cylinder into another cycle.

When the "Stop" button is momentarily pressed at any position in the cylinder stroke, Relay 2-CR drops out. This opens Contacts 2-CR-A which removes all current from the circuit. Solenoid B, being de-energized, unloads the pump, and the loss of pressure causes the cylinder to stop.

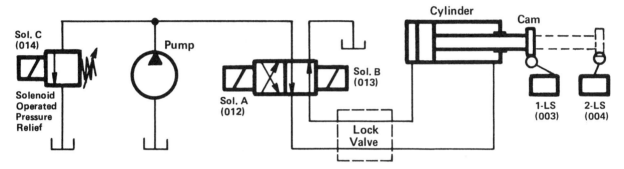

FIGURE 3-20, Part A, Hydraulic Circuit. Continuous reciprocation of a cylinder featuring a 2-position double solenoid valve, solenoid vent pump unloading. See electrical circuit on next page.

Figure 3-20. Double Solenoid Valve Reciprocation. Part A of this figure shows a double solenoid, 2-position 4-way valve for simplified control of a hydraulic cylinder in continuous reciprocaton.

The solenoid valve has only two working positions but the cylinder can be stopped in mid-stroke by de-energizing Solenoid C which unloads the pump through the relief valve. As in the preceding circuit, a lock valve must be added to the circuit if necessary to lock the ports on the cylinder while it is stopped.

Electrical Circuit. Figure 3-20, Part B. Characteristics of electrical components are given in this box. Three pushbuttons are provided and can be marked "Forward", "Reverse", and "Stop". If the cylinder was last stopped in mid-stroke, the operator can start it in either direction with the appropriate button. The "Forward" or "Reverse" button in conjunction with the "Stop" button can be used for jogging during work set-up. Limit Switch 1-LS, although its N.O. terminal is used, is shown with contacts closed because it is held

ELECTRICAL PARTS LIST — Figure 3-20.

Relay 1-CR, with 1 set of N.O. contacts.
"Stop" pushbutton with 1 set N.C. contacts.
"Forward" pushbutton, with 2 sets N.O. contacts.
"Reverse" pushbutton, with 2 sets N.O. contacts.
Standard limit Switch 1-LS. Wire to N.O. terminal.
Standard limit Switch 2-LS. Wire to N.O. terminal.
Standard limit Switch 3-LS. Wire to N.O. terminal.

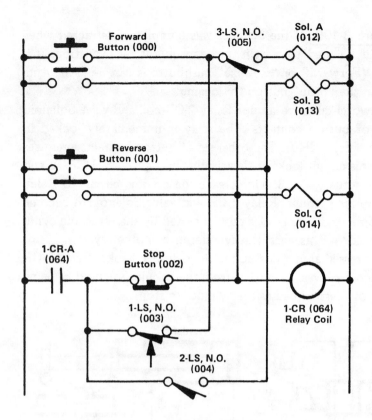

FIGURE 3-20, Part B. Electrical circuit for preceding fluid circuit. Features 2-position double solenoid valve, solenoid vent unloading and pushbutton control.

actuated while the cylinder is at home. As soon as the cylinder starts forward, the switch will return to its N.O. state.

Operation of the Electrical Circuit, Figure 3-20, Part B. Switch 3-LS is a safety switch on a guard which must be closed before the "Forward" button becomes active.

When the "Forward" button is pressed, two circuits are set up. One energizes valve Solenoid A for directional control. The other energizes 1-CR relay and Solenoid C on the relief valve. Relay 1-CR immediately locks in through its own contacts, 1-CR-A. The cylinder moves forward and actuates limit Switch 2-LS. This energizes valve Solenoid B to reverse cylinder direction but does not disturb the relay or Solenoid C. The cylinder travels toward home until it actuates Switch 1-LS. This energizes valve Solenoid A to start another cycle. When the "Stop" button is pressed, Relay 1-CR drops out and this de-energizes relief valve Solenoid C, unloading the pump and stopping the cylinder at this point in its stroke.

Figure 3-21, Part A. Reciprocation With 3-Position Solenoid Valve. This fluid circuit uses a 3-position closed center 4-way valve. The valve neutral gives an oil lock on cylinder ports while the cylinder is stopped. And, unloading the pump through the relief valve produces far less shifting shock than if a tandem center valve were used, particularly on higher power systems.

Figure 3-21, Part B. Electrical Circuit. Two holding relays are required. Configuration of relay, switch, and pushbutton contacts can be determined from the electrical circuit and the parts list.

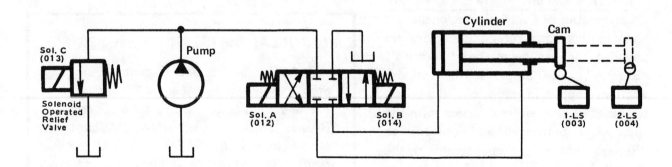

FIGURE 3-21. Part A, Hydraulic Circuit. This circuit features a double solenoid, closed center 4-way valve, solenoid vent pump unloading, and "Forward" and "Reverse" pushbutton start.

The limit switches are placed at reversal points of cylinder travel. The cylinder can be stopped at any point in its stroke, and on re-starting, the operator can start it in either direction. As in previous circuits, the pump becomes unloaded when the relief valve solenoid, C, is de-energized.

Operation of Electrical Circuit, Figure 3-21, Part B. When the "Forward" button is pressed, relay Coil 2-CR and relief valve

---

ELECTRICAL PARTS LIST – Figure 3-21

Relay 1-CR, with 1 N.O. and 1 N.C. contact sets.
Relay 2-CR, with 1 N.O. contact set.
"Stop" pushbutton, with 1 N.C. contact set.
"Forward" button, with 1 N.O. contact set.
"Reverse" button, with 2 N.O. contact sets.
1-LS, wire to common and N.C. terminals.
2-LS, wire to common and N.O. terminals.

FIGURE 3-21, Part B.

Reciprocation circuit using a double solenoid, 3-position 4-way valve with closed center spool. Features solenoid vent pump unloading, and 3-button operator control. The 3-digit codes under each component are terminal assignments for a programmable controller. This circuit is used for demonstration in Chapter 10.

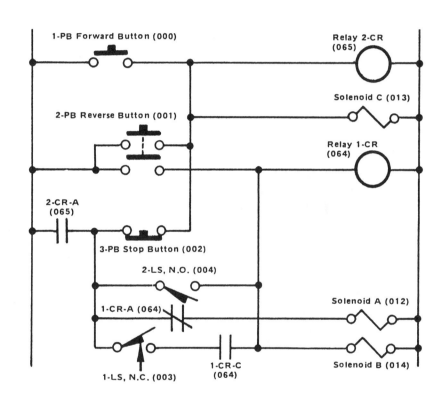

Solenoid C becomes energized and Contacts 2-CR-A close. This locks in Relay 2-CR through the N.C. "Stop" button contacts. Closure of 2-CR-A contacts energizes Solenoid A through Contacts 1-CR-A. The cylinder moves forward and actuates 2-LS. This energizes Relay 1-CR coil. Contacts 1-CR-A now open, de-energizing Solenoid A. Switch 2-LS also energizes Solenoid B, reversing the cylinder. Relay 1-CR remains locked in during cylinder retraction with a holding circuit through 1-LS and 1-CR-C contacts. When the cylinder reaches home, 1-LS is actuated. This breaks the holding circuit and releases Relay 1-CR. Solenoid A now becomes energized through 1-CR-C and 2-CR-A. Solenoid B becomes de-energized by 1-CR-C contacts. The cylinder now starts into another cycle.

At any time, either while the cylinder is extending or retracting, the 3-PB "Stop" pushbutton is pressed, the holding circuit to Relay 2-CR is broken. Solenoid C becomes de-energized and the pump becomes unloaded through the relief valve. The circuit to both Solenoids A and B is also broken. To start the cylinder again, either the "Forward" or "Reverse" button can be pressed. This locks in Relay 2-CR and energizes Solenoid C. Pump pressure is now developed and the cylinder will start moving.

THE USE OF FORK LEVER LIMIT SWITCHES

A fork lever limit switch is described on Page 22. It has a special kind of rotary arm which can be fitted to switches which have a "maintained" action. The contacts on these switches, when actuated, will remain in this state until actuated to their other state; they do not spring back to a "normal" state when an actuating cam is withdrawn.

There are two rollers on the actuator arm. Both can be mounted on the same side of the arm and actuated by the same moving cam. Circuits in this book, however, use an actuator arm with the two rollers mounted on opposite sides of the arm so each can be actuated by a separate cam. The use of a fork lever limit switch can greatly simplify some electrical circuits but there are limitations which may be unacceptable on some applications. For example, when a cylinder has been stopped in mid-stroke, the operator can only start it in the direction it had been moving. The cylinder can only be jogged in one direction. Although it is possible to add safety or "panic" circuits, these auxiliary controls are more difficult to design into the circuit.

A fork lever switch is particularly useful during the mid-stroke travel of a cylinder. If used at the end of the stroke, its position must be carefully adjusted so its contacts will be fully actuated at the precise position the cylinder reaches before coming against a positive stop. Cams which operate a fork lever switch should be designed according to information in Chapter 6, Page 120.

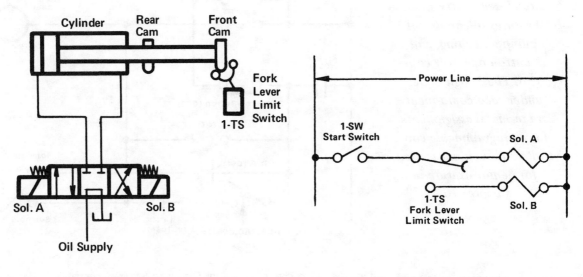

Part A. Hydraulic Circuit.   Part B. Electrical Control Circuit.

FIGURE 3-22. Limit switch with fork lever actuator will control cylinder reciprocation with a very simple electrical circuit. Circuit features tandem center pump unloading, flip switch start/stop control.

Figure 3-22, Part A. To illustrate the basic application of a fork lever actuated limit switch we have selected a hydraulic circuit which uses a 4-way, tandem center, double solenoid valve. The front and rear cams each actuate a separate roller on the fork lever arm. For illustration, the cams are shown attached to the cylinder rod, but actually must be mounted on a moving member of the machine which will keep their stroke axes accurately aligned with the rollers on the switch.

A simple hook-up is all that is required in the electrical circuit, Figure 3-22, Part B. A toggle switch, 1-SW, allows the operator to start and stop the reciprocation. When 1-SW is turned off, both valve solenoids become de-energized, and the valve spool returns to center by spring action, stopping the cylinder with an oil lock on both ports, and with incoming oil pressure unloaded to tank. When 1-SW is turned ON, the cylinder resumes its travel in the same direction as when it was stopped.

Figure 3-23. Pushbutton Control. For more sophisticated control, a pair of momentary Start/Stop pushbuttons and a holding relay can be substituted for toggle Switch 1-SW in the preceding circuit. Accurate contour and alignment of actuating cams are quite important. The action of a holding relay with pushbutton control has been shown in Figures 3-3 through 3-6.

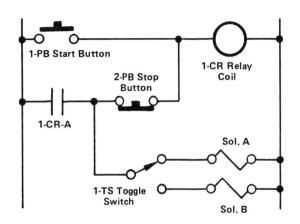

FIGURE 3-23. This electrical circuit provides pushbutton control of hydraulic circuit of Figure 3-22 which uses a fork lever limit switch.

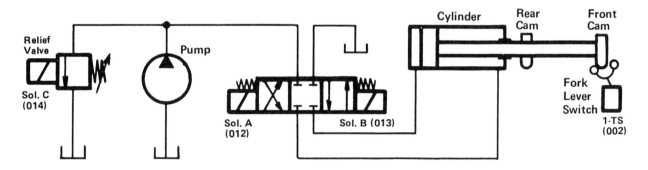

Figure 3-24, Part A. Hydraulic Circuit.

Figure 3-24. This circuit may be preferred for high power systems but solenoid vent unloading, while eliminating start and stop hydraulic shocks, will not minimize shock created at the moment of cylinder reversal.

Since the action in this circuit is similar to that in circuits already described, it will not be described further. When the circuit is in operation, Solenoid C (on the pump relief) is kept energized in combination with either Solenoid A or Solenoid B, depending on the direction of cylinder travel.

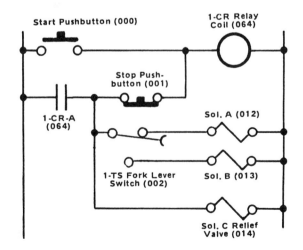

Figure 3-24, Part B. Electrical Circuit.

FIGURE 3-24. Fork lever reciprocation for higher power systems. The 3-digit codes under each symbol are used for programmable controller ladder diagrams in Chapter 10.

ELECTRICAL CONTROL OF REGENERATIVE CIRCUITS

For a study of regenerative hydraulic circuits and the methods for calculating force, speed, and oil flow in such circuits, please refer to the Womack book "Industrial Fluid Power — Volume 2".

The regenerative state of a hydraulic circuit gives double the normal forward speed at one-half the normal maximum force. When regenerative fluid circuits are controlled with solenoid valves, a pressure switch is often used to take the circuit automatically out of high speed regeneration when load pressure has built to near maximum relief valve pressure, and to place it in a normal speed, full force non-regenerative state.

Pressure switch take-out circuits must be carefully designed to avoid a severe "hunting" or "fluttering" of the pressure switch and associated valve at the take-out pressure. The cause of this "flutter" can be understood from the fluid circuit, Figure 3-25, below. When maximum pressure has been reached and the pressure switch has tripped, the circuit drops out of regeneration and back into a conventional state and the pressure behind the cylinder piston drops to one-half its regenerative value. This causes the pressure switch to drop out or re-set and the circuit again goes into regeneration. The system pressure then immediately increases to maximum and again trips the pressure switch. This hunting action may continue indefinitely. To avoid this condition the electrical circuit must be designed to disconnect the pressure switch for the remainder of the cycle after it first trips.

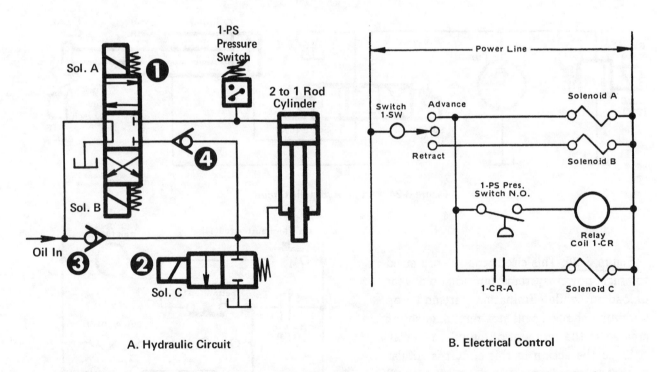

A. Hydraulic Circuit   B. Electrical Control

FIGURE 3-25. Elementary regeneration circuit with pressure switch take-out. Control is by means of a 3-position rotary selector switch.

Figure 3-25. Circuit operation is as follows: When selector Switch 1-SW is turned to "Advance", Solenoid A becomes energized and starts the cylinder advance. Return oil from the rod end of the cylinder passes through check Valve 3 and joins pump oil to rapidly advance the cylinder piston forward in a regenerative state. As load pressure builds up and actuates 1-PS pressure switch contacts, Relay 1-CR and Solenoid C become energized. Rod oil is now vented directly to tank. The cylinder slows its advance to its normal, non-regenerative speed. Relay contacts 1-CR-A lock the relay in electrically so the pressure switch, when it re-sets will not cause the circuit to again go into regeneration. This prevents the "flutter" described before.

When selector Switch 1-SW is turned to "Retract", Solenoid B becomes energized while the Relay 1-CR, Solenoid C and Solenoid A become de-energized. The cylinder retracts to home position. The operator now must move the rotary selector switch to neutral to unload the pump. All solenoid and relay coils are now de-energized.

The circuit of Figure 3-25 is extremely simple, to illustrate the kind of electrical action required to prevent the pressure switch and valve from fluttering. In practice, the circuit action is undesirable from several standpoints. A rotary selector switch is not a good starting switch. In practice it would be better to use a momentary pushbutton for starting the cylinder. One or more holding relays would be needed to hold the solenoid valves in a shifted position when the pushbutton was released. Most circuits should have a switch at the end of the cylinder stroke for automatic retraction. A pump unloading circuit should be designed to automatically unload the pump when the cylinder reaches home position rather than relying on an operator to center a selector switch. The basic idea of pump unloading was shown in Figure 3-15, Page 50. Some of the holding relay principles shown in Figure 3-21, Page 58 could be employed. Other circuits in Chapters 3 and 4 also illustrate principles of pump unloading.

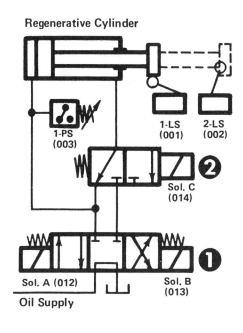

Regenerative Cylinder

A. Hydraulic Circuit

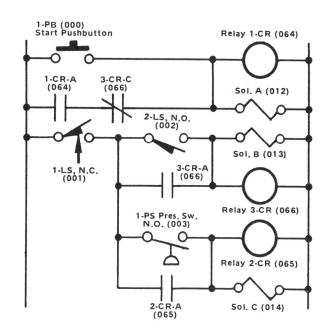

B. Pushbutton Electrical Control

FIGURE 3-26. Regenerative cylinder circuit featuring pushbutton start, complete automatic cycle, forward and reverse, and tandem center pump unloading.

Figure 3-26. Pushbutton Start, Pressure Switch Take-Out. Circuit operation is as follows: Pressing the "Start" button energizes Relay 1-CR and Solenoid A, and the relay locks in through 3-CR-C and 1-CR-A contacts. As the cylinder starts to move, 1-LS is released and returns to its N.C. state. The cylinder advances rapidly in the regeneration mode until load pressure build-up actuates 1-PS pressure switch. Relay 2-CR and Solenoid C become energized and the relay locks in through 2-CR-A contacts.

Solenoid C shifts Valve 2 spool and the circuit goes out of regeneration and into a normal advance mode. Its speed drops to one-half and the pressure behind its piston drops to one-half. It continues to advance at slow speed but with double the tonnage capability. At the end of its forward stroke, when 2-LS is actuated, Relay 3-CR and Solenoid B become energized while Relay 2-CR and Solenoid C become de-energized. Solenoid A and Relay 1-CR also become de-energized when Relay 3-CR closes. The cylinder retracts to home position and actuates 1-LS switch. This de-energizes Solenoid B. The spool of Valve 1 becomes centered by internal spring action, unloading the pump flow through the valve spool center.

Figure 3-27. Instead of a pressure switch to take the circuit out of regeneration, this circuit uses a limit switch, 2-LS, mounted at the position in the stroke where full cylinder force is needed. This arrangement can also be used for applications where cylinder speed must be reduced prior to engagement with the work. The cam which operates the limit switches must have sufficient length to keep 2-LS actuated for the remainder of the forward stroke. Switch 2-LS, in this circuit, is non-functional on the cylinder return stroke. As an alternative, a 1-way roller actuator, with short cam, could be used for 2-LS, but would require one more holding relay in the electrical circuit.

This basic hydraulic circuit is presented in "Industrial Fluid Power – Volume 2" with a more complete description than given here. It has been adapted in this book for a completely automatic 1-cycle reciprocating action with a workable electrical control circuit.

Operation of this regenerative system is as follows: When the "Start" button is

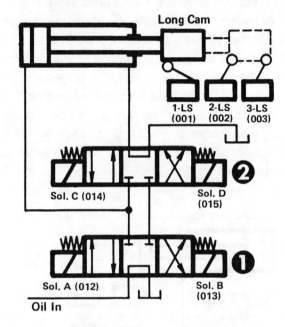

A. Hydraulic Circuit

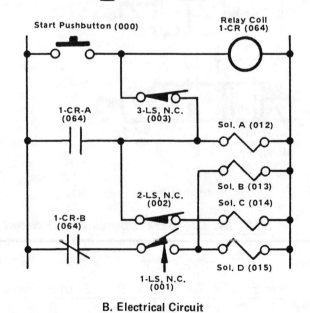

B. Electrical Circuit

FIGURE 3-27. A limit switch, 2-LS is used instead of a pressure switch for regenerative take-out.

SOLENOID SEQUENCE	
Cyl. Condition	Sol. Condition
Stopped	All De-Energized
Regen. Advan.	A & C Energized
High Tonnage	A Only, Ener.
Retract	B & D Energized

pressed, Solenoids A and C, and Relay 1-CR become energized and lock in electrically through 1-CR-A contacts. After the first small advance of the cylinder, Switch 1-LS is allowed to return to its N.C. state. The cylinder advances in a high speed regenerative mode with discharged oil from its rod end joining incoming pump oil for high speed forward travel. When 2-LS is actuated, Solenoid C becomes de-energized and Valve 2 spool centers. Cylinder speed decreases to its normal, full tonnage, speed. When 3-LS is actuated, Relay 1-CR and Solenoid A become de-energized. This fulfills the conditions for normal retraction stated in the sequence table on the preceding page. At home position, 1-LS is actuated, and this de-energizes Solenoids B and D. Both valves are now centered and the oil supply is unloaded through Valve 1 spool center.

Note: The 3-digit codes under each component symbol in Figure 3-27 are terminal assignments to a programmable controller. This is one of the circuits used in Chapter 10 to demonstrate the conversion of a JIC electrical diagram into a ladder diagram for entering into a controller.

SPEED CONTROL IN PRESSURE SWITCH CIRCUITS

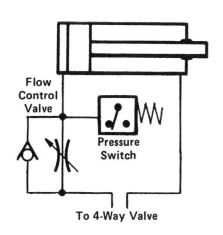

Flow Control Valve

Pressure Switch

To 4-Way Valve

FIGURE 3-28. If a speed control valve is used in pressure switch circuits, it must be connected for meter-in control.

Several circuits in Chapters 3 and 4 use pressure switches instead of limit switches to produce a signal to reverse direction of the cylinder. When flow control valves are used in these circuits to reduce cylinder maximum speed, it is important to connect the valves for meter-in speed control and to connect the pressure switch downstream of the valve, directly at the cylinder port.

Meter-out speed control cannot be used successfully because pressure behind the piston will immediately rise to its maximum level whether there is any load on the cylinder or not. There will be no rise in pressure at the end of the stroke to trip the switch. When the flow control is connected meter-in, pressure behind the piston will be in proportion to the load build-up on the cylinder.

Flow control valves must be connected as shown in this figure for both air and hydraulic cylinders.

CHAPTER 4

Directional Control: Sequencing of Cylinders

SEQUENCING DEFINED

As defined by the dictionary, a "sequence" is a regular order of progression. In fluid power this means a regular order of operation of several branch circuits on the same machine. More specifically, it means the operation of several cylinders (or motors) in a regular and repetitive progression or "program". It includes automatic reciprocation as studied in the preceding chapter but involves more than one cylinder. When one of them finishes a specific movement, which could be its complete forward and reverse cycle, its half cycle, or even a part of a half cycle, a switching signal is produced by one of several means to be described, and this signal starts the next cylinder into motion. In electrically controlled fluid circuits switching signals come from limit switches, pressure switches, timers, etc. Any number of cylinders can be "programmed" into an automatic machine cycle, depending on the ingenuity of the designer. "Automation" depends on, and usually implies, automatic programming.

Figure 4-1. The three most often-used methods of establishing a sequence between cylinders are shown in these block diagrams. On a given machine more than one method might be employed.

Position Sequencing, Part A, Figure 4-1. If sequencing is to take place when Cylinder 1, for example, reaches a certain position in its stroke which may be its full stroke or any part of its stroke, a switching signal is usually produced by mounting a limit switch at the desired position. The signal from this switch is applied to Solenoid B to start Cylinder 2 into motion. If the sequencing position is at an intermediate point in the stroke, Figure 6-9, Page 119, shows precautions to be observed to obtain the type of signal desired — momentary or maintained.

Load Sequencing, Part B, Figure 4-1. A pressure switch can be teed into a cylinder port on Cylinder 1, for example, to give a switching signal when load resistance against the piston causes fluid pressure to build up to a pre-set level on the pressure switch. This method may be the one to use when the main requirement is to start Cylinder 2, not when Cylinder 1 has reached a certain point in its stroke but when it has reached a certain force against its load. It could reach this level of force at any point in its stroke or when its piston stalls against the cylinder end cap or against an external positive stop. With a pressure switch installed in the blind end cylinder port as shown, the switching signal is obtained on the forward stroke only, with no signal at the end of its return stroke. If instead, the switch is teed into the rod end port, a switching signal is obtained during the retraction stroke only.

Time Sequencing, Part C, Figure 4-1. A third method of sequencing is with a time delay relay or a program or re-set timer. Program timing is shown on Page 123, and dwell timing on Page 125. The timer gives a switching signal after a pre-set interval of elapsed time. In the figure, Solenoid A, which controls Cylinder 1 would remain energized with Cylinder 1 stalled until the elapsed time is completed and Solenoid B becomes energized. This method is wasteful of cycle time but can be used if other methods are not practical. For example, on bonding or curing, or as a timed re-loading period.

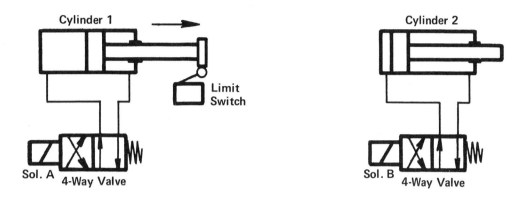

A. Position Sequencing. Cylinder 2 starts when Cylinder 1 reaches the limit switch.

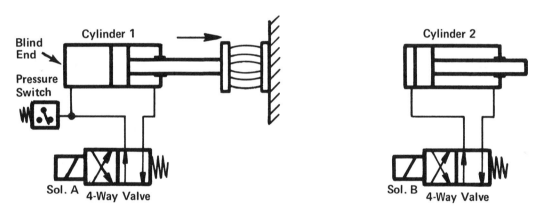

B. Load Sequencing. Cylinder 2 starts when reaction load on Cylinder 1 reaches a pre-set level.

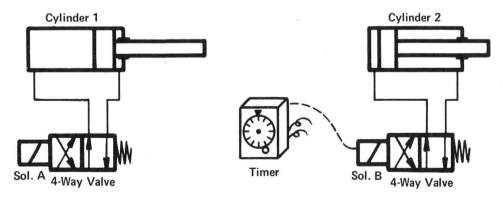

C. Time Sequencing. Two cylinders operate independently from a timed program.

FIGURE 4-1. Block diagrams showing the three most often used methods of operating two cylinders in a sequential relationship in an electrically controlled fluid power system.

SEQUENCING OF AIR CYLINDERS

Review of Air Cylinder Action and 4-Way Valve Types . . .

First, let us briefly review the action of an air cylinder. A more complete study will be found in the Womack book "Industrial Fluid Power – Volume 1". See listing inside rear cover.

Whenever possible an air system should be designed so the cylinder operates from one extreme of its stroke to the other, never stopping in mid stroke. External positive stops should be used if the stroke is more than needed. When stopped, it should be held with full pressure against its end caps or the external stops. It is difficult to stop an air cylinder at a precise point in mid stroke because, when air pressure is cut off it will continue to travel until air pressure behind its piston reaches a balance with the load. And while stopped, if external load is added or removed the cylinder piston will move forward or backward until a balance point is again reached. Therefore, 3-position valves are not often used with air cylinders. Most air circuits should use 2-position models with single or double solenoid actuators. In choosing between single and double solenoid, a designer will have several factors to consider:

Single Solenoid Valves. The action in controlling a double-acting air cylinder is explained on Page 8. Current must be maintained on its coil to keep its spool in a shifted position. This model may be preferred when the starting signal is maintained, as from a toggle or selector switch. It can be operated from momentary starting signals by using a holding relay. Such circuits are shown later in this chapter. A single solenoid model has a "fail safe" action in the sense that if control current fails the valve spool will return to a "normal" state, retracting the cylinder. Its spool can never accidentally drift because of excessive flow or vibration, and it will usually tolerate a higher "g" rate than a double solenoid model when used on moving equipment. Cost may also be a factor, and this model is always priced less than a comparable double solenoid model.

Double Solenoid Valves. The action in controlling a double-acting air cylinder is explained on Page 10. The spool will shift and stay in shifted position on a momentary impulse of current. Often can be operated directly from a set of momentary pushbuttons with simpler wiring and fewer components than needed for single solenoid models. Should always be mounted with spool horizontal to minimize the possibility of spool drift from causes mentioned above.

Simple Sequencing Circuits for Air Cylinders Using Limit Switches . . .

In the majority of sequencing applications, limit switches seem to be the more satisfactory way of operating several cylinders in a planned program. Pressure switches and timers are more often used on applications where limit switches are impractical or unsuitable.

Several air cylinders can be programmed to each other in a number of combinations. The circuits to follow show principles for programming two cylinders. By understanding these principles, a designer can extend them to systems using more than two cylinders and operating in any sequence.

Sequence Combinations for Two Cylinders

A. Cylinder 1 advance; Cylinder 2 advance; both cylinders retract in random sequence.

B. Cylinder 1 advance; Cylinder 1 retract; Cylinder 2 advance; Cylinder 2 retract.

C. Cylinder 1 advance; Cylinder 2 advance; Cylinder 1 retract; Cylinder 2 retract.

D. Cyl. 1 advance; Cyl. 2 advance; Cyl. 2 retract; Cyl.1 retract. (Standard clamp & work sequence).

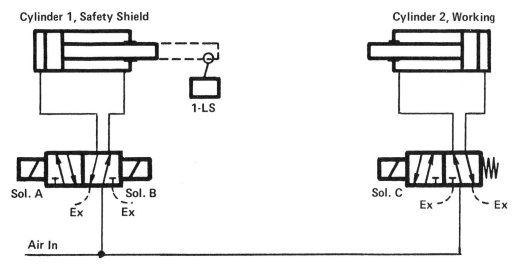

Figure 4-2, Part A. Air Circuit

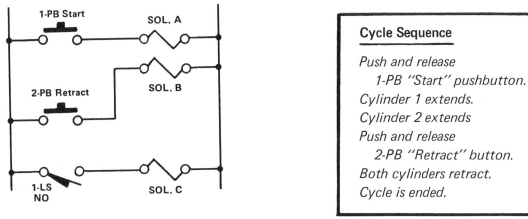

Cycle Sequence

*Push and release
    1-PB "Start" pushbutton.
Cylinder 1 extends.
Cylinder 2 extends
Push and release
    2-PB "Retract" button.
Both cylinders retract.
Cycle is ended.*

Figure 4-2, Part B. Electrical Circuit

FIGURE 4-2. Priority-type sequence circuit. Two cylinders are arranged so the second one cannot start until the first one has advanced to a designated position and has actuated a limit switch.

Figure 4-2, Parts A and B. This is the basic circuit for electrically programming two (or more) cylinders to operate in a definite sequence. When Cylinder 1 is started, it must make its forward stroke and must actuate limit Switch 1-LS before Cylinder 2 can start. The sequential relationship between the cylinders is shown in the box and stated in Part A at the bottom of Page 67. This arrangement is often used to assure safety for the operator, the workpiece, or the tooling. For example, Cylinder 1 may operate a safety shield, guard, or door. Cylinder 2 may operate a working device and cannot start until the safety shield is in place. In this simple circuit, the cylinders must operate in sequence while extending, but are allowed to retract at random. If this is not a safe condition, then a more elaborate circuit must be used, for example the "clamp and work" sequence stated in Part D on Page 67. These circuits will be covered later.

Figure 4-2, Part A. Air Circuit. This circuit is set up for pushbutton start and pushbutton retract. The appropriate 4-way valves are a double solenoid, 2-position model for Cylinder 1 and a single solenoid model for Cylinder 2. A limit switch must be placed at the position in the stroke of Cylinder 1 where it is safe for Cylinder 2 to start.

68

Figure 4-2, Part B. Electrical Circuit. A very simple electrical circuit will control the action. A pair of momentary pushbuttons are used to energize Solenoids A and B to control Cylinder 1. In addition to the solenoid valves, the only components required are the pushbuttons and one limit switch.

Electrical Action in Detail. When Pushbutton 1-PB is pressed, Solenoid A is energized. The valve will shift and remain shifted on a pushbutton signal as short as 1/2 second. Cylinder 1 starts forward and will actuate Switch 1-LS. This energizes Solenoid C and starts Cylinder 2 forward. Cylinder 1 will remain stalled at the end of its forward stroke. Cylinder 2 will also stall at the end of its forward stroke. The operator must press Pushbutton 2-PB to retract both cylinders. Both retract at the same time in a random sequence, although placement of speed control valves in the lines connecting 4-way valves to cylinders can be adjusted to cause one cylinder to retract faster than the other one.

Circuits later in this chapter will show how to make retraction automatic and in a preferred sequential order.

Figure 4-3. Automatic Retraction. This circuit has the added feature of automatic retraction of both cylinders when the extension stroke of Cylinder 2 has been completed. The sequence between

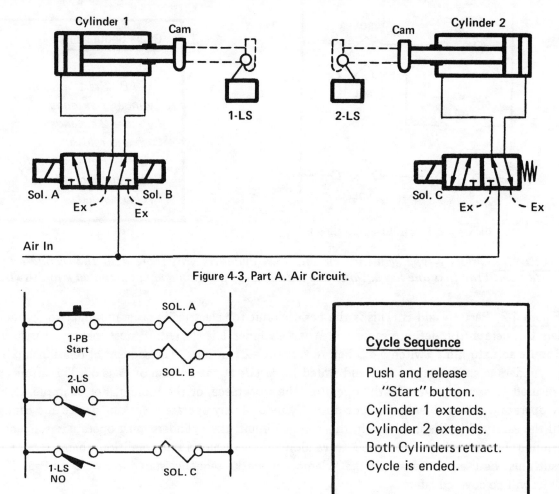

Figure 4-3, Part A. Air Circuit.

Figure 4-3, Part B. Electrical Circuit.

Cycle Sequence

Push and release
    "Start" button.
Cylinder 1 extends.
Cylinder 2 extends.
Both Cylinders retract.
Cycle is ended.

FIGURE 4-3. Complete automatic cycle, forward, reverse, and stop. Sequencing occurs on forward cylinder movements with random retraction. Pushbutton electrical control.

the cylinders is the same as in the preceding circuit, and is defined in Part A at the bottom of Page 67.

Applications for this circuit are similar to those for the preceding circuit: holdback of the second cylinder until the first one has reached a safe point in its stroke.

Other applications may include successive motions of two cylinders on the same workpiece. For example, a 180° turnover of a workpiece by a pair of cylinders. Cylinder 1 may turn the piece 90° then activate the second cylinder to complete the turnover. Both cylinders may then return to their home positions in any random order. See example on Page 138.

Another useful application is in handling a workpiece in two planes. For example, Cylinder 1 lifts a workpiece to the height of a platform, then activates Cylinder 2 which pushes the workpiece horizontally on to the platform. The two cylinders may then retract in any random order. A typical example is shown on Page 135. For applications like these it is imperative to hold back the second cylinder until the first one has extended to a reference position. *(Text continues on Page 71)*

Sequencing Steps in a Standard "Clamp and Work" Action Between Two Cylinders

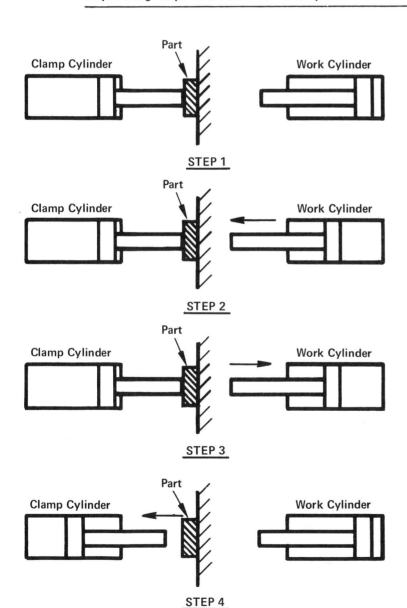

Step 1. *Clamp cylinder advances first, contacts the work, and stalls against it with full air line pressure on its piston. At the moment the work is contacted a switching signal is produced either with a limit switch, pressure switch, or other sensor to start the work cylinder.*

Step 2. *Clamp cylinder continues to exert full active force against the workpiece while the work cylinder is advancing to the work and while the work operation is being performed.*

Step 3. *With the work operation completed, the work cylinder reverses either automatically or by operator control. During retraction of the work cylinder, the clamp cylinder must continue to maintain full active force against the workpiece.*

Step 4. *After the work cylinder reaches home position, or at least has completed critical withdrawal from the work area, a switching signal is generated either by a limit or pressure switch, or other sensor, to reverse the clamp cylinder.*

"Clamp and Work" Sequence Circuits . . .

The cylinder sequence described on Pages 68 and 69 is easy to design but may not be safe for certain applications if retraction must be in a designated sequence where Cylinder 1 (the clamp) cannot release its grip on the workpiece until Cylinder 2 (work cylinder) has either completely retracted or has retracted to a safe distance. This sequence is defined in Part D on Page 63 and shown graphically on the preceding page. In this book this sequence is called "clamp and work". It is probably used more often than any other but is more difficult to design. For this reason it will be used in the following examples. If a student can learn the tricks of designing a clamp and work he should have little difficulty with the others.

An important difficulty develops in a clamp and work circuit when one cylinder actuates, then stands on, a limit switch, keeping it actuated. If the switch is used to energize a valve solenoid, some way must be found to break the switch circuit later in the cycle so the opposite solenoid on the same valve can shift the valve spool into its opposite position. If this is not done the cycle will stall. There are several ways of breaking the switch signal which will be covered in circuits to follow.

Figure 4-4. Clamp and Work Action. The two (or more) cylinders must not only extend in a sequential order but equally important, must retract in the proper sequence. This sequence is mandatory for applications mentioned earlier and for others such as bending, punching, shearing, sawing, milling, etc. where the workpiece must be firmly clamped while being worked on and must be firmly held during retraction of the work cylinder. Step 4, retraction, is especially important on sawing and milling operations in which the blade or cutter must clear the work before the clamp releases.

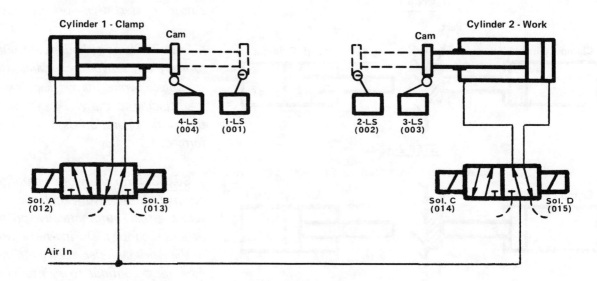

FIGURE 4-5A. Clamp and work air circuit using limit switches at all points of reversal.

Figure 4-5, Part A. Air Circuit. Both cylinders are controlled with 4-way, double solenoid, 2-position air valves. These valves are easy to use on air circuits because a brief impulse (1/2 second) to one solenoid or the other is sufficient to shift the valve spool to its opposite position. A limit switch must be mounted at both ends of the stroke on both cylinders.

Please note that this circuit cannot be used for hydraulic cylinders. Cylinder 1 would release its grip at the moment Cylinder 2 started its advance.

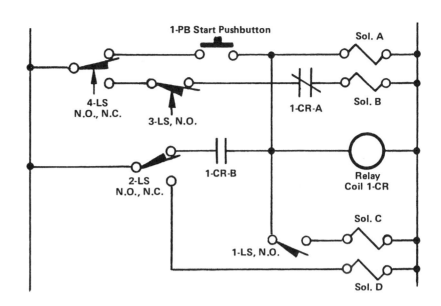

Cycle Sequence:

Push "Start" Button.
Cylinder 1 Extends.
Cylinder 2 Extends.
Cylinder 2 Retracts.
Cylinder 1 Retracts.

FIGURE 4-5, Part B.

Electrical Circuit.

Figure 4-5, Part B. Electrical Circuit. Before the cycle starts, limit Switches 3-LS and 4-LS are held in an actuated state by moving cams on the machine. This is indicated on the diagram by side arrows on the switch arms.

The circuit difficulty described in the second paragraph on Page 71, that of having Cylinder 1 actuate, then stand on, limit Switch 1-LS, has been solved in this example by adding a relay to break the circuit from 1-LS later in the cycle. This makes it possible for Solenoid D to reverse the valve.

Figure 4-5B. Circuit Action in Detail. When the start button, 1-PB, is pressed, Relay 1-CR and Solenoid A both become energized. The relay locks in through 2-LS and 1-CR-B. A contact, 1-CR-A on the relay prevents Solenoid B from being energized at this time.

Cylinder 1 advances, and after a brief travel releases Switch 4-LS. This disconnects the pushbutton for the rest of the cycle. Cylinder 1 advances until it actuates 1-LS. This energizes Solenoid C to start Cylinder 2 while Cylinder 1 remains standing on 1-LS.

Cylinder 2 advances and actuates 2-LS. This de-energizes Solenoid C, energizes Solenoid D, and re-leases Relay 1-CR. The valve shifts and Cylinder 2 starts to retract. When it has backed off of 2-LS, Solenoid C remains de-energized. At home, Cylinder 2 actuates 3-LS. This energizes Solenoid B, causing Cylinder 1 to retract. At home position, 4-LS is actuated and this restores power to the push-button so another cycle can be started. The cycle ends with both cylinders stalled at home position.

Figure 4-6. Sequence Diagram. (For air and electric circuits of Figure 4-5). The purpose of a sequence diagram is to show graphically for each component the time period in which it functions during the cycle. This can be of value in assisting a reader to grasp a clear understanding of circuit action, even though the diagram may not convey information not already contained in the air and electric schematics and the written description of circuit action. The student can construct a sequence diagram for circuits he finds difficult to understand, and for new circuits he designs.

A suggested method is shown in Figure 4-6 for constructing such a sequence diagram for the "clamp and work" circuits of Figures 4-5A and B. One horizontal line is assigned for each component, includ-ing valve and relay coils, switch and relay contacts, etc. The heavy portion of each horizontal line shows the time during which the component is actuated or energized. Insofar as possible, horizontal lines should be placed in the same vertical order in which each component is actuated or energized during the cycle. See Page 36 for further information on how to construct a sequence diagram.

The diagram, as well as adding clarity to a circuit description, can serve as a check to see whether both solenoids of a double solenoid valve are ever energized at the same time. Sometimes this is permissible, sometimes not. It will confirm that all solenoid and relay coils become de-energized at the end of the cycle.

Comments on Sequencing Diagram (Below) . . .

Line 1. Pushbutton. The solid part of this line is short because the pushbutton will automatically be disconnected as soon as 4-LS is actuated and will remain inactive for the remainder of the cycle.

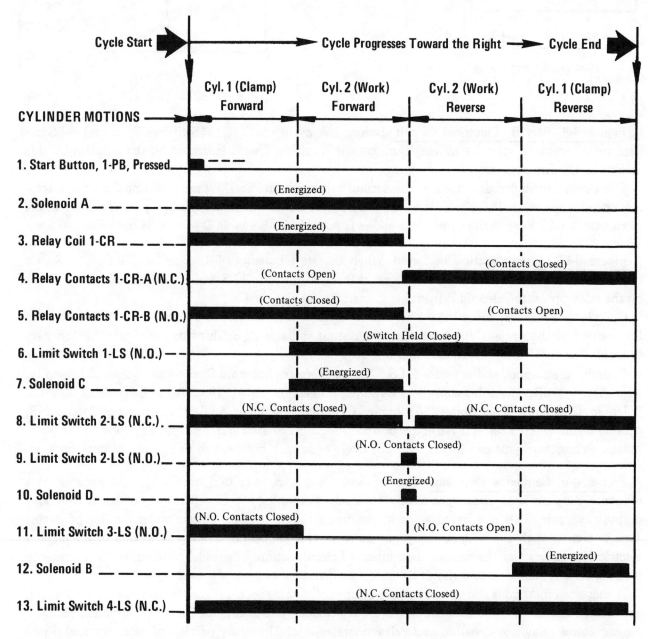

FIGURE 4-6. Sequence diagram for the clamp and work circuit of Figure 4-5 on the preceding page. One complete cycle is shown, starting at the left and ending on the right side of the diagram.

Circuits are included in this section for disconnecting the pushbutton. Interlocking methods for pushbuttons are also a part of Chapter 8, starting on Pages 145 and 148.

Line 2. All solenoid valves in this circuit will shift on an impulse of current, but to avoid the possibility of self-shift due to vibration or excessive air flow, it is better to hold current on each solenoid as long during the cycle as possible without over-complicating the circuit. Of course, one solenoid on a double solenoid valve must be de-energized before the other one can reverse the spool.

Line 7. Compare with Line 6. Switch 1-LS energizes Solenoid C, but some means must be included in the circuit to break the connection to Solenoid C before time to energize Solenoid D, even though Cylinder 1 is still standing on 1-LS. Several circuits to do this are included in this section.

Safety Interlock on "Start" Pushbutton ...

On applications where a safety hazard might be created for the operator, for the machine, or the workpiece or tooling if the starting pushbutton were accidentally pressed while the cycle was in progress, the electrical circuit should be designed to remove power from the pushbutton as soon as the cycle starts. In Figures 4-5B and in others to follow, a limit switch is placed at home position of the cylinder which starts first. Power is removed from the pushbutton as soon as the cylinder starts. On some applications a different cylinder may be the last to retract at the end of the cycle. A second limit switch can be placed at home position of that cylinder. Figure 4-24 illustrates such a case.

If the operator weights the button down or continues to hold it through the entire cycle, another cycle will immediately start when the last cylinder reaches home position.

We recommend this feature on all circuits with this hazard. It can be added to most circuits in this book. More information on safety interlocks is on Pages 149, 150, and in Example 2 on Page 187.

Other Ways of Solving "Clamp and Work" Electrical Circuits ...

The circuit difficulty described in the second paragraph on Page 71, of having a cylinder actuate, then stand on a limit switch, was solved in Figure 4-5B by adding a relay. Contacts on this relay break the limit switch circuit later in the cycle. Here are some other ways the problem can be handled:

Figure 4-7 on the next page uses a re-set electrical timer to break the switch circuit after the elapse of (so many) seconds. The time can be set from 1/2 second up to any value short of the time required for the other solenoid on the same valve to be energized.

A dashpot relay of the kind used with magnetic motor starters can be used to provide the short delay in contact closing required in Figure 4-7. See relay description on Page 117.

Figure 4-8 on the next page shows a method of using a pressure switch, supplied from one source of air pressure and exhausting to a cylinder port which becomes vented at the right time.

If an impulse-type limit switch is available it is a very simple and inexpensive way of producing a short duration impulse. Too short an impulse can be generated by a cylinder moving too fast. Use this switch with caution. It is described on Page 19 and a circuit for its use is on Page 76.

When using a programmable controller to handle the electrical control, any of the suggested methods can very easily be programmed without addition of extra parts. Programmable controller operation is described in Chapter 10.

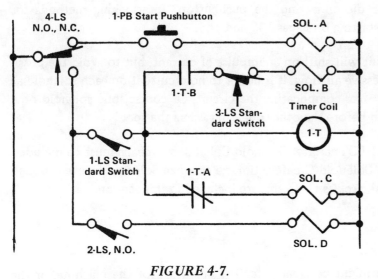

FIGURE 4-7.

Cutting off the switching signal with a timer.

Solving Clamp and Work With a Timer.
Figure 4-7. Alternate electrical circuit for air circuit of Figure 4-5A. A timer is employed to disconnect the switching circuit from 1-LS to Solenoid C. This solves the circuit difficulty stated in the second paragraph of Page 71.

The timer can be set for about half the time required for extension of Cylinder 2. When its coil is energized, its contacts do not transfer until completion of the time delay. When its coil is de-energized, its contacts will immediately re-set to time zero.

When 1-PB is pressed, Solenoid A is energized. Cylinder 1 starts forward and releases 4-LS. This removes power from the pushbutton for the rest of the cycle. When 1-LS is actuated, the timer coil and Solenoid C become energized. Cylinder 2 starts forward, releasing 3-LS. At about mid-stroke, the timer contacts transfer, de-energizing Solenoid C and preparing Solenoid B to be energized when Cylinder 2 retracts. When 2-LS is actuated, Solenoid D becomes energized and Cylinder 2 retracts. At home it actuates 3-LS. This energizes Solenoid B, causing Cylinder 1 to retract. At home, Cylinder 1 actuates and stands on 4-LS, disconnecting power from all circuits except the pushbutton.

Solving Clamp and Work With a Pressure Switch. Figure 4-8A. This is the air circuit of Figure 4-5A with the addition of a pressure switch and two check valves. Circuit action is the same except for the means to cut off the switching signal to Solenoid C after that solenoid has been energized. It is another means for solving the circuit problem in the second paragraph on Page 71. When Cylinder 1 has extended and actuated 1-LS, it continues to stand on it. Solenoid C is energized and causes Cylinder 2

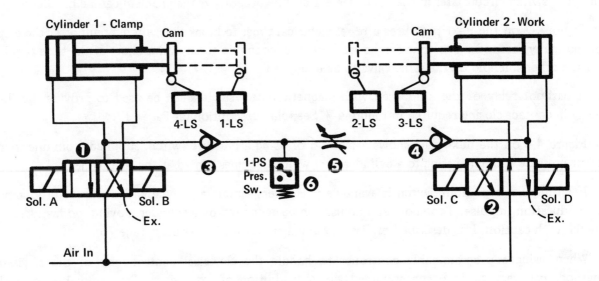

FIGURE 4-8A. Cutting off a switching signal with a pressure switch between two check valves.

to extend. Air pressure passes through check Valve 4 and actuates the pressure switch. The switch is now locked in between the two check valves and will remain actuated while Cylinder 2 is retracting. At home, actuation of 3-LS will cause Cylinder 1 to retract. This vents the blind end of Cylinder 1 and allows the pressure switch to vent to atmosphere. Two versions of electrical control are shown below.

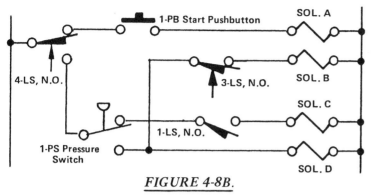

FIGURE 4-8B.
Electrical control circuit for the preceding air circuit.

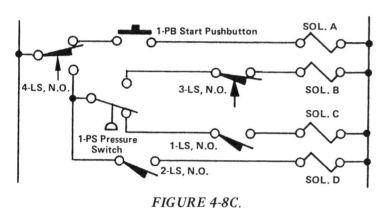

FIGURE 4-8C.
Another electrical circuit for the preceding air circuit.

Figure 4-8B. Limit Switch 2-LS is omitted and retraction of Cylinder 2 is by the pressure switch which is actuated during the forward stroke and switches the circuit from Solenoid C to Solenoid D. The pressure switch should be set a little below the stall-out pressure of the cylinder. Later, when Solenoid B is energized to retract Cylinder 1, the pressure switch can vent off through check Valve 2 and re-set.

Figure 4-8C. Alternate electrical circuit for Figure 4-8A for applications where 2-LS rather than the pressure switch is more appropriate for retraction of Cylinder 2. The pressure switch can be set to actuate either while Cylinder 2 is extending or when it stalls on its forward stroke. The pressure switch in this circuit disconnects Solenoid C and prepares a circuit for actuation of Solenoid B when Cylinder 2 returns home and actuates 3-LS.

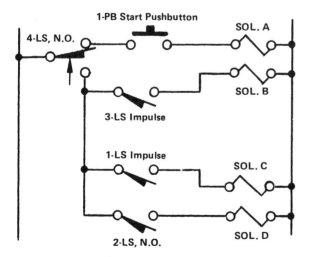

FIGURE 4-9. *Circuit with impulse limit switches to control the air cylinder circuit of Figure 4-5A.*

Solving Clamp and Work With Impulse Switches.
Figure 4-9. Alternate electrical control for air circuit of Figure 4-5A. Limt Switches 1-LS and 3-LS are the special type described on Page 19.

When the start pushbutton is pressed, Solenoid A becomes energized and Cylinder 1 starts forward, releasing 4-LS. Power is removed from the pushbutton for the rest of the cycle. Cylinder 1 actuates 1-LS, and a short impulse is produced which energizes Solenoid C and starts Cylinder 2 forward. When 2-LS is actuated, Solenoid D becomes energized and Cylinder 2 retracts, At home, Cylinder 2 actuates 3-LS, producing an impulse which energizes Solenoid B causing Cylinder 1 to retract. At home, 4-LS is actuated which removes power from all circuits except the pushbutton.

CLAMP AND WORK EXAMPLE

The example shown on these two pages has been selected for complete illustration because it typifies the requirements and problems found on most applications for clamp and work. Refer to Pages 190 and 202 for additional details of the application.

Job Specifications. This is an application for drilling end holes in one or both ends of a work-piece with drill units which use compressed air at shop air pressure for quill advance, and which use electric motors for rotating the spindles. The workpiece, after being loaded into the drilling fixture, must be held securely with an air clamp while holes are being drilled in one or both ends. The circuit must be arranged so either drill unit can be used singly or both drill units can operate together. Another requirement is that each cycle shall start when a momentary "Start" button is pressed by an operator, and that the pushbutton shall immediately be disconnected from control when the cycle starts.

On this application the choice of running either drill by itself or both together is made by using auxiliary contacts inside the magnetic motor starter. See Figure 4-12 on opposite page.

Drill Units. Several manufacturers offer self-contained drill units of the kind described above. Each drill unit can have a single-bit chuck or can have a multiple-spindle drill head designed for the job. Built-in limit switches sense hole depth and retracted position. Hydraulic checking devices can be added to minimize drill lunge if the bit breaks through the work.

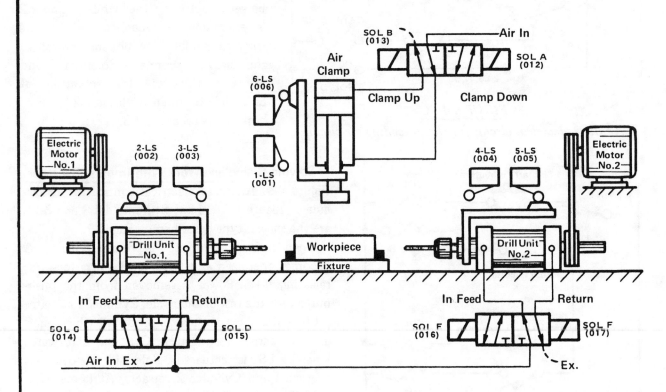

FIGURE 4-10. Air circuit with vertical air clamp in center and two opposing drill units for end hole drilling. Flow control valves can be added to each drill unit for speed restriction during free air travel. The electrical circuits are shown on the opposite page. Note: the 3-digit codes shown under each component are terminal assignment numbers when using a programmable controller to operate the system. Controllers are described in Chapter 10.

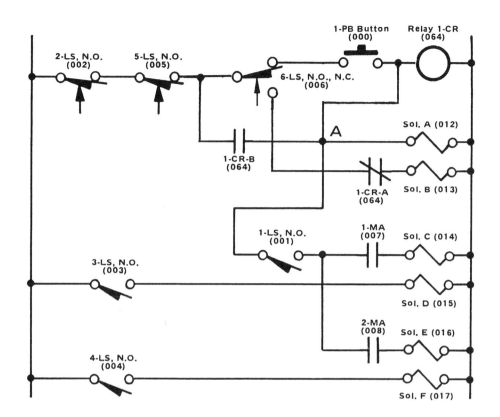

The cycle sequence is similar to the clamp and work circuit of Figure 4-6 shown in the box on Page 72.

To select choice of either drill unit or both together to operate, Contacts 1-M-B and 2-M-B on the magnetic motor starter, shown below, will prevent Solenoids C and/or E from being energized unless the drill motor is running.

"Panic" buttons can be added to this circuit in a manner similar to that shown on Page 146.

This application is used to illustrate the method of converting a JIC hard wired circuit to a ladder diagram acceptable to a programmable controller. See information on Pages 186 to 190.

FIGURE 4-11. Electric Circuit for Solenoid Valves Which Control the Drill Units and Air Clamp.

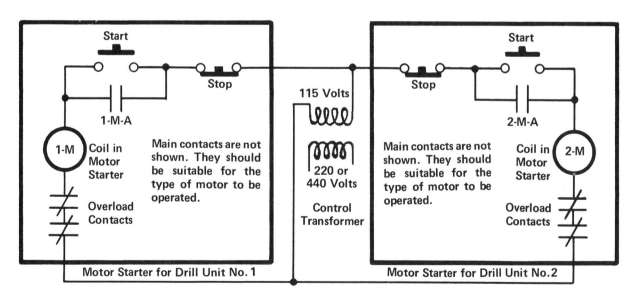

FIGURE 4-12. Partial Circuits for Magnetic Motor Starters Which Control Rotation of the Drill Unit Motors.

Partial circuits for the magnetic motor starters controlling Drill Units 1 and 2. Only the "Start" and "Stop" pushbutton circuits are shown; power circuits are omitted. Symbols 1-M and 2-M are the coils which close the main contacts; they also operate auxiliary Contacts 1-M-A and 2-M-A for the purpose of selecting operation of either one or both drill units as shown in diagram above. More on magnetic motor starters in Chapter 9.

Impulse From a Switch With a One-Way Roller Actuator. On suitable applications a very easy and reliable way of producing a short duration switching signal or "impulse" is with the use of a limit switch fitted with a one-way roller actuator or with a flattened roller as described on Pages 19 and 122. A switching signal is produced by a cam moving in one direction but no signal on the return direction of cam movement. More often used to produce an impulse while the cylinder continues to move.

Sequencing of Air Cylinders With Pressure Switches . . .

On those applications where it may not be practical to mount a limit switch for sequencing to the next cylinder, a pressure switch can usually be substituted for a standard limit switch, often with no other change in the fluid or electrical circuit. Pressure switches cannot replace impulse limit switches; the circuit must be re-designed. Any application where the cylinder may not necessarily make an exact repetition of stroke length on every cycle is an application for improved performance by using a pressure switch instead of a limit switch for cylinder sequencing. For example, a clamp cylinder holding workpieces of varying thickness, or a cylinder working against compressible material.

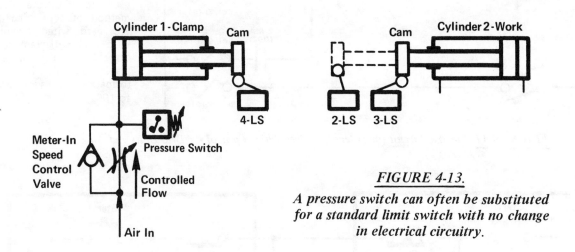

FIGURE 4-13.

A pressure switch can often be substituted for a standard limit switch with no change in electrical circuitry.

Figure 4-13. On a standard "clamp and work" application, the circuit of Figure 4-5, Part A, has been modified to replace 1-LS with a pressure switch. No modification of the electrical circuit of Figure 4-5, Part B, is necessary to accommodate this substitution.

Speed Control Considerations. When a limit switch is used to reverse an air cylinder, a speed control valve usually works equally well in either a meter-in or meter-out arrangement. But when a pressure switch is substituted, meter-in speed control as shown in Figure 4-13 is almost mandatory to avoid premature tripping of the switch during the cylinder stroke. See more details of speed control with pressure switches on Page 64.

On fully loaded moving cylinders, pressure switch reversal is usually not practical because there may not be a sufficient rise of pressure when the cylinder stalls to reliably operate the switch.

Regulation of Air Supply on Multiple-Cylinder Applications . . .

Figure 4-14. Where several cylinders are supplied from a common air line, the incoming supply of air must be sufficient so when one cylinder is operating in a free-running, no-load condition, the heavy

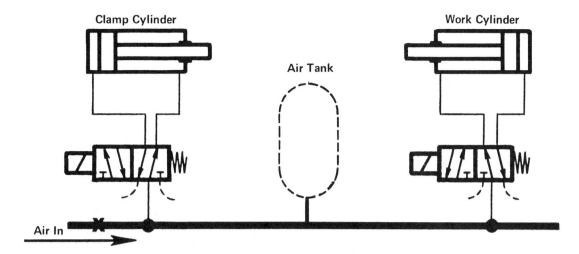

FIGURE 4-14. Multiple cylinder systems should operate from adequately sized feeder lines. An auxiliary air storage tank may be installed to improve flow regulation, and/or a check valve can be installed at Point X to prevent a momentary loss of pressure by backflow of air into another branch circuit.

air flow will not cause a significant drop in line pressure to other cylinders. If the air distribution system has been properly designed, this should not be a problem. But if the air is supplied through a long line of small diameter, pressure regulation can become a problem. Air pressure regulators installed near each cylinder will not solve the problem if the input line to the regulators is restricted. On some applications and under certain conditions, even a momentary drop in line pressure could be diastrous. For example, a clamp cylinder might momentarily lose its grip when another cylinder starts forward in free travel. A simple test can be made by gauging the line pressure on the critical cylinder while the other cylinder is stopped, then while it is moving. The pressure gauge for such a test should be installed directly at the cylinder port.

One solution to a starved air supply may be to install an additional receiver tank as close as possible to the valve inlet port of the second cylinder as shown above.

Please refer to the Womack books "Industrial Fluid Power — Volumes 1 and 2" for a detailed treatment of meter-in and meter-out speed control methods.

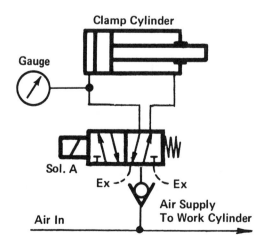

Figure 4-15. To prevent momentary loss of clamping force because of backflow of air when another cylinder operating on the same air supply starts into motion, a check valve can be installed at the pressure inlet of the 4-way valve which controls the clamp cylinder, or at Point X in the feeder line in Figure 4-14. This often provides a simple, reliable, and inexpensive safety measure. Pressure gauging directly at the port of the critical cylinder (not at the 4-way valve inlet) will show whether a safety check will be effective.

The remedies suggested in Figures 4-14 and 4-15 are effective only for malfunctions caused

FIGURE 4-15. Check valve at 4-way valve inlet may prevent clamp from losing its grip on a momentary loss of pressure.

by momentary pressure drop due to friction losses in the supply line. They cannot solve the problem if the air compressor is undersize and cannot maintain adequate pressure.

Sequencing Air Cylinders With Electric Timers . . .

Sometimes, sequencing problems which are so highly involved as to require complicated electric circuitry, can be handled with a program timer. See Page 123. This solution, although easy, is not necessarily recommended in every case because it may require more time on every cycle. Each function must have an over-allotment of time to make sure one cylinder has completed its movement before the next one is started by the timer. This is especially true on air circuits where cylinder speed is influenced by magnitude of the load. No extra allotment of time is necessary when using limit switches.

This method of sequencing must be used with caution, to be sure that premature starting of the next cylinder by a timer would not endanger personnel, the machine, or the workpieces. To safeguard against this kind of disaster, a limit switch can be mounted at the end of a cylinder stroke to shut down the machine if the next cylinder starts before the previous one has finished its stroke.

A compromise in difficult circuitry is to use a combination of limit switch sequencing for the easy steps in the sequence, and combine this with one or more re-set timers to handle the difficult steps.

SEQUENCING OF HYDRAULIC CYLINDERS

General Requirements . . .

When two or more hydraulic cylinders must work in an automatic programmed relation to each other such as the "clamp and work" program described on Page 70, several requirements must be met either in the hydraulic or the electrical circuit, or both. A means must be provided for unloading the pump at the end of each cycle and during periods when the cylinders are not moving. Sequence circuits in this section are illustrated with several unloading arrangements. Although there may be a few exceptions, most applications require that an oil lock be maintained on one or both ports of a hydraulic cylinder while it is stopped. Several ways of providing this oil lock are illustrated later. Most hydraulic circuits use double solenoid, 3-position valves for the main directional control. Single solenoid valves sometimes are adequate for auxiliary or branch circuits. Since current must be maintained on the solenoids of a valve with spring centered or spring returned spool to keep the cylinder in motion, electrical circuitry for hydraulic valves is usually more difficult than for an air circuit with similar action.

When designing any hydraulic system the first and most important step is to decide what kind of a fluid circuit will best fit job requirements. Since job results are produced by the hydraulic and not the electrical circuit, the fluid layout is of primary importance and the electrical means for controlling it are secondary.

Pump Unloading Methods Suitable for Sequencing Circuits . . .

The four unloading methods shown in Figure 4-16 on the next page are the common ones used in most hydraulic systems. Examples of hydraulic sequencing circuits with each of these methods will be described in this section. All of these methods have been covered in more detail in the Womack book "Industrial Fluid Power — Volume 2", but will be briefly reviewed here.

Full Tandem Center. Figure 4-16, Part A. Two or more tandem center valves are connected in a series string with the outlet of one valve feeding the inlet of the next. When all solenoids are de-ener-

(Text continues on Page 83)

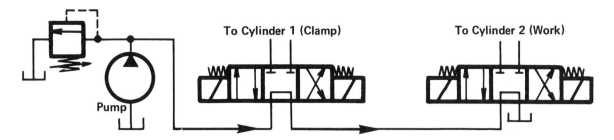

<u>A</u>. The pump is unloaded through a string of tandem center control valves. This method can only be used on those applications where full pump pressure is never needed on more than one cylinder at a time.

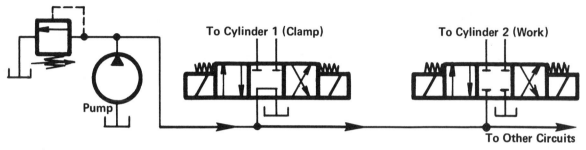

<u>B</u>. A modified tandem center unloading circuit where full pump pressure can be maintained on several cylinders at the same time. Can be used only on selected applications as explained in the text.

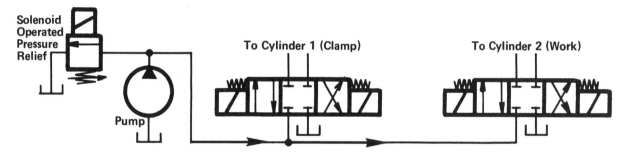

<u>C</u>. Solenoid vent unloading for operation of several branch circuits in parallel. Closed center 4-way valves are generally used. Some designers consider this the best arrangement for operation of multiple branch systems.

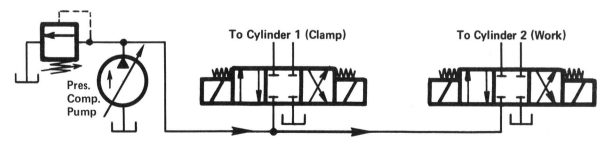

<u>D</u>. Operating parallel branch circuits with a variable displacement, pressure compensated pump. When all valves are centered, the rise in pressure causes the compensator to reduce pump displacement to near zero.

FIGURE 4-16. Block diagram for four popular methods of unloading a hydraulic pump.

gized, all valve spools return to center position and pump oil can flow to tank with a flow resistance equal to pipe and valve flow loss. Usually no more than two or three valves are connected in this way because flow loss becomes too high.

When any solenoid on Valve 1 or 2 is energized, pump flow is intercepted and is diverted to the associated cylinder. Return oil from the cylinder enters the series plumbing and flows downstream to the next valve.

If two solenoids, one on each valve were to be energized at the same time, pump oil would be connected to two cylinders in series. Neither cylinder could receive full pump pressure; it would be divided between them in proportion to their respective loads. Therefore, tandem center unloading is suitable only for hydraulic circuits where no more than one cylinder will be operating at any one time. This is a true condition for sequencing, so if sequence valves are used to separate cylinder action, all cylinders can receive oil through the same 4-way valve which can be a tandem center type. This is illustrated later in Figure 4-24. But on circuits other than sequencing, where each cylinder must operate independently from the others, but where only one is in operation at a time, these must be controlled with individual 4-way valves which can be tandem center type.

On circuits where several branches must have full pump pressure at the same time, cylinders in those branches must be placed in parallel across the pump line, controlled with closed center 4-way valves.

Modified Tandem Center. Figure 4-16, Part B.

Modified Tandem Center. Figure 4-16, Part B. This is a modified version of the full tandem center. Pressure ports of both (or all) valves are connected in parallel across the pump line. This gives all circuits equal access to the full pressure. When both solenoids of all valves are de-energized, the valve spools are centered and the pump can unload through the spool of Valve 1.

The modified tandem center arrangement will provide access to the full pressure on both cylinders provided Valve 1 is the first one to be shifted at the start of the cycle and is the last one to be centered at the end of the cycle. During the cycle, Valve 1 spool can be shifted from side to side but must not be centered. This action makes the modified tandem ideally suited for "clamp and work" applications where Cylinder 1 is the clamp and Cylinder 2 the work cylinder.

Solenoid Vent Unloading for Sequence Circuits. Figure 4-16, Part C. Although tandem center unloading is simple to use and the least expensive method of unloading a pump, there are cases where it may be unacceptable. The solenoid vent unloading method in Part C can be used in almost any system. This is a method where, with a miniature 2-way solenoid valve connected in the relief valve vent port, the pump relief valve can be opened to dump the full pump flow through the relief valve poppet. On any system the solenoid vent method may offer these advantages:

(1). Will permit operation of any number of branch circuits from a common pump with full pump pressure available to all branches at the same time.

(2). Will accommodate a program with any desired sequence between branch cylinders, and is not limited to any priority order in which the branch circuit valves must be shifted.

(3). Will give smoother starts and stops and less pressure shock than tandem center systems. This is particularly important on higher powered systems.

(4). Tends to produce less heating of the oil because the pump can be unloaded to a pressure of about 50 PSI. With several cylinders in a tandem circuit the back pressure, with the pump unloaded, may be from 100 to several hundred PSI depending on number and size of valves in the series loop.

At the heart of solenoid vent unloading is an electrically operated pressure relief valve called a solenoid controlled, pilot-operated relief valve. The solenoid can be incorporated as part of the valve structure, or a 3/8" 2-way solenoid valve can be used externally, connected between the vent port of the relief valve and tank.

The solenoid venting principle is completely described on Page 99, and briefly its action can be summarized in this way: When the solenoid is de-energized, the pump flow goes to tank across the main poppet — the only resistance to flow being the cracking pressure of the non-adjustable main spring, usually about 50 PSI. When the solenoid is energized it blocks the vent line flow, causing the pump pressure to build up to equal load resistance but no higher than the setting of the adjustable main knob. There is little shock because of the slight delay in build-up and decay of pressure.

Directional valves used with solenoid vent unloading are usually double solenoid, spring centered models with full closed center. Or, at least the pressure port and one cylinder port closed.

Pressure Compensated Pump Unloading. Figure 4-16, Part D. A variable displacement, pressure compensated pump replaces the fixed displacement pump shown in other circuits of Figure 4-16. Any number of branch circuits can be operated in parallel by a common pump. When all 4-way valves are centered the pump is "deadheaded" across the circuit. This causes pump pressure to build up to the adjusted setting of the pressure compensator. The compensator "fires" and reduces pump displacement to near zero, with only enough oil being pumped to make up slippage in closed center valve spools and in the pump itself. A small relief valve, about 1/2" size is recommended across the pump line to cushion high pressure spikes which may be produced by shock loads before the compensator has time to mechanically reduce pump displacement. The relief valve can be set about 500 PSI higher than the compensator to prevent a steady oil discharge during normal running.

Directional valves used in these circuits should have pressure port closed in neutral. Usually full closed center models are used.

Note: Single lobe vane pumps and some piston pumps are mechanically unbalanced — that is, hydraulic pressure creates a bearing load in proportion to the pressure. When one of these pumps is running at full pressure, even though it may be compensated to zero flow, running time must be counted as part of its B-10 bearing life rating just as if it was producing full power. For most variable displacement piston pumps a load sensing control is available which will have the compensating action described but will allow the pump to run at a reduced pressure while fully compensated. Running time at 3/4 or less of maximum pressure rating is not counted as reducing the B-10 bearing rating. If the pump will remain idling at full pressure for an appreciable time between cycles, a load sensing control should be used if available.

Oil Lock on Cylinder Ports . . .

Figure 4-17. In addition to selecting the method of pump unloading, another important consideration in a hydraulic system is that a cylinder may have to be stopped at a mid point in its stroke and held in this position with an oil lock on one or both of its ports. Three ways of locking a cylinder are shown in this figure. However, no matter how leaktight the external valving may be, if a cylinder must hold a load stationary in mid stroke for a long time, it may slowly drift out of position because of cylinder piston leakage or valve spool leakage. Drifting is usually in the extension direction because of less cavity volume in the rod end. If it can be mounted with rod up, cylinder drift may not be as severe.

Part A. Most often used for an oil lock is a 3-position 4-way valve with blocked cylinder ports in center, or at least the cylinder port blocked which is in the direction of drift. Most often used are tandem or closed center spools. Open center spools do not provide the blocked cylinder ports.

Part B. If a 4-way valve is used which does not have a blocked cylinder port, a pilot-operated check valve can be installed in one or both cylinder ports to hold the cylinder in position when pump pres-

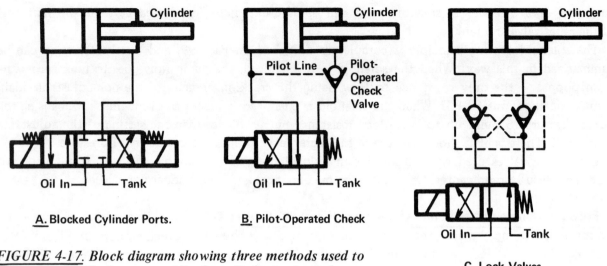

A. Blocked Cylinder Ports. B. Pilot-Operated Check C. Lock Valves.

FIGURE 4-17. Block diagram showing three methods used to oil-lock cylinder ports while the cylinder is stopped.

sure is removed from the valve inlet. Pilot-operated check valves can also be used in the circuit of Part A. Hovever, these check valves will not prevent drift due to piston seal leakage.

Part C. If pilot-operated check valves are to be used in both cylinder ports, a more economical means is to use a lock valve. This is two pilot-operated check valves in one package. All cross port pilot connections are made through holes drilled in the body.

SEQUENCING IN HYDRAULIC CIRCUITS

Sequencing involves the interaction between two or more cylinders through an automatic cycle. Before the electrical circuit can be designed, the hydraulic circuit must be designed with specifications

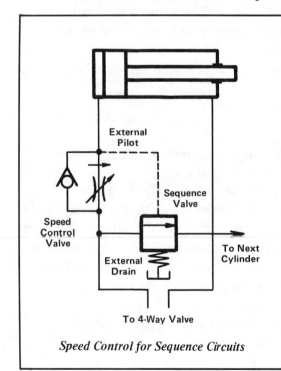

Speed Control for Sequence Circuits

Notes on Sequence Valve Operation

The drain port on a sequence valve must always be connected directly to tank. If internally drained it will act like a relief valve.

On applications where a speed control valve must be used, the meter-in speed control method must be used. The sequence valve must be externally piloted and must take pilot pressure downstream of the speed control valve, directly at the cylinder port. If connected for internal piloting, it may open prematurely.

If several sequence valves are used in series as in Figure 4-24, each valve can be set for a different opening pressure. When a sequence valve opens, since it is externally piloted, there will be no power or pressure loss through it to the next cylinder. Each cylinder, when it stalls, will be exposed to maximum pressure as set on the pump relief valve.

Each sequence valve must be set higher than the normal operating pressure, while in motion, of the cylinder which will feed into it. If set lower, the sequence valve will open prematurely, diverting some of the oil to the next cylinder. Sequence valves are described in detail in the Womack book "Industrial Fluid Power – Volume 2".

as to the order in which each cylinder extends and retracts. For applications described in this section we are using two cylinders operating in a "clamp and work" sequence because this kind of action is typical of most sequencing applications. The order in which the cylinders extend and retract is the same as shown in the box on Page 72 for air cylinders. The clamp cylinder extends first and must remain in this position with full active pressure on its piston while the work cylinder advances and retracts. Only then can the clamping force be released and the clamp cylinder retracted. We refer the reader to the Womack book "Industrial Fluid Power — Volume 2" for other sequencing circuits.

Sequence Circuit With Solenoid Vent Pump Unloading

Figure 4-18. Directional valves for both cylinders are double solenoid, 3-position, closed center models. Closed center valves must be used so the two branches can be connected in parallel with full pump pressure available to both branches at the same time.

A fixed displacement pump is used. At the end of each cycle the pump must be unloaded to tank. The unloading method chosen for this circuit is to vent the pump relief valve. The method is shown in Part C of Figure 4-16 on Page 82 and described in detail on Page 99.

In most sequencing circuits, especially those for clamp and work, it is necessary to allow the clamp cylinder to remain at forward stall with full pressure behind its piston while the work cylinder is advancing (or retracting) at a lower pressure. A sequence valve is the only practical way of doing this. It

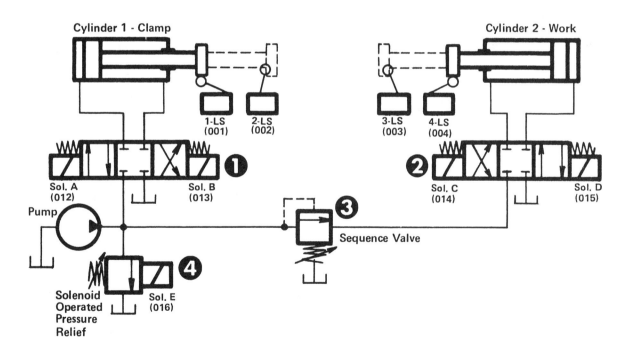

FIGURE 4-18. Working hydraulic circuit showing the use of 3-position spring centered valves for "clamp and work" sequence program. Solenoid vent pump unloading.

will withhold oil flow to the work cylinder until the clamp has fully advanced and has stalled at the pressure level set on the sequence valve. Note: The air sequence circuit of Figure 4-5 is not suitable for hydraulic cylinders. The clamp would lose its grip when the work cylinder started to move. Sequence valve action can be reviewed in the Womack book "Industrial Fluid Power — Volume 2".

Specifications for Electrical Control of Figure 4-18. The electrical circuit of Figure 4-19 is designed for "clamp and work" control of the preceding fluid circuit. If a different sequencing order is required, the circuit must be modified, but will usually be simpler. Requirements are as follows:

(1). Some kind of electrical sensor is required at each end of the stroke on every cylinder in order to start the next action. In this circuit limit switches are shown. At some locations pressure switches or proximity switches might be more suitable.

(2). Each time one or more of the valve solenoids is energized, Solenoid E on the relief valve must also be energized through a separate circuit at the same time to produce hydraulic pressure.

(3). As precautions against accidents, as soon as the cycle starts, the pushbutton should be disconnected from its power for the remainder of the cycle. Also, before the cycle starts, all limit switches which could be accidentally actuated should be isolated from the power bus.

(4). At the end of each cycle the pump should be left in an unloaded state. All current should be removed from valve solenoids and other load devices.

(5). On some valves a solenoid coil may burn out if both solenoids of a double solenoid valve are energized at the same time. Be aware of possible valve limitations.

(6). After a valve coil is energized, current must be held on it until its cylinder completes its stroke. And on some applications, like Figure 4-18, current must be maintained after the cylinder stops, to keep the cylinder stalled under full pressure.

(7). On some applications a cylinder may have to stop, or stop and reverse, in the middle of its stroke. A switch or other electrical sensor must be placed at each location where a new or repeat action must start or finish, except where a sequence valve may start the next action.

Drawing an Electrical Ladder Diagram. Rules for drawing these diagrams have been given on Page 34. Please review those rules before attempting to draw your first diagram.

Description of Electrical Circuit Action. Figure 4-19. This electrical circuit has been developed for operation of the "clamp and work" hydraulic circuit of Figure 4-18. To help in understanding the circuit action it will help immensely to make 7 or 8 copies of Figure 4-19 on an office copy machine. Use a felt tip pen to color in the current flow as it changes every time a limit switch is actuated. For example, use one copy to color in the current flow before the pushbutton is pressed. Use the next copy to color in current flow when the pushbutton is pressed. The next copy can show current flow when the clamp cylinder moves far enough to release limit Switch 1-LS, etc. When designing a new circuit, this technique can detect circuit mistakes which might ordinarily go unnoticed. See Page 41 for more details of this procedure. Circuit action in Figure 4-19 is as follows:

When 1-PB pushbutton is pressed, Solenoid A becomes energized through 1-LS. Relay 1-CR is also energized through 1-LS and 2-CR-B contacts. This relay locks in electrically through its own contacts 1-CR-A. Contacts 1-CR-B in Rung 5 close to energize Solenoid E.

Cylinder 1 starts forward and releases 1-LS. This removes power from the pushbutton for the rest of the cycle and provides power for the rest of the circuit from the auxiliary bus.

When Cylinder 1 extends and actuates 2-LS (shown in Rung 7), this energizes Solenoid C through 4-CR-C. It also energizes Relay 3-CR and this relay locks closed through Contacts 3-CR-A. Cylinder 2 advances with oil flowing across the sequence valve while Cylinder 1 remains stalled against 2-LS under full pressure.

As Cylinder 2 advances a short distance LS-4 switch is released. This does not change current flow through the circuit at this time, but it does prepare Solenoid B to be energized later in the cycle when Cylinder 2 reaches home.

Cylinder 2 advances and actuates 3-LS. Solenoid D and Relay 4-CR become energized. Relay 4-CR locks in through 4-CR-A. Solenoid C becomes de-energized. Cylinder 2 retracts.

When Cylinder 2 reaches home it actuates 4-LS. This energizes Relay 2-CR and Solenoid B. Contact 2-CR-B breaks the circuit to Relay 1-CR. Solenoid A becomes de-energized when Contacts 1-CR-A open. Cylinder 1 retracts to home and actuates 1-LS. This drops out relays which are still holding and restores power to the pushbutton for starting the next cycle.

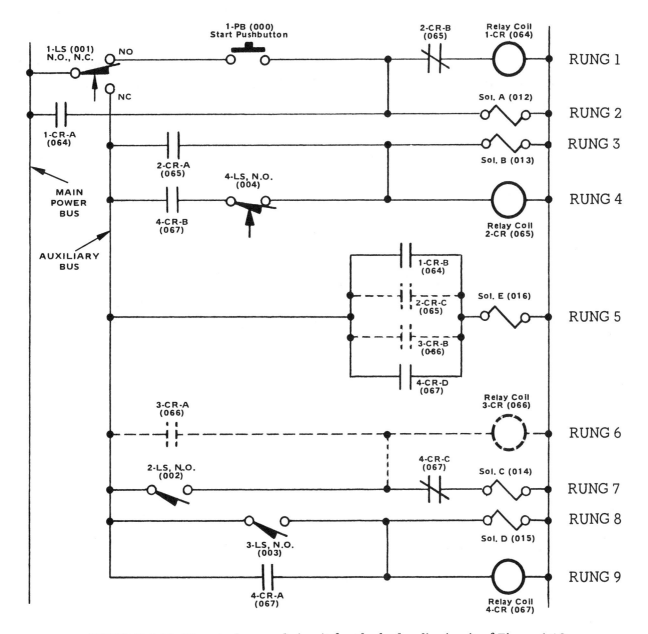

FIGURE 4-19. Electrical control circuit for the hydraulic circuit of Figure 4-18.

Suggestions for Making a Diagram for a New Circuit. If you are just learning to draw electrical diagrams these suggestions may help you develop an orderly procedure. Please refer to Figure 4-19 as you study these suggestions.

If using spring centered or spring return solenoid valves, plan on using one holding relay (CR) for each valve solenoid to start off with. These are shown as 1-CR, 2-CR, 3-CR, and 4-CR on Rungs 1, 4, 6, and 9. Sometimes one or more of these relays can be eliminated when the diagram has been fully developed. For example, on Figure 4-19, after the diagram was completed, Relay 3-CR was found to be unnecessary and was eliminated. It is retained in dotted lines for illustration.

When using the solenoid vent method of pump unloading, Solenoid E (on the relief valve) must also be energized every time one of the other solenoids is energized. Four contacts, one from each relay, are connected in parallel to Solenoid E. In this case, contacts from 1-CR and 4-CR are sufficient to keep Solenoid E energized, and Contacts from 2-CR and 3-CR (in dotted lines) can be omitted.

Limit Switch 1-LS is an excellent way of removing power from the pushbutton as soon as the cycle starts. Relay 1-CR becomes energized as soon as the pushbutton is pressed. But its holding contact, 1-CR-A, must receive power from the main bus to avoid the possibility of the relay dropping back out during transfer of 1-LS switch contacts. All other rungs can receive power from the auxiliary bus connected to the N.C. terminal of 1-LS.

Switch 2-LS presents the old problem of what to do when a cylinder remains standing on a limit switch after actuating it. Later in the cycle, by some means, Solenoid C must be disconnected from 2-LS before Solenoid D is energized to retract Cylinder 2. In this circuit it was done by placing a N.C. contact from 4-CR relay in series with Solenoid C. When Cylinder 2 extends and actuates 3-LS, this breaks the circuit from 2-LS to Solenoid C. Other means could probably be used if found compatible with the circuit.

Modified Tandem Center Pump Unloading.

Figure 4-20, Hydraulic Circuit. See Pages 82 and 83 for this kind of circuit. Valve 1 to operate the clamp cylinder must have a tandem center spool for pump unloading. Valve 2 for the work cylinder

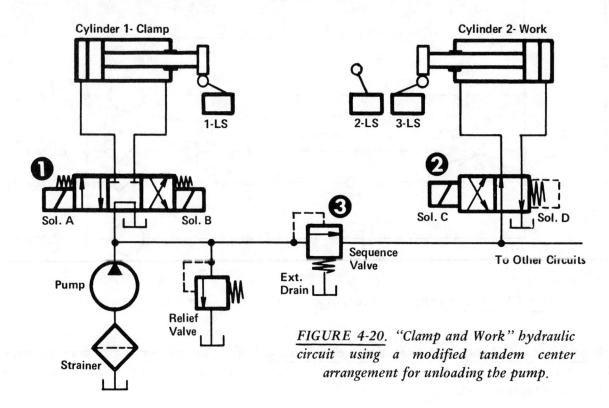

FIGURE 4-20. "Clamp and Work" hydraulic circuit using a modified tandem center arrangement for unloading the pump.

can be a 2-position model, either single or double solenoid. A single solenoid model is, however, less expensive.

When the clamp cylinder extends and stalls against the work, the sequence valve opens and supplies flow to advance Cylinder 2. A limit switch is not needed at full extension of Cylinder 1 because no electrical action takes place there.

There are limitations on the use of sequence valves which are explained on Page 85. No attempt should be made to use meter-out speed control of a cylinder which is just ahead of a sequence valve. If speed control is needed for controlling advance of Cylinder 1, use the circuit in the box on Page 85.

Electrical Action. Figure 4-21. When the pushbutton is pressed, Solenoid A and C and Relay 1-CR become energized. The relay locks in through 1-CR-A contacts. Cylinder 1 starts forward but Cylinder 2 cannot move until it receives a flow of oil across the sequence valve. After a short movement of Cylinder 1 the pushbutton becomes inactive for the rest of the cycle.

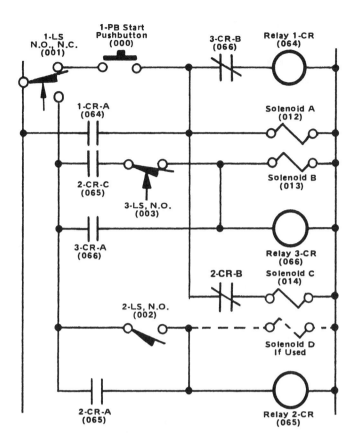

FIGURE 4-21.

Electrical circuit for controlling the hydraulic circuit of Figure 4-20.

Cylinder 1 extends and stalls against the work. Pressure rises in the pump line and oil flows across the sequence valve to extend Cylinder 2.

As Cylinder 2 advances a short distance, 3-LS is released. This does not change current flow through the circuit at this time, but it does prepare Solenoid B to be actuated when Cylinder 2 returns home.

Cylinder 2 extends and actuates 2-LS. This locks in Relay 2-CR. Solenoid C is de-energized and Solenoid D is energized. Cylinder 2 retracts to home and actuates 3-LS. This locks in Relay 3-CR and energizes Solenoid B. Solenoid A is de-energized by opening of Contacts 3-CR-B. Cylinder 2 now retracts to home and actuates 1-LS. Relays 2-CR and 3-CR drop out and the pushbutton is re-activated.

Pressure Compensated Pump Unloading

Figure 4-22. The principle of using a pressure compensated pump to supply several branch circuits connected in parallel has been covered in Figure 4-16, Part D on Page 82 and on Page 84.

A "clamp and work" sequence circuit between two cylinders, using a pressure compensated pump, could be designed in a similar way to that shown in Figure 4-18 on Page 86 by replacing the fixed displacement pump and solenoid vented relief valve with a pressure compensated pump and a small (1/2" size) adjustable, direct-acting, relief valve. The electrical control circuit of Figure 4-19 could be used by simply omitting Rung 5.

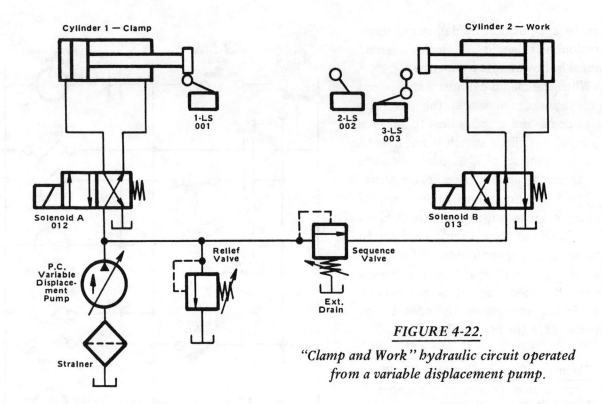

FIGURE 4-22.

*"Clamp and Work" hydraulic circuit operated
from a variable displacement pump.*

Variable Displacement Pump. Figure 4-22. This is another "clamp and work" circuit powered with a variable displacement, pressure compensated pump. It is shown in its simplest form, both hydraulic and electrical, and is suitable for many applications where no greater sophistication is required.

Hydraulic Circuit. Figure 4-22. Directional 4-way valves for both cylinders can be single solenoid, 2-position models. These valves will not permit the cylinders to be stopped at any intermediate position in their strokes. But for many simple applications this is not necessary.

The sequence valve is a vital part of this circuit just as it is on every program where one cylinder is allowed to stall under full pressure while other cylinders are advancing or retracting at a lower pressure. At the completion of every cycle, both cylinders have retracted and remain at stall under full pressure at their home positions. Pump line pressure rises and the compensator then causes the pump displacement to be reduced to near zero. This unloads the pump although it may still be running at maximum pressure but producing only a small flow to make up for circuit leakage.

If necessary, review sequence valve action on Page 85 and in the Womack book "Industrial Fluid Power — Volume 2". If a speed control valve must be added to any cylinder operating into a sequence valve it must be connected as shown in the box on Page 85.

Electrical Circuit. Figure 4-23. This circuit, too, has been stripped down to bare essentials. A limit switch must be mounted at home position of Cylinder 1 and at both ends of the stroke of Cylinder 2. Limit Switches 1-LS and 2-LS are standard switches. Switch 3-LS is a standard switch which has been fitted with a one-way roller actuator. This actuator is described on Page 19. In one direction of cam movement the switch contacts are actuated. In the opposite direction of cam movement, the contacts are not actuated. Thus, a short duration switching impulse, either make or break, is produced in only one direction of cam movement. Be sure 3-LS is mounted so it will be actuated as Cylinder 2 retracts, and that its roller is released before Cylinder 2 stalls at home position. Where these switches can be used, the electrical circuit can be simplified, and sometimes several holding relays can be omitted.

Circuit Action. When the pushbutton is pressed, Solenoids A and B and Relay 1-CR become energized. The relay locks closed through 1-CR-A contacts. Cylinder 1 will start but Cylinder 2 cannot move until Cylinder 1 has stalled and oil is received across the sequence valve.

When Cylinder 1 has started to advance, Switch 1-LS is released. This removes power from the pushbutton for the rest of the cycle.

Cylinder 1 advances to stall, then Cylinder 2 starts to advance. No switching impulse is produced by 3-LS in this direction of movement. When Switch 2-LS is actuated, Relay 2-CR becomes energized and locks closed through Contacts 2-CR-A. Contacts 2-CR-B cause Solenoid

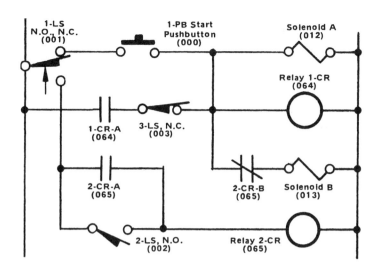

FIGURE 4-23. Electrical control circuit for the hydraulic circuit of Figure 4-22.

B to become de-energized. Cylinder 2 retracts and near home position an impulse BREAK from Switch 3-LS causes Relay 1-CR to drop out and Cylinder 1 to retract.

At home position of Cylinder 1, limit Switch 1-LS is actuated. This restores power to the pushbutton for the start of the next cycle, and releases Relay 2-CR.

Tandem Center Pump Unloading in Sequence Circuits

Tandem center pump unloading was described on Pages 81 and 82. Only one cylinder at a time can be operated with full pump pressure, so this circuit cannot be used on some applications for serving two or more branch circuits from a common pump. But most clamp and work applications have only one cylinder in motion at any one time, so tandem center operation may be ideal for those applications.

In this section we are still dealing with "clamp and work" circuits in which one (or several) cylinders must stall under full pressure while another cylinder is working at a lower pressure.

Hydraulic Circuit. Figure 4-24. Three cylinders are shown. They can be arranged to operate in a desired sequence on extension and in the same or a different sequence while retracting. Sequence valves prevent the next cylinder from starting until the preceding cylinder has reached sequence valve setting or has stalled. One requirement is that each cylinder which precedes a sequence valve must be able to move its load at or below sequence valve setting. When it stalls it will come up to the pressure of the pump relief valve. If any cylinder must move at higher than sequence valve setting, the next cylinder will start prematurely. Sequence valves are usually set about 10% below relief valve pressure.

In Figure 4-24 the sequence has been set up for the cylinders to extend in 1, 2, and 3 order. For retraction the order is 3, 1, then 2. If a speed control is needed on any cylinder, either for extension or retraction, it must be connected for meter-in control and connected in reference to the sequence valve as shown in the box on Page 85.

Electrical Circuit. Figure 4-25. A limit switch must be placed at home position of the first cylinder to extend (Cylinder 1 in this case), at the extended position of the last cylinder (Cylinder 3), and at home position of the last cylinder to retract (Cylinder 2 in this example). All are standard limit switches.

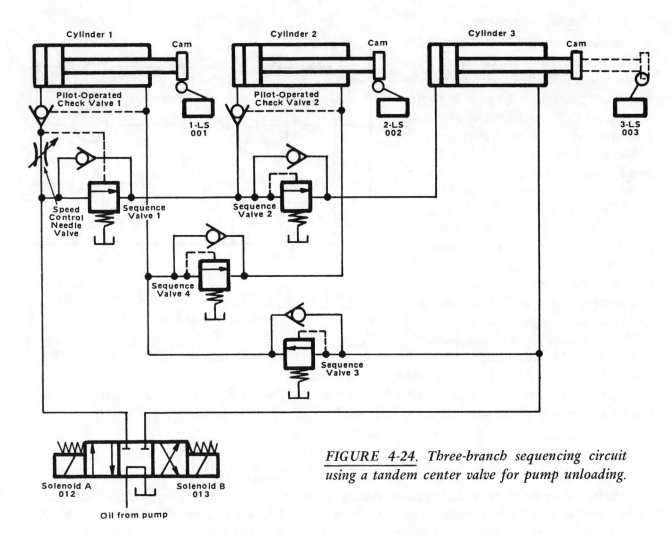

FIGURE 4-24. Three-branch sequencing circuit using a tandem center valve for pump unloading.

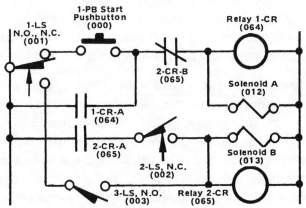

FIGURE 4-25. Electrical control circuit for the hydraulic circuit above.

Circuit Action. When the pushbutton is pressed, Solenoid A and Relay 1-CR become energized. The relay locks closed through 1-CR-A and 2-CR-B contacts. Cylinder 1 advances, releasing Switch 1-LS. This de-activates the pushbutton. Cylinder 1 extends and stalls, then Cylinder 2 starts forward, releasing Switch 2-LS. This does not change circuit action until the end of the cycle. Cylinder 2 extends and stalls, then Cylinder 3 starts forward. When Switch 3-LS is actuated, this starts reversal. Solenoid B and Relay 2-CR become energized. The relay locks closed through 2-CR-A and 2-LS (now closed). Cylinder 3 retracts and stalls, then Cylinder 1 retracts. Cylinder 1 stalls at home, then Cylinder 2 retracts. At home, 2-LS is actuated and power is restored to the pushbutton.

CHAPTER 5

Pressure Control by Electrical Means

When we speak of controlling the pressure in a compressed air or hydraulic system, we are usually concerned with controlling the *maximum* level, beyond which the fluid pressure will not be permitted to rise. Students of fluid power will remember that pressure limiting devices are necessary to keep the system operating within the safe power handling capacity for which it was designed. Additional reasons might be to produce a very precise force against a workpiece, with neither too much or too little force. Or, to prevent distorting or crushing a workpiece, or to prevent tool damage. In all fluid systems, pressure limiting is accomplished with some sort of valving device. This is usually a pressure regulator in a compressed air system, and a relief, or by-pass valve in a hydraulic system. By using a solenoid valve in conjunction with these devices, a degree of control over their maximum pressure setting can be established from a remote point through electrical circuitry.

The operating principle of air pressure regulators has been covered in "Industrial Fluid Power — Volume 1", and the construction and operation of hydraulic pressure control valving in Volume 2 of the same series. The student may wish to review those descriptions. In this book we are concerned only with electrically controlling their pressure settings.

ELECTRICAL CONTROL OF AIR PRESSURE

The variation of air pressure level by electrical control, while not common in industrial applications, can sometimes be used to advantage. One application which comes to mind is for marking or staking an assortment of parts made from different materials, using the same die. An electric switch provides a rapid and precise means of changing the force level on the tool according to the hardness of the material being stamped. Another application is on a small tapping machine where air pressure is used to "crowd" the tap. When using taps of different diameter or lead, the crowding pressure can be quickly changed with a flip switch to a choice of several accurately pre-set pressures.

The simplest method of step level air pressure control is to provide one standard regulator for each pressure level desired, and to divert air flow through a selected regulator by means of solenoid diverter valves. Sometimes, on very critical applications, precision regulators may be necessary, but on most applications standard regulators will be satisfactory. Miniature regulators may not be as accurate as standard regulators and should be used only after evaluation to be sure they will maintain the accuracy required. Those brands built strictly for economy may not be sufficiently accurate.

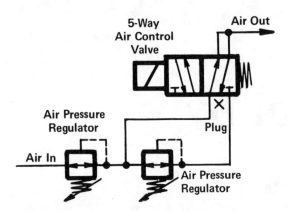

FIGURE 5-1. *Normally, two regulators should not be used in series. A parallel connection will give more accurate pressure control.*

Figure 5-1. *Do not* connect two pressure regulators in series as shown here. The error in the first regulator will be added to the error in the second regulator. But even more important, there will probably be a gap in the pressure range between the lowest setting of the first regulator and the highest setting of the second regulator. Regulators in the diagrams of Figure 5-2 on the next page are always connected in parallel. If desired, one of them can be a high range model, the other a low range model. This will produce a more accurate control with no gaps in the pressure range.

Figure 5-2. The examples in this figure show various ways of using solenoid selector valves to deliver step increments of pressure by remote electrical control.

Best results can probably be obtained with circuits of Parts D and E using relieving-type regulators installed *ahead* of the solenoid selector valve. Circuits in Parts A, B, and C have the regulator installed *following* the solenoid valve. On those circuits, relieving regulators cannot be used because they would permit a backflow of air to atmosphere through the regulator with the lower setting while the other regulator(s) was in operation. Non-relieving regulators have a disadvantage on some applications: if the regulators happen to be feeding into a dead-end circuit (no air flow), and if the selector valve should be shifted to a regulator with a lower setting, the system pressure could not adjust downward to the lower level until excess trapped pressure could be vented.

Note: On circuits shown in Figure 5-2, where a valve port is shown plugged, be sure to use a valve brand which is so constructed that plugging a port will not unseat the seals.

Figure 5-2, Part A. Since the double solenoid valve will shift and remain in shifted position on a momentary electrical impulse, the desired pressure level can be selected with momentary pushbuttons. Or, instead of manual pushbuttons, the valve solenoids can be wired to shift automatically from signals produced elsewhere in the system when a different pressure is required. The air regulators must be the non-relieving type, or, relieving regulators can be used if a check valve is placed at Point X following each regulator. This will prevent unwanted backflow as described above.

Figure 5-2, Part B. A 3-position, double solenoid air valve with closed center spool will allow electrical selection of high pressure, lower pressure, or no pressure (Off). The valve must be operated from a maintained-type switch such as a 3-position toggle switch with center off. Non-relieving type regulators must be used, or a check valve must be installed at each Point X to prevent backflow.

Figure 5-2, Part C. A 3-position, double solenoid air valve with open pressure port in neutral must

(Text continued on Page 97)

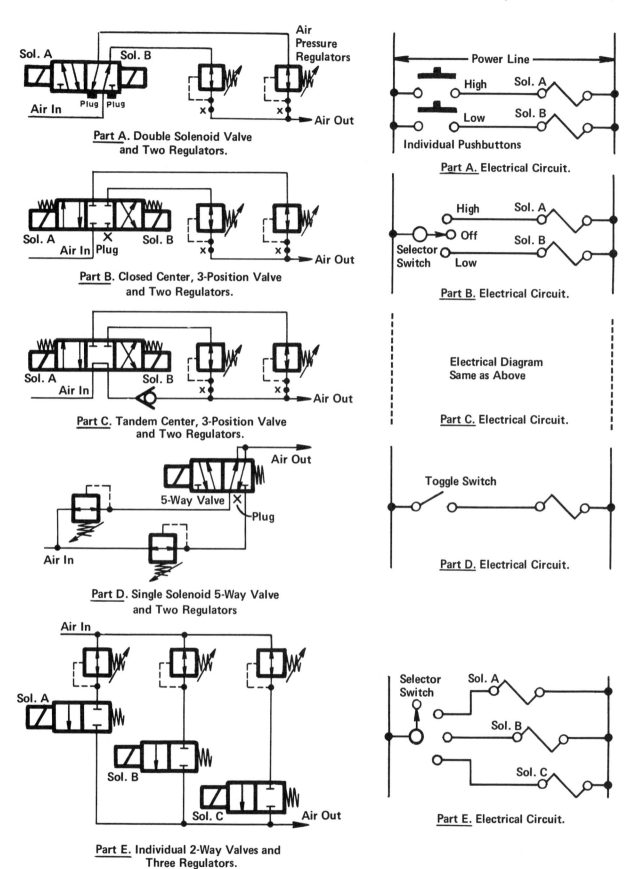

FIGURE 5-2. Examples of Solenoid Valve Selection of Air Pressure Level.

be used. Such a spool may not be available from all valve manufacturers. Energizing the solenoids will permit selection of two intermediate pressures, and de-energizing both solenoids will select full air line pressure, established by another upstream regulator.

Figure 5-2, Part D. Two pressure levels can be selected by using a single solenoid, spring return air valve. The valve shown is a 5-way type with two inlets, two outlets, and one exhaust port. Some brands of 4-way, dual exhaust air valves can be used for 5-way service by using the original exhaust ports for inlets and the original pressure inlet as a common exhaust. Be sure the 4-way valve used will tolerate air pressure on its exhaust ports without unseating the seals. Although a single solenoid model is shown, a double solenoid, 2-position or 3-position model could be used just as well. Since the regulators are installed ahead of the valving, they may be either the relieving or non-relieving type.

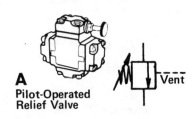

A
**Pilot-Operated
Relief Valve**

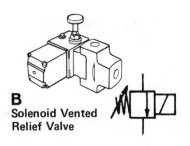

B
**Solenoid Vented
Relief Valve**

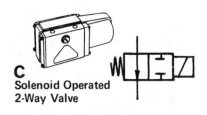

C
**Solenoid Operated
2-Way Valve**

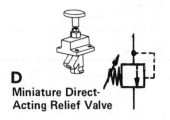

D
**Miniature Direct-
Acting Relief Valve**

FIGURE 5-3.

Some of the components used for electrical control of relief valves.

Figure 5-2, Part E. Where more than two step levels are needed, individual 2-way N.C. solenoid valves in any reasonable number, can be combined in this way with selector switch control. The regulators can be either relieving or non-relieving since they are installed ahead of the valves.

ELECTRICAL CONTROL OF RELIEF VALVES

The pressure level in a hydraulic system can be electrically controlled by using a solenoid actuator installed in the "vent" line of a pilot-operated relief valve. Or, relief valves are available with integral solenoid for remote electrical control. The relief valve must be of the pilot-operated type and must have a port marked "vent" or "RC". Students who are not familiar with the venting operation of a relief valve can review this material in "Industrial Fluid Power — Volumes 1 and 2".

Two distinct modes of control can be obtained with solenoid actuators working in conjunction with relief valves. Pump loading/unloading in response to an electrical signal, and step control of maximum pressure level through a grouping of 2-way solenoid valves and miniature relief valves. Each of these modes will be described separately.

Pilot-Operated Relief Valve. Part A, Figure 5-3. Most industrial hydraulic systems already use a pilot-operated relief valve on the pump line, and in most cases it can be controlled by adding a 2-way solenoid valve. On new designs, these valves are available in sizes from 3/8" up to 6". When selecting a model to be used with electrical control, be sure it has an external "vent" port. This port, even on large valves will usually be 1/4 or 3/8" NPT or equivalent straight thread size. The simplified symbol shown alongside the sketch is the symbol used on schematic diagrams.

Relief Valve With Built-in Solenoid Control. Part B, Figure 5-3. Some manufacturers offer relief valves with a solenoid venting valve built into the structure. This is a convenience for assembling and plumbing. However, the same functions can be obtained by adding a separate solenoid venting valve to any pilot-operated relief valve which has an external vent port.

The composite assembly shown in this figure can only be used for loading and unloading of a hydraulic pump; it cannot be used for step level pressure control. The simplified symbol shows that the relieving pressure is adjustable (slash arrow) and that the relief poppet can be vented with built-in solenoid action.

Solenoid Actuator. Part C, Figure 5-3. This is a 2-way solenoid valve which can be combined with a pilot-operated relief valve for pump unloading in response to de-energization of the solenoid. Most circuits can use a 1/8, 1/4, or 3/8" size valve. It should be N.O. so it will automatically unload the pump if coil connections should become loose, the electric current should be interrupted, or if the coil should burn out. It must have a pressure rating equal to the maximum setting of the relief valve to which it is connected. Miniature direct-acting 4-way valves can be used by using the P port and A port, plugging the B port and connecting the T port to tank. A diagram appears on Page 107.

Control Relief Valve. Part D, Figure 5-3. Circuits for step level pressure control will require one or more direct-acting miniature relief valves of 1/8" or larger flow capacity. Any miniature, direct-acting, relief valve which can be adjusted to the desired pressure level can be used in these circuits.

Pump Loading and Unloading in Response to Electric Signal . . .

The pilot-operated relief valve pictured on the preceding page can serve a dual purpose. Its prime function is to set a maximum limit on pressure in the pump line. A knob or a wrench adjustment is provided. Its secondary function is to provide a free flow unloading path for pump oil when its external vent port is drained to tank.

Figure 5-4. (See next page). To illustrate the venting principle, a pump is shown here working deadhead into a pressure gauge. Pump flow must pass to tank through the relief valve main poppet. A 1/4 or 3/8" steel tube connects the relief valve vent port to the inlet of the 2-way, N.O., solenoid valve. The solenoid valve outlet port must be connected to tank. A very small flow, usually less than 1 GPM on small relief valves to 3 GPM on large valves passes out through the vent port when it is open to tank. A 1/8 to 3/8" size solenoid valve is quite sufficient to handle the vent flow from even a large valve. By energizing and de-energizing the solenoid, the relief valve can be made to build up pressure to its knob setting or to dump the pump flow to tank through its main poppet at 50 to 75 PSI.

Unloading. Part A, Figure 5-4. When the solenoid valve is de-energized, the vent port of the relief valve is connected through the valve spool to tank. This causes the pump oil to flow to tank (through the relief valve main poppet) at a very low back pressure, usually no more than 50 to 75 PSI. The amount of back pressure in the flowing oil relates to the strength of the non-adjustable main spring, and is the minimum pressure to which the relief valve can be adjusted. At a back pressure of 50 to 75 PSI the pump is said to be in an unloaded state.

Loading. Part B, Figure 5-4. When the solenoid is energized, this blocks flow from the vent port of the relief valve. In turn, this causes the relief valve to build up to the pressure which has been set on the adjusting knob. At that pressure, pump flow passes through the relief valve main poppet to tank. Under these conditions the pump is said to be in a loaded state.

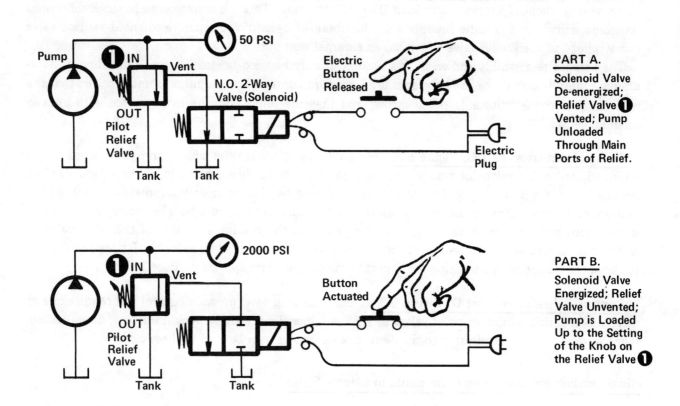

FIGURE 5-4. *Solenoid Vent Pump Unloading With a 2-Way Normally Open Valve.*

JIC Safety Code . . .

From Paragraph E5.4.2.3 of the 1967 JIC (Joint Industry Council) Electrical Standards: "Stop functions shall be initiated through de-energization rather than energization of control devices where possible". To meet this safety code, a N.O. solenoid valve is preferred to a N.C. type for vent un-loading of a hydraulic pressure relief valve. By de-energizing the solenoid valve the pump is placed in an unloaded state and pressure is removed from the hydraulic circuit. If a solenoid coil should burn out, if a wire in the solenoid circuit should break or become disconnected, or if the electrical supply to the machine should fail, the machine would return to a safe condition.

Solenoid Vent Unloading Applied to Hydraulic Cylinder Operation . . .

Figure 5-5. The principle of using solenoid vent pump unloading in combination with 4-way directional valves is illustrated here. Referrinq to Part B, the electrical circuit must be designed to simultaneously energize Solenoids A (for direction) and C (to develop pump pressure) to extend the cylinder. Usually these solenoids must be energized through separate circuits on switches or relay contacts. Likewise, Solenoids B and C must be simultaneously energized (through separate circuits) to retract the cylinder. Center position of the switch causes all solenoids to become de-energized. This is the stop position for the cylinder, with the pump unloaded. A 2-pole selector switch is used to keep the solenoid circuits isolated. The dash line connecting the rotors of the selector switch indicates that both sections are rotated in unison with one control knob.

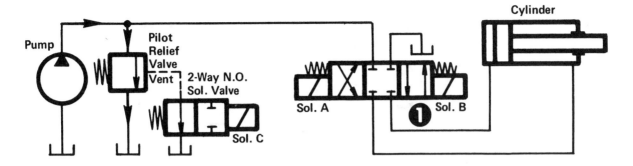

Part A. Hydraulic Circuit

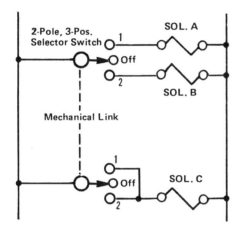

Part B. Electrical Circuit

FIGURE 5-5.

Solenoid Vent Pump Unloading

The hydraulic circuit, Part A above, uses a pilot-operated relief valve for pump unloading. A 2-way solenoid valve in the relief valve vent line controls pump unloading.

Part B, electrical circuit, demonstrates only the principle of solenoid vent control. A 3-position selector switch operates the cylinder in forward and reverse and stops the cylinder with the pump unloaded. A more complete working circuit is shown in Figure 5-7.

Two-Pump High-Low Circuit With Electrical Take-Out . . .

Figure 5-6. A standard "high-low" system with pilot pressure "take-out" or unloading of the high volume pump (only) has been described in "Industrial Fluid Power — Volume 2". A similar "high-low" system with *electrical* take-out is shown in this figure and operates as follows:

Its purpose is to obtain, with a minimum of horsepower, rapid cylinder advance (but at less than maximum force), then full cylinder force (but at a reduced speed). Two pumps are required, one rated for relatively low pressure but having a high volume flow for fast cylinder speed under light or no load; the other rated for full system pressure for high cylinder tonnage but at a slower speed. At the start of a cycle when there is little or no load against the cylinder, both pumps combine their flows to give a rapid cylinder advance. Then, as load resistance builds up to the point that there is insufficient horsepower in the driving motor to carry both pumps to a higher pressure, the high volume pump is automatically unloaded to near zero pressure while the full driving horsepower is applied to the high pressure pump, to continue the cylinder advance, at a slower speed, up to the maximum load resistance for which the system was designed.

Figure 5-6. Part A of Figure 5-6 shows a basic hydraulic circuit for "high-low" operation. Parts B, C, and D of Figure 5-6 show several methods of electrical control. Pump 1-PF is a high volume pump to operate during the low pressure, high speed cylinder advance, and during the cylinder return stroke. It will be dropped out or unloaded during the forward stroke when load pressure rises to a certain

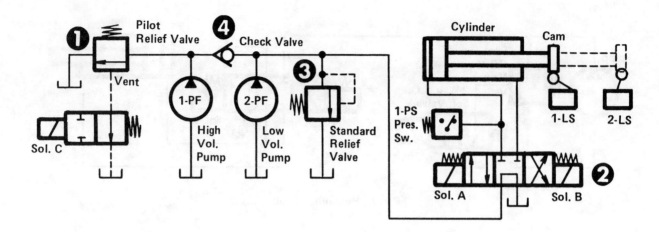

FIGURE 5-6, Part A. Hydraulic diagram for "high-low" pump circuit with electrical take-out.

level. Pump 2-PF is a low volume, high pressure pump rated for maximum system pressure. This pump will remain pumping all of the time the cylinder is advancing or retracting. At the start of each cycle, both pumps will deliver oil to the cylinder, 2-PF directly and 1-PF through the check valve. A pressure switch, 1-PS, is set to trip when load pressure builds up to a level where the driving motor would be overloaded if pressure were to rise higher. When 1-PS trips, Solenoid C becomes de-energized, opening the vent line on relief Valve 1. The flow from 1-PF can then flow to tank through the main poppet of Valve 1 at almost no back pressure, thus removing most of its load from the driving motor. After 1-PF unloads, the entire driving horsepower is then available to 2-PF for producing a higher pressure against load resistance. Valve 1 is a standard pilot-operated relief valve with vent port. However it is not used as a relief but as an unloading valve in this circuit. Setting of its adjustment knob makes no difference in the circuit except that it must be set at least 200 PSI higher than the pressure switch to avoid premature loss of part of 1-PF flow before the pressure switch trips. See Page 99 for venting action.

This circuit, with electrical take-out of high to low speed, has a much more abrupt action than the pilot pressure take-out used in many "high-low" circuits, and on some applications the abrupt action may be undesirable. However, on applications where load build-up is gradual, as when compressing a bale of cotton, the abrupt action is beneficial in reducing oil heating if the system should linger in the "gray" or changeover pressure area for an appreciable time with oil from 1-PF partly delivered to the load and partly discharging to tank.

Electrical Circuit. Figure 5-6, Part B. This partial circuit shows that Pump 1-PF becomes unloaded when load build-up against the cylinder trips the pressure switch. Maximum pressure take-out can be determined by measuring line current to the motor. Set switch to trip when full load current is reached. The cylinder can be manually controlled by using a 2-circuit, 3-position selector switch. With the switch in Position 1, Solenoids A and C are energized, Solenoid A for forward direction and Solenoid C to block the vent port on Valve 1 to cause 1-PF to build up pressure. With the switch in Position 3, Solenoids B and C are energized, Solenoid B to retract the cylinder and Solenoid C to cause 1-PF to build pressure. In center position all solenoids are de-energized. Pump 2-PF is unloaded through 4-way Valve 2, and 1-PF through relief Valve 1, and the cylinder is stopped. The pressure switch can be adjusted, as described above, to open the circuit to Solenoid C when the electric motor becomes fully loaded. In practice, an automatic control circuit would be more like Figure 5-7 in which relay contacts replace the rotary switch.

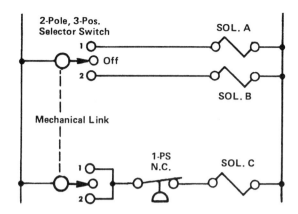

FIGURE 5-6, Part B. Demonstrates electrical circuit for control of solenoid valves.

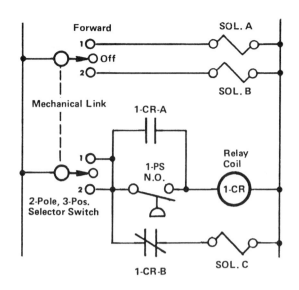

FIG. 5-6C. To soften the take-out action, this modification will eliminate instability.

The circuit of Figure 5-6, Part B above, is only for demonstration of electrical take-out of Pump PF-1 in a high-low system. Figure 5-7 on the next page is more typical of a complete control circuit for such an application.

Modified Electrical Circuit. Figure 5-6, Part C. On some applications of the electrical take-out circuit the take-out action may be too abrupt and a condition of "hunting" can be set up. When the pressure switch trips, the pressure behind the piston may drop momentarily, causing the pressure switch to re-set. If this should be a problem, a holding relay, 1-CR can be added to the circuit. Once the pressure switch trips it is locked out for the rest of the cycle. This modification has also been incorporated into the complete electrical circuit, Figure 5-7 on the next page.

"Jog" or "Slow" Control. Figure 5-6, Part D. Electrical unloading by venting a pilot-operated relief valve as shown in preceding circuits offers an opportunity to add a "Slow" control switch to a 2-pump "high-low" circuit.

During set-up of a press it may be desirable to operate the cylinder through a number of cycles at a reduced speed. This can be done easily by keeping the high volume pump, 1-PF, in Figure 5-6, Part A, unloaded and using only the low volume pump, 2-PF, to operate the entire cycle. The "Slow" switch, 1-SW, in this circuit can be any kind of maintained action switch such as a rotary or toggle switch. It has been added to the basic circuit of Part B. When 1-SW is open, Solenoid C will be kept de-energized. Relief Valve 1 will remain vented and will keep 1-PF in an unloaded state.

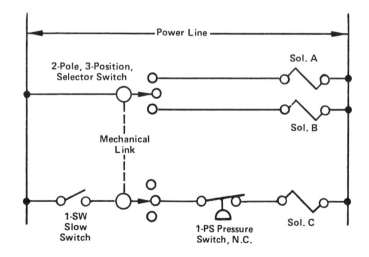

Figure 5-6D. "Slow" switch added to circuit.

Complete Electrical Circuit. Figure 5-7. This is one possible electrical circuit for operation of the 2-pump "high-low" hydraulic circuit of Figure 5-6, Part A. It has these special features:

(1). Electrical take-out action from high speed, low force, to full force at a lower speed.

(2). Cycle start by a momentary pushbutton.

(3). Disconnection of the pushbutton during cylinder retraction to prevent accidental re-start.

(4). Lock-out of the pressure switch after it has tripped, to prevent flutter or hunting.

(5). Automatic cylinder return after completion of its forward stroke.

(6). Automatic unloading of both pumps at the end of every cycle.

A limit switch must be mounted at each end of the cylinder stroke, and a pressure switch must be teed into the blind end port of the cylinder.

Electrical action is as follows: The operator presses a pushbutton to start the cycle and must hold the button down a few moments until the cylinder starts and moves far enough to release limit Switch 1-LS. This immediately energizes Relay 1-CR, Solenoid C, and Solenoid A. The cylinder starts forward, and when load pressure builds up to the take-out level, the pressure switch closes. This energizes Relay 3-CR and this relay locks in through its own contacts, 3-CR-B. Contacts on 3-CR also disconnect solenoid Valve C, venting relief Valve 1 and unloading 1-PF pump. The cylinder continues to travel to the end of its stroke with oil from Pump 2-PF. Limit Switch 2-LS is actuated. This breaks the holding circuit to 3-CR, allowing Pump 1-PF to load up again for the return stroke. It also energizes Relay 2-CR and this relay locks in through its own contacts, 2-CR-C. The cylinder makes its return stroke and during the stroke the pushbutton is disconnected with 2-CR-D contacts to avoid an accident if it should accidentally be pressed again. At home position the cylinder actuates Switch 1-LS. This drops out all the holding relays; all solenoids become de-energized and the pump unloaded.

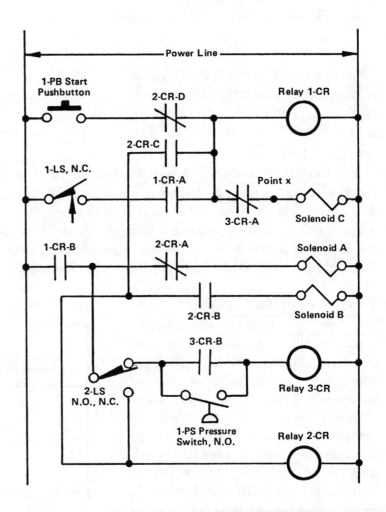

FIGURE 5-7. Complete circuit for the "high-low" system with electrical take-out.

Note: A "Slow" speed switch, as shown in Figure 5-6, Part D, can be added to this circuit by installing a toggle switch at Point X.

Pressure Manifold Hydraulic System . . .

Figure 5-8. Although most hydraulic systems are designed with a hydraulic pumping unit to serve only one machine, some systems are designed to operate much like a compressed air system — with a

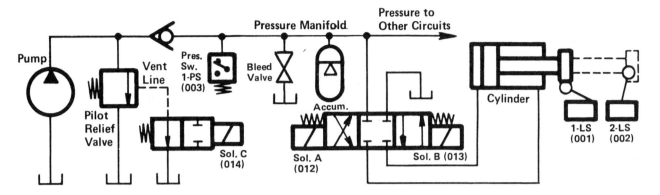

FIGURE 5-8. Hydraulic Circuit. Only one branch is illustrated.

central hydraulic power supply serving several unrelated machines. In this kind of a system, hydraulic oil is pumped into an accumulator or a bank of accumulators under pressure, and stored for future use. The hydraulic pump runs continuously until sufficient oil is stored in the accumulators to raise their pressure to the cut-off level, and this is usually 3000 PSI. A special accumulator unloading valve then opens a line to tank to allow the pump, still running, to discharge its flow at near zero back pressure to tank. The pump remains in this unloaded state until sufficient oil has been discharged from the accumulators to drop their pressure to the cut-in level. The unloading valve then closes and the pump re-charges the accumulators. Accumulators and their circuits are described in "Industrial Fluid Power — Volume 1".

The special accumulator unloading valve mentioned above is usually a pilot-operated type, with a differential between cut-in pressure and cut-out pressure of about 20%. This differential can be reduced by unloading with a pressure switch instead of the accumulator unloading valve. The switch must be wired to a solenoid operated dump valve in the pump line.

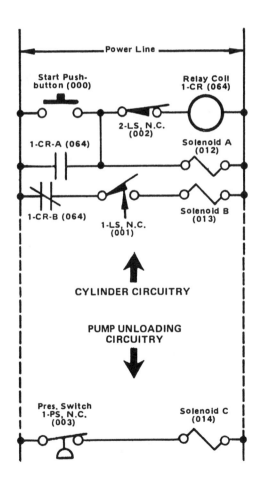

PART B. Electrical. A cylinder control circuit is shown at the top of this diagram. One such circuit is required for each branch connected to the manifold. A pump unloading circuit is shown below. One such circuit is required per pump.

FIGURE 5-8. *Pressure manifold hydraulic system using electrical pump unloading.*

Hydraulic Circuit. Figure 5-8, Part A. This is the one-cycle reciprocation circuit from Page 50 shown here in greater detail, and with an accumulator added. Refer to that page for additional description. In a pressure manifold system, high pressure is continually maintained in the system, and pump unloading does not have to be designed into the electrical control circuit. It can be handled with a separate circuit as shown on the bottom rung of the electrical diagram in Part B.

Any number of hydraulic branch circuits can be operated from one manifold, although only one branch is shown in Figure 5-8. Each branch would have an independent electrical control circuit. All branch circuits must be controlled with 4-way valves having their pressure port blocked in neutral center position. Typically, a closed center 3-position valve. Tandem center and open center valves cannot be used. Accumulator size must be selected according to the number of branch circuits to be in operation at the same time, the oil flow required for each branch, and rate of cycling.

One important item on the diagram is the bleed-down valve across the accumulator. Unless this valve is installed before operating the system there is no way to get the pressure safely out of the accumulator. It can be a 1/8 or 1/4" size high pressure, leaktight valve of any kind.

Electrical Circuit. Figure 5-8, Part B. The control circuit for the cylinder is shown in the top rungs of this diagram, and is similar to Figure 3-15, Page 50. A separate electrical system is required for each hydraulically powered machine operating from this central power system.

An unloading circuit for the hydraulic pump is shown in the bottom rung. Only one of these rungs is required regardless of the number of branches in the hydraulic system. One pressure switch, 1-PS, is required with a set of N.C. or "break on rise" contacts. Solenoid C is the coil of a 2-way, N.O. solenoid valve for the vent line of the pilot-operated relief valve. When the pump has charged the accumulator up to the cut-off setting of the pressure switch, the switch opens and de-energizes Solenoid C. This unloads the pump. The power source to the pressure switch and Solenoid C can be obtained from the motor starter which operates the pump motor. When the motor is started, Solenoid C becomes energized and keeps the pump loaded until the cut-off pressure level is reached. Refer to Page 99 for details of relief valve venting. The relief valve not only unloads the pump when the accumulator is fully charged, it also serves to protect the pump if the pressure switch should fail. It should be set about 300 to 500 PSI higher that the pressure switch setting.

Step Level Control of Maximum Pump Pressure . . .

Using a pilot-operated relief valve with vent port, two modes of pump control can be obtained with 2-way solenoid valves installed in the vent line. One mode, that of loading and unloading a hydraulic

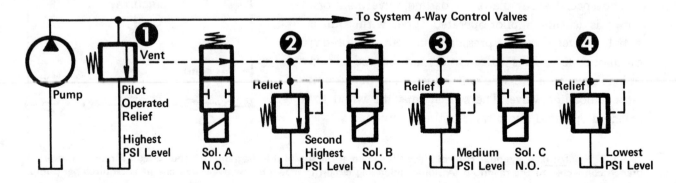

FIGURE 5-9. A step-level system for selecting four different pressure levels.

pump has just been described. The other mode is that of selecting any one of several pre-set pressure levels through remote electrical control. This is accomplished in very much the same way as venting, described on Page 99, except that instead of being connected directly to tank through a solenoid valve, the vent line can be switched to any one of several pre-set miniature relief valves. This kind of operation is referred to in this book as "step level pressure control". The object of step level pressure control is to be able to select, by electrical control, a choice of several accurately pre-set operating pressures for a press or other hydraulically powered machine.

Figure 5-9. There are several ways in which 2-way solenoid valves and miniature direct-acting relief valves can be combined for step level control. The particular arrangement shown in this figure is "fail safe". If for any reason control current should fail, all solenoid valves would return to an open state, reducing pump pressure to its lowest level. If one solenoid should burn out, pump pressure would drop to the next lower level.

In the hydraulic circuit, Valve 1 is a pilot-operated relief valve of sufficient capacity to by-pass the entire pump flow to tank at a very low back pressure. The highest desired pressure level must be set on the knob of this valve. Valves 2, 3, and 4 are miniature direct-acting relief valves, usually

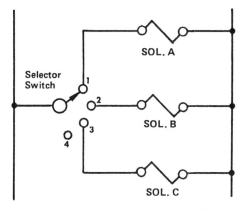

Selector Switch Control of Step Level Pressures.

1/8 to 1/4" size, set for the lower pressure levels and selected by electrical control. Each relief valve from left to right must be set for a progressively lower pressure. This circuit gives a choice of four levels. Additional levels can be obtained by adding a solenoid valve and miniature relief valve for each additional level.

Electrical control is very simple, obtained with a 4-position rotary selector switch. See figure above. In Position 1, Solenoid A becomes energized and blocks the relief valve vent line. This causes pressure to build up to the level set on the main knob. Positions 2 and 3 energize Solenoids B and C respectively for successively lower pressure levels. Finally, at Position 4 all solenoids are de-energized and relief Valve 4 takes over, giving the lowest pressure level.

Figure 5-10. Pushbutton Control of Pressure Level. While the selector switch control shown above is a very simple method, it may not be suited to applications where control must be exercised from more than one location. In Figure 5-10, four pushbutton stations are shown for selection of four pressure levels. Additional relief and solenoid valves can be added for a greater number of pressure levels. To operate from a second location, four more pushbuttons can be installed at that location and wired in parallel with corresponding buttons at the original location.

In the hydraulic circuit, double solenoid 2-way valves adapt very easily to pushbutton control without using holding relays. In event of coil burn-out or interruption of control current, the pump pressure remains just as it was but cannot be changed. This is considered a safe condition.

In the electrical circuit, each pushbutton has three sets of N.O. contacts. For example on 1-PB, the three contacts energize Solenoids B, D, and F to re-set Valves 5, 6, and 7 (on the hydraulic diagram) to their closed positions. This blocks the vent line and the system develops, as a maximum, the pressure set on the adjustment knob of the main relief valve, 1. On 2-PB, the three contacts energize Solenoids A, D, and F. This opens Valve 5 and closes Valves 6 and 7. Relief Valve 2 now takes over control of pressure. Pushbutton 4-PB energizes Solenoids B, D, and E for the lowest pressure.

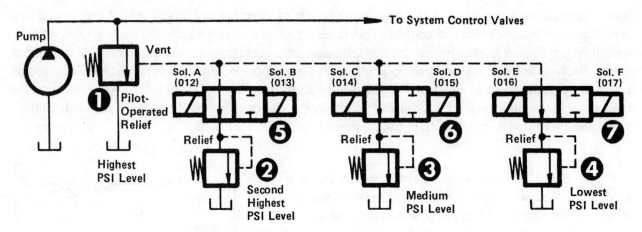

FIGURE 5-10. Part A, *Hydraulic Circuit for Four Levels of Pressure.*

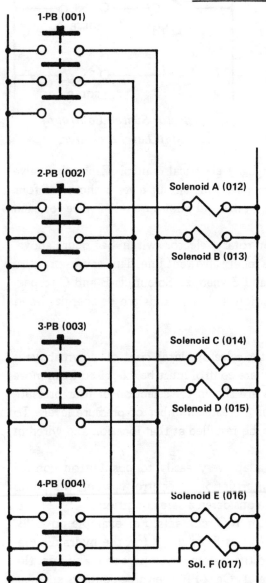

If double solenoid, 2-position valves are not available, 4-way valves can be substituted if connected as in the diagram below. Pressure should be handled only on the P, A, and B ports. High pressure should be kept off the T port and it should be vented to tank.

When using a 4-way valve for 2-way or 3-way service, do not exceed manufacturers pressure rating on tank (T) port. Drain this port if possible. Full pressure may be used on all other ports.

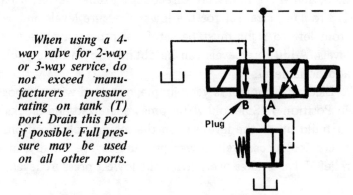

Figure 5-11. Three Pressure Levels. (Next page). By using a 3-position double solenoid valve there is a choice of three pressure levels. The highest pressure must be set on the control knob of the pump relief valve, 1. It is a pilot-operated type with vent port. Two lower levels can be set on miniature direct-acting relief Valves 2 and 3. A 3-position selector switch is used for control. For safety, the lowest pressure should be set on Valve 2. Then if a solenoid should burn out, the valve spool will center and system pressure will drop to the lowest level.

FIGURE 5-10, Part B. *Electric Circuit for Pushbutton Control of Hydraulic Circuit Above.*

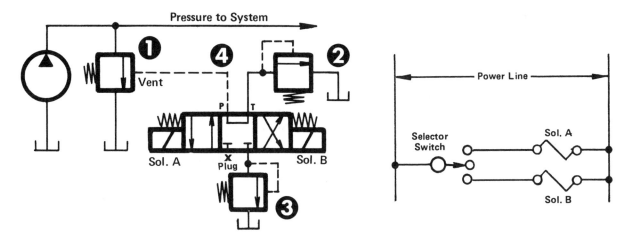

FIGURE 5-11. Choice of three pressure levels with 3-position solenoid valve.

ELECTRICAL CONTROL OF PRESSURE REDUCING VALVES

A pressure reducing valve is the hydraulic equivalent of a pressure regulator in a compressed air system and works on the same principle except that an air regulator uses air pressure against a diaphragm to open and close the main poppet, and a hydraulic reducing valve ordinarily uses outlet pressure working against the end of the main spool to regulate outlet pressure.

Both these valves are used for the same purpose in their respective systems, that of providing a regulated maximum pressure downstream regardless of variations of inlet pressure as long as the inlet pressure is as high as or higher than the adjustment set on the reducing valve. The air regulator supplies a constant pressure to a branch circuit regardless of wide variations between the "cut-in" and "cut-out" pressure of the compressor. A hydraulic reducing valve makes possible the operation of a branch circuit at a lower pressure than maintained on the rest of the system.

Direct-acting hydraulic pressure reducing valves cannot be readily controlled electrically. They are not widely used and may no longer be available. They were replaced many years ago by pilot-operated reducing valves and these can easily be controlled remotely with solenoid valves. Reducing valves do not have a "vent" line but they do have an external drain, and it is in this drain line that control of outlet pressure can be exercised. A reducing valve is never used in place of a relief valve to reduce

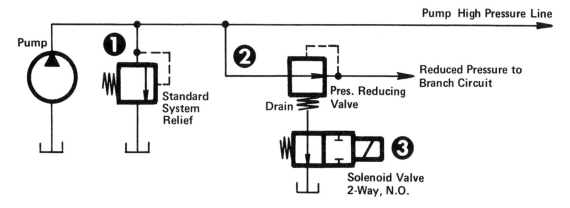

FIGURE 5-12. Solenoid valve selects full or reduced pressure to branch circuit.

or limit maximum pressure in the pump line. It is always used in a branch circuit to limit pressure to less than in the pump line. Please refer to "Industrial Fluid Power — Volume 2" for description of operation of reducing valves.

Figure 5-12. One Reduced Level. This is a typical application for remotely selecting either a reduced pressure or full pump pressure from a pressure reducing valve into a branch circuit.

Valve 1 is the main pump relief valve to limit maximum pump pressure. Valve 2 is a pilot-operated reducing valve with a 1/4" 2-way, N.O. solenoid valve, 3, installed between the drain port on the valve and the tank. By energizing and de-energizing Valve 3, the operator can select by remote electrical control his choice of full high pressure or a selected level of reduced pressure to the branch circuit.

When Valve 3 is de-energized, it connects the reducing valve drain port to tank and the valve works normally, delivering a reduced pressure into the branch circuit, the exact level of which is controlled by the knob setting of Valve 2. When Valve 3 is energized, it blocks the action of the reducing valve, and full inlet pressure is delivered through to the outlet port. Solenoid action is "fail-safe". If a coil should burn out, the branch circuit pressure would drop to the reduced pressure level. Electrical control of solenoid Valve 3 can be with a 2-position toggle or rotary selector switch.

Figure 5-13. Two Reduced Levels. The operator can remotely select by electrical control a choice of two pre-selected reduced pressure levels into a branch circuit. Solenoid Valve 3 is a 1/4" direct-acting 3-way valve. If a 3-way valve is not available, use a 4-way model by plugging and/or draining unused ports. See information on Page 107.

For choice of two reduced pressures, the *lower* pressure must be set on the main knob of reducing Valve 2. If solenoid Valve 3 remains de-energized, reducing Valve 2 functions normally, giving an outlet pressure equal to its knob setting. When Valve 3 is energized, the pressure drop of relief Valve 4 is added in series with the internal adjusting spring of the main reducing valve, giving a pressure level in between full inlet pressure and the normal reduced pressure. Figure 5-13 also has the "fail-safe" action described in the preceding figure.

Electrical control is exercised with a simple toggle switch, or Solenoid 3 could be tied into the machine electrical circuit to automatically produce a pre-set reduced pressure at the proper time in the cycle.

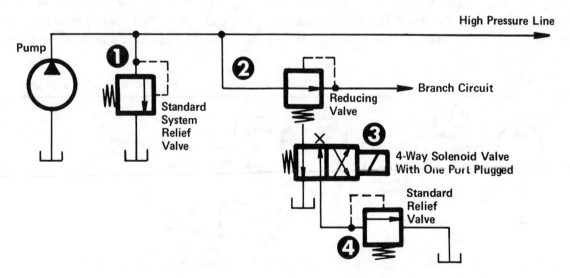

FIGURE 5-13. *Solenoid valve selects two levels of reduced pressure to branch circuit.*

CHAPTER 6

Solving Design Problems in Electrical Circuitry

Most circuits in this book show standard fluid power movements controlled with more or less standard electrical circuits. In this chapter we will show examples of special circuit problems which may be encountered by a designer when he designs a circuit for a special application.

PROBLEMS ASSOCIATED WITH THE STARTING SIGNAL

All electrically controlled fluid power machines must be started every cycle with some kind of electric signal. This may come from an operator, from the output of another machine, or from a programmer such as a tape or card reader or from a programmable controller. But no matter where the signal may come from, it will be one of two kinds: (1), momentary, as from a pushbutton: (2), maintained, as from a toggle switch or rotary selector switch. Several distinct problems must be considered in dealing with such starting signals:

(1). A momentary signal of short duration, as from a pushbutton, must sometimes be converted into a maintained signal if it is used to energize (and hold) a spring return or spring centered valve. Design Problem No. 1 on the next page shows how this can be done with a holding relay.

(2). A maintained signal, as from a toggle switch, must be interrupted after it has done its work so it cannot interfere with normal progress in the cycle. The circuit must be designed with delay relays, timers, relay or switch contacts so the circuit can be broken ready for the next cycle.

Momentary Signal from Electric Pushbutton   Maintained Signal from a Toggle Switch

FIGURE 6-1. Starting signals will be either momentary or maintained.

DESIGN PROBLEM No. 1

How to convert the momentary signal from a pushbutton into a maintained signal.

When operating a 4-way valve with spring return or spring centered spool, the spool will not remain in shifted position when the pushbutton is released. To keep the spool shifted, current must be kept on the valve coil by using a holding relay.

For operation of compressed air cylinders, only 2-position valves, either single solenoid with spring return or double solenoid no-spring models are normally used. Three-position air valves are seldom used because an air cylinder is unstable when stopped in mid-stroke.

Double solenoid, no-spring models adapt easily to pushbutton control because they will stay in shifted position when the pushbutton is released. However, single solenoid spring return models are more resistant against spool drift due to high "g" acceleration (when mounted on moving machines), by excessively high air flow across the spool, or by machine vibration. Their spools are positively retained at all times in one position or the other by solenoid force or by return spring force.

Single solenoid valves are, therefore, preferred for spool stability but they are more difficult to adapt to pushbutton control. A holding relay must be added to the electric circuit. It will accept a momentary signal and will lock in electrically to keep current on the valve solenoid coil. A "holding" relay is simply a standard relay wired through a set of its own contacts to keep itself (and the valve coil) energized. See Page 27 for more information.

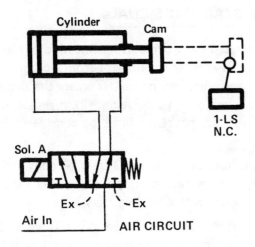

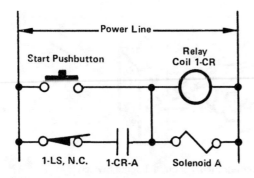

FIGURE 6-2. A holding relay circuit.

Air Circuit. Example of an air cylinder controlled with a single solenoid air valve. Cycle start will be from a momentary pushbutton. The cylinder will make a forward stroke, actuate limit Switch 1-LS, retract automatically and stop. Design an electric circuit to work from a momentary pushbutton and provide an automatic cycle.

Electric Circuit. A momentary signal from an operator's pushbutton would energize the solenoid valve and start the cylinder forward, but if the button were released, the cylinder would immediately retract without completing its full stroke. A holding relay, 1-CR, must be added to take over for the operator and keep the cylinder moving after the button has been released.

Electrical action is as follows: When the button is pressed, Solenoid A and relay Coil 1-CR become energized. After closing, the relay keeps itself and the valve solenoid energized by electrically locking in through 1-CR-A and 1-LS contacts. The solenoid valve shifts and starts the cylinder forward. When Switch 1-LS is actuated, its contacts open and unlock the relay coil. Solenoid A then becomes de-energized, its spool is released and returns to its normal state by spring force, and the cylinder retracts.

DESIGN PROBLEM No. 2

How to use the momentary signal from a starting pushbutton to operate a hydraulic cylinder controlled by a 3-position spring centered 4-way valve.

Most hydraulic cylinders are controlled with double solenoid, 4-way valves having 3-position spring centered spools. These valves present a problem when trying to control them from momentary pushbuttons because the spool springs back to center neutral when the button is released. Obviously, holding relays must be added to the electric circuit to maintain current on a valve solenoid after the pushbutton has been released. Control circuit design is more difficult than for an air cylinder on a similar application, (a), because holding relays may be necessary on both forward and reverse strokes, and (b), the oil supply must be unloaded to tank at the end of the cycle.

Hydraulic Circuit. The problem is to initiate a cylinder action with a "Cycle Start" momentary pushbutton, and to cause the cylinder to go through one complete cycle automatically, forward and reverse. At the end of the cycle, with the cylinder stopped, the oil supply must be in an unloaded condition. A tandem center 4-way valve is chosen for this illustration. When its spool is centered, the cylinder ports are oil-locked and the oil supply unloaded to tank.

Electric Circuit. Two limit switches must be used. Switch 2-LS is placed at the forward end of the stroke to reverse the cylinder. Switch 1-LS senses the completion of a cycle and unloads the oil supply by de-energizing both solenoids of the 4-way valve. Wiring to 1-LS is to its COM and N.C. terminals. A cam on the machine keeps this switch actuated while the cylinder is retracted.

When the pushbutton is pressed, Solenoid A and the relay coil, 1-CR, become energized. The relay locks in through 1-CR-A and 2-CR-A contacts and maintains current on Solenoid A during the forward stroke, even though the button is released. When 2-LS is actuated, Relay 2-CR becomes energized and locks in through 2-CR-C and 1-LS. Solenoid B becomes energized through 2-CR-B while Solenoid A becomes de-energized when 2-CR-A opens. Relay 1-CR drops out at this time. The cylinder retracts and actuates 1-LS. This releases 2-CR relay. Both valve solenoids are now de-energized, the valve spool centers by spring action, and the oil supply is unloaded to tank through the valve spool.

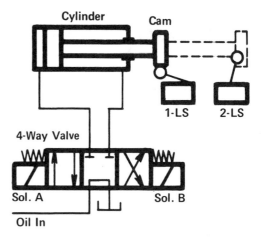

HYDRAULIC CIRCUIT

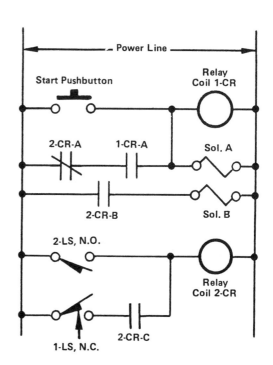

FIGURE 6-3. Holding relays enable a hydraulic cylinder to be operated from a 3-position, spring centered, tandem center valve.

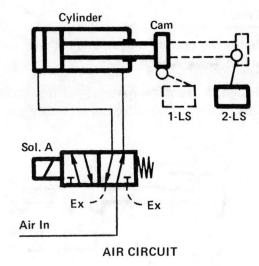

AIR CIRCUIT

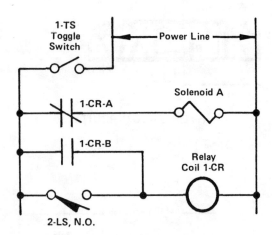

ONE-CYCLE ELECTRIC CIRCUIT

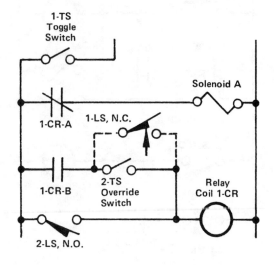

CONTINUOUS RECIPROCATION

FIGURE 6-4. Air cylinder reciprocation started from a maintained signal.

DESIGN PROBLEM No. 3

How to use the maintained switching signal from a toggle switch to cause an air cylinder to go through one automatic cycle, forward and back, and stop.

<u>Air Circuit.</u> The starting signal can come from the closure of a toggle or rotary selector switch, or may come from the output of another machine or from a programmer. The cylinder must make only one cycle and then stop. For a 1-cycle action such as this, limit Switch 1-LS is not required.

<u>Electric Circuit.</u> On closure of toggle Switch 1-TS, valve Solenoid A becomes energized, shifts, and the cylinder makes its forward stroke. When limit Switch 2-LS is actuated, Relay 1-CR coil becomes energized. One set of relay contacts, 1-CR-B, locks the relay in electrically. The other set, 1-CR-A, de-energizes Solenoid A. The cylinder retracts and stalls at home position. Toggle Switch 1-TS must first be opened, then closed, to start another cycle. If the starting signal comes from a programmer, it must be interrupted, then re-applied, to start another cycle.

DESIGN PROBLEM No. 4

How to use a maintained signal from a toggle switch to start an air cylinder into continuous reciprocation.

<u>Air Circuit.</u> Use the same circuit shown at top of this page, adding limit Switch 1-LS.

<u>Electric Circuit.</u> The action is much the same as described above for 1-cycle reciprocation except that when the cylinder returns to home position, Switch 1-LS breaks the holding circuit to Relay 1-CR, starting the cylinder forward again.

To stop the cylinder, toggle Switch 1-TS must be opened, or the input signal, if from a programmer, must be interrupted. The cylinder will immediately retract to home position from wherever it may be in its stroke at the time.

An override toggle Switch 2-TS can be added in parallel with limit Switch 1-LS to give a choice of 1-cycle or continuous reciprocation. With override Switch 2-TS closed, the cylinder will stop after completing one cycle.

DESIGN PROBLEM No. 5

How to use a maintained starting signal, as from a toggle switch, to cause a hydraulic cylinder to go through one reciprocation cycle and stop with the pump unloaded.

A typical application is on a hydraulic press operated with a foot switch. The operator presses and remains standing on the switch while the press goes through one cycle and stops. To start the next cycle he must release the foot switch and press it again. He can instantly stop the press at any time in case of emergency by raising his foot from the switch.

Hydraulic Circuit. Operation is with a 3-position, tandem center valve. A limit switch is placed at each end of the cylinder or press travel.

One-Cycle Cylinder Action. When foot Switch 1-FS (or a hand switch) is closed, valve Solenoid A becomes energized and the cylinder advances until it actuates Switch 2-LS. Relay 1-CR becomes energized. One set of relay contacts locks the relay closed, the other two de-energize Solenoid A and energize Solenoid B, causing the cylinder to retract. At home position 1-LS is actuated, de-energizing Solenoid B, stopping the cylinder and unloading the oil supply. The relay remains energized until the operator removes his foot from the switch. A new cycle starts when he again presses the switch.

DESIGN PROBLEM No. 6

How to use a toggle switch to start a hydraulic cylinder into continuous reciprocation. When the toggle switch is opened, the oil supply must unload to tank.

Hydraulic Circuit. The same hydraulic circuit shown above is also used for continuous reciprocation.

Electric Circuit. The action for continuous reciprocation is similar to that described above except that when the cylinder retracts to home position and actuates 1-LS, the holding circuit to Relay 1-CR is broken. When the relay contacts change, Solenoid A is again energized for another cycle. If 1-TS is opened during progress of the cycle the solenoid valve spool centers, unloading the oil supply and stopping the cylinder immediately at that point in its stroke.

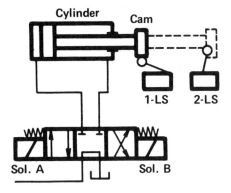

HYDRAULIC CIRCUIT

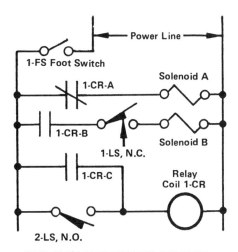

ONE-CYCLE ELECTRIC CIRCUIT

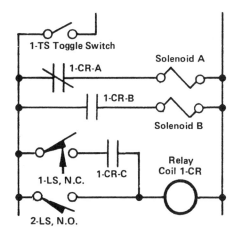

CONTINUOUS RECIPROCATION

FIGURE 6-5. Hydraulic cylinder reciprocation started from a maintained signal.

DESIGN PROBLEM No. 7

How to use a maintained signal from a toggle switch to give an impulse for operation of air cylinders controlled with 2-position, double solenoid valves. Delay relay method is illustrated in this problem.

<u>Air Circuit.</u> An electric circuit is to be designed for 1-cycle reciprocation of an air cylinder. When the cylinder is started by an electric signal, it makes a forward stroke, actuates limit Switch 1-LS, automatically retracts and stops.

The starting signal, in this case, is to be obtained from a maintained source such as a toggle switch or a switch on another machine or process. The control circuit must be designed so no matter how long the starting signal is maintained it will not interfere with cycle action and stopping at the proper time.

A double solenoid 4-way valve with two positions was selected for directional control of the cylinder.

<u>Electrical Circuit A.</u> This illustrates the nature of the problem to be solved when attempting to operate a 2-position solenoid valve from a toggle switch start.

When toggle Switch 1-TS is closed, Solenoid A becomes energized, the valve spool shifts, and the cylinder starts forward. When it actuates 1-LS, Solenoid B becomes energized but the valve cannot reverse because current is still held on Solenoid A, and this circuit must be broken before the valve can be reversed with Solenoid B. One way to solve this problem is shown in Electrical Circuit B. Note: Energizing both coils at the same time, on some valves, may burn out one coil.

<u>Electrical Circuit B.</u> A timer or a delayed action relay as shown on Page 117 can be added to Circuit A. Now, when the starting toggle switch is closed, Solenoid A is energized through N.C. delayed action contacts, 1-TR-A. After a delay of about 1 second, these contacts open, removing current from Solenoid A. However, the valve spool stays in its shifted position. At the end of the forward stroke, Switch 1-LS is actuated. This energizes Solenoid B, causing the cylinder to retract and stall at home position.

Delay Relay 1-TR converts the steady signal from the toggle switch into a short pulse. After one cycle the cylinder stops even though the toggle is still closed. To start another cycle the toggle must be opened then re-closed, allowing the relay to re-set.

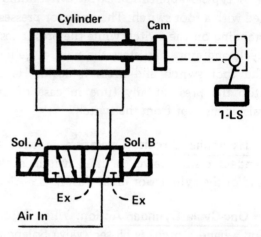

AIR CIRCUIT. This cylinder is to have 1-cycle reciprocation controlled with a toggle switch.

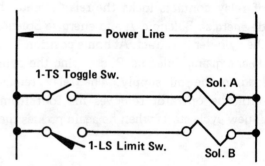

Electrical Circuit A. The basic circuit shown here is unworkable without the addition of a time delay relay as shown in the circuit below.

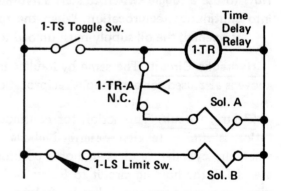

Electrical Circuit B. A relay with delayed action contacts provides one solution for the problem of the previous circuit.

FIGURE 6-7. Delay Relay Circuitry.

DESIGN PROBLEM No. 8

How to release a sustained signal, developed during progress of a cycle and usually caused by a cylinder actuating a limit switch then continuing to stand on it.

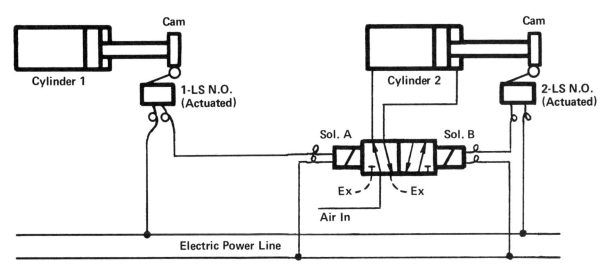

FIGURE 6-8. Illustration of the problem.

This is a frequent and serious problem encountered during the design of an electrical control circuit and one which is sometimes difficult to solve. First an explanation of the problem:

Figure 6-8. This is only a partial circuit to show the components usually involved in the problem. Cylinder 1 has made its forward stroke and actuated limit Switch 1-LS. This energizes valve Solenoid A to start Cylinder 2 forward while Cylinder 1 continues to hold at full extension and keeps 1-LS in its actuated state. Cylinder 2 makes its forward stroke and actuates 2-LS. The signal from this switch is intended to reverse Cylinder 2 by energizing Solenoid B. But with the other cylinder standing on 1-LS, the valve will not reverse and the circuit stalls. To solve this problem, some means must be found to interrupt current to Solenoid A after it is no longer needed. Several methods may be used:

Standard Limit Switches. The problem has been solved in Figure 4-5B on Page 72. A holding relay has been used to break the circuit to Solenoid A. The following description refers to Figure 4-5B.

When PB pushbutton is momentarily pressed, valve Solenoid A and Relay 1-CR become energized. The relay locks in through 2-LS and 1-CR-B. Cylinder 1 moves forward, actuates Switch 1-LS, and continues to stand on this switch. Valve Solenoid C becomes energized while Solenoid A continues to be energized. Cylinder 2 moves forward and actuates 2-LS. This drops out Relay 1-CR and disconnects Solenoid A while energizing Solenoid D. Cylinder 2 retracts and actuates 3-LS. This energizes Solenoid B to retract Cylinder 1. At home position, Switch 4-LS is cammed open to remove current from Solenoid B. The cycle is ended with current removed from all solenoids.

Impulse Switching. Other methods of solving this problem are with short duration switching signals produced when Switch 1-LS is actuated. Several methods are described on Pages 74, 75, and 76. After Solenoid A has been briefly energized, current is removed from it.

The time delay relay circuit on the preceding page can be adapted for this purpose. Other methods include the use of an impulse limit switch, or the use of a mechanical or electronic timer to disconnect Solenoid A after a brief delay. Impulses of any time duration can be readily programmed electronically when using a programmable controller to operate the electrical system.

THE USE OF TIME DELAY RELAYS

Relays with delayed contact action are shown on Page 115 for controlling a cylinder from a maintained starting signal, on Page 126 for cylinder dwell, on Page 139 for oil decompression, on Page 145 for two-hand safety circuits, and on Page 159 for starting a string of electric motors one at a time.

Figure 6-6 shows graphic symbols of timing relays for use on diagrams. The model most often used in fluid power for converting a maintained signal into a short pulse is one having N.C. contacts that do not open until an elapsed time interval after the coil has been energized. It is indicated with an asterisk in the chart below. It use is shown in Design Problem No. 7 on Page 115.

Relay coils operating delayed action contacts are indicated by a circle, and are marked 1-TR, 2-TR, 3-TR, etc. (Symbol TR indicates a timing relay).

Contact sets activated by these coils are drawn as shown in the box, and are marked 1-TR-A, 1-TR-B, etc., for contacts operated by Coil 1-TR.

If Contact Action is Retarded After Coil is Energized.		If Contact Action is Retarded After Coil is De-energized.	
N.O.	N.C.*	N.O.	N.C.

*This type most often used in starting cylinders.

FIGURE 6-6. This table shows the correct way to draw time delay relay contacts on diagrams.

Timing Relays Available . . .

There is a wide variety of electrical timing devices available from many sources. Information can be readily obtained from any distributor of industrial electrical components. Our discussion in this book will be limited to a brief description of some of the types available.

1. Industrial Control Relays. These are available in several NEMA sizes with delayed action contacts or with a combination of instant closing and delayed action contacts. In general these are the same structures used in magnetic motor starters but without thermal overload protective devices. Delay action is usually produced by a small pneumatic dashpot with adjustable orifice which can be set from 0 to 2 or 3 minutes. These relays can be ordered either with delayed action on energization of the coil or on de-energization, but not both on the same relay. These relays are reliable and are recommended as one of the best ways of obtaining short delays in electric control circuits.

2. Silicone Fluid Dashpot Relays. These are available from several manufacturers with delays up to 5 to 10 seconds. The models we have seen are for light duty and should be used to energize a relay. All inrush solenoid current should then be handled through a contactor operated from this relay.

3. Solid State Electronic Timers. These timers feature almost unlimited life, great accuracy, and are available with adjustable delays from fractions of a second to minutes, hours, days, weeks, or months.

4. Thermal Delay Relays. Relatively inexpensive and with good reliability, although repetitive accuracy is not as good as with other types. For better accuracy, the element must be allowed to cool before being energized again. Cooling time could be approximately the same as heating time. They are available in non-adjustable delays up to about 3 minutes.

5. Motor-Driven Re-Set Timers. Very accurate but with probably a shorter life than industrial timing relays or solid state timers. Available with adjustable delays up to 5 minutes, sometimes longer.

GENERAL RULES FOR ELECTRICAL DESIGN

The rules given on this page should apply to most applications of electrical control of air and hydraulic systems, and should apply not only to JIC hard wired electrical control but to solid state control by programmable controllers covered in Chapter 10. Of course deviations are always permitted to obtain special effects or to simplify circuitry.

(1). All valve solenoids, relay coils, timer coils, and other load devices should be left in a de-energized state at the end of every cycle. Exceptions are permitted if for a special reason.

(2). Fluid power valves should be ordered with "oil immersed" or "high temperature" coils instead of standard coils on applications involving any of these unusual conditions: (a), Where the solenoid must be kept continuously energized for long periods (more than a few minutes) and especially on deadend service where there is no movement of fluid through the valve during this period. The fluid (hydraulic or air) serves an important role in carrying away heat; (b), If a solenoid will be cycled at a high rate of speed (this applies only to valves with A-C solenoids). Because of the higher inrush current, the *average* current over a period of time may be greater than the coil can tolerate. (c), Where surrounding (ambient) temperature is unusually high; and (d), On applications operating in locations of unusually high humidity.

(3). On hydraulic applications, the circuit must be designed to unload the pump at the end of every cycle or during extended idling periods within the cycle. Pump unloading is automatic in circuits using pressure compensated pumps and in central hydraulic systems. On circuits using fixed displacement pumps, the electrical circuit must be designed to take care of the pump unloading. Exceptions may be on low power, low flow applications where it may not be necessary to unload the pump.

(4). Usually the electric control circuit should be designed for a completely automatic cylinder cycle, stopping only at places in the cycle where operator attention is required such as for unloading parts. The circuit should be designed to be self-monitoring, insofar as possible, instantly stopping the machine if any condition should develop which would be hazardous to the operator, to the machine, or to the material being processed. Limit switches and other sensors can often be used to detect abnormal conditions.

(5). Electrical circuits should be laid out so both solenoids on a double solenoid valve are not energized at the same time. On some valves this would cause one of the solenoids to burn out. Over a long period of operation, even a momentary overlap of energization on each cycle might cause internal heat to build up to damage the coil. Certain other valves are not harmed by this condition. If necessary to protect valve coils on those models which could be damaged, they can be interlocked on opposite sets of contacts of a relay or pushbutton in circuits similar to those on Page 149.

(6). Valve solenoids can be operated directly from limit switch contacts if their current is within the switch rating. However, on electric circuits designed for extremely long life on important or heavy duty applications, we suggest the limit switches operate relays. Valve solenoids, with their high inrush current, can be switched by the relay contacts. Even small limit switches are suited for operation of relay coils, panel lamps, and other light loads.

Note: Electrical circuits in this book show valve solenoids operated directly from limit switches. This is for circuit simplicity. On any circuit, additional relays can be interposed to carry valve solenoid current. A designer must use judgement in deciding whether to interpose additional relays.

PLACEMENT OF LIMIT SWITCHES AND CAMS

Enclosed switches should be used in locations where they may be exposed to water or oil splash or chip accumulation. A slotted mounting or other provision should be made for precise adjustment of switch position. Switches should be mounted so they will not be damaged if the cylinder should accidentally overrun, as it could in event of control current failure or burn-out of a valve solenoid or relay coil. In addition to these points of good design, suitable provisions should be made to get desired switch action on those applications where the circuit is intentionally designed for the cylinder to overrun a switch as part of its normal operation. See next figure.

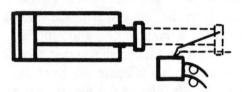

Part A. A long actuator arm attached to the limit switch.

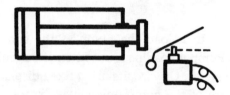

Part B. A long actuator arm hinged to a fixed member of the machine.

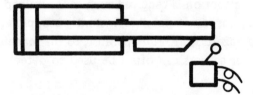

Part C. A long cam on a moving part of the machine.

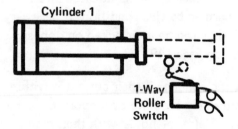

Part D. Switching impulse produced at intermediate point in stroke.

FIGURE 6-9. Switching signals produced at an intermediate point in a cylinder stroke.

Figure 6-9. While in most cases a limit switch is placed to actuate very close to the end of a cylinder stroke, there are applications where a switching signal is needed at an intermediate point in the stroke. For example, if a sustained switching signal is needed from the point of switch actuation to the end of a cylinder stroke, a long actuating arm can be attached to the switch as in Part A. Or, as in Part B, with a long actuator arm hinged at a fixed point on the machine. An alternative method is to have a long cam on the moving member of the machine as in Part C.

Note: One of these arrangements should be used as a safety precaution on any cylinder set-up where the cylinder after accidentally overriding a limit switch could get behind its actuating arm with resultant damage when the machine is re-started.

A method of producing a limited duration electrical impulse is to use a standard limit switch fitted with a 1-way roller actuator with knee action (Part D of Figure 6-9). This actuator is described on Pages 19 and 122. The switch can be positioned at the point in the cylinder stroke where the impulse must start. The duration of the impulse can be established by design of cam length, considering the cylinder travel speed. The switch is actuated by the cam and then must be released by the cam before completion of the cylinder stroke.

When the switch faces the direction shown in Part D of Figure 6-9 it will give a switching impulse while the cylinder is retracting, but no impulse will be produced on the cylinder extension stroke. If turned the other way it will produce the impulse while the cylinder is extending.

Other means for producing switching signals of limited duration for use in circuitry are shown on Pages 74, 75, and 76. The time delay circuit on Page 115 can also be adapted for this purpose.

Figure 6-10. If any limit switch is mounted for head-on actuation, and if it is not mounted at the end of the stroke, a means of protecting the switch from physical damage should be provided in case the cylinder should accidentally over-travel. This could happen if electrical control current should fail. Switches mounted at the end of a cylinder stroke are protected from damage by the cylinder end cap.

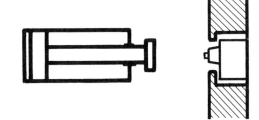

FIGURE 6-10. Protect head-on switches from damage by cylinder over-travel.

PROPER CAM ACTUATION OF LIMIT SWITCHES

Too often there is a lack of attention given to properly actuating a limit switch. A designer may think that the only requirements for a dog or cam for actuating a limit switch are that it can be adjusted to actuate at exactly the right time and have good repetitive accuracy. He may not be aware that the size and shape of the cam have a great deal to do with life expectancy of the switch. The highest percentage of breakdowns in an electrical control system in the past have been caused by limit switch failures, and these failures have largely been due to one or more of the poor design practices discussed in this section.

(1). Many failures have been due to the use, for reasons of economy, of light-duty or non-enclosed switches where heavy-duty industrial switches should have been used.

(2). Improper Cam Angle. Figure 6-11. The leading edge of the actuating cam should be approximately parallel with the switch arm, or at right angles to direction of lever movement. No more than 15° variation should be allowed in either direction.

(3). Excessive Rotational Movement. Cams should be designed so they do not over-rotate switch levers. Excess movement can result in unnecessary strain on mechanical parts and springs in the switch.

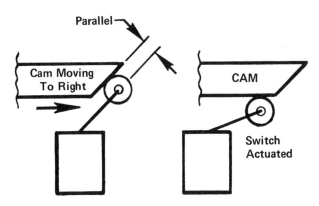

Leading edge of cam should be parallel with switch lever arm.

FIGURE 6-11. Cam shape for approach velocity of 50 feet per minute or less.

(4). Excessive Impact. Figure 6-12. Fast-traveling cams should have sloped or contoured surfaces. Excessive impact is without a doubt the major cause of premature switch failure. At slow approach speeds there is no problem, but as approach velocity increases, the destructive impact becomes greater, and can cause physical damage to the mechanical parts of the switch. But more important, it can cause the contacts to "bounce", thus making and breaking the circuit more than once during the period of high inrush current to a solenoid valve. Of course, this will greatly reduce contact life.

For cam velocities of 50 feet per minute or less, the cam shape shown in Figure 6-11 is satisfactory. For higher speeds a straight slope should be provided on the leading edge of the cam as shown in Part A of Figure 6-12. Although this straight slope does not give uniform acceleration to the switch

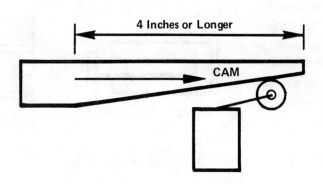

A. Cams with straight slope leading edge are suitable for moderately high speeds.

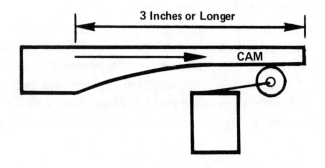

B. For very high speed cam approach, leading edge of cam should be contoured.

FIGURE 6-12. Special cam shapes should be used for high approach speeds.

arm, it may be satisfactory for speeds up to 200 feet per minute provided the part of the slope which causes movement to the switch arm is at least 4 inches long. The switch should be so located that its arm can be adjusted to be parallel with the sloping surface of the cam.

At cam speeds faster than 200 feet per minute the cam surface should be shaped in a curve which will give a uniform acceleration to the switch lever as illustrated in Part B of Figure 6-12. Surface length should be at least 3 inches, longer if space permits. As in all cam designs, the limit switch should be so mounted and its lever so adjusted that the arm is approximately parallel with the leading cam surface.

A designer should consider the replacement of limit switches with other actuating devices such as proximity switches, photoelectric sensors, or accoustic switches on applications where approaching cam velocity is high.

(5). Overriding Cams. Figure 6-13. On those applications where a cam must override a limit switch, traveling beyond it, the switch arm should never be allowed to drop off the cam abruptly. This "fly-back" can produce severe strains on mechanical parts and springs in the switch, and will shorten switch life by producing double pulsing of its contacts.

The trailing edge of an overriding cam should be sloped or contoured to prevent rapid "fly-back" of the switch arm. Although not as critical as slope of the leading edge, the angle between trailing edge

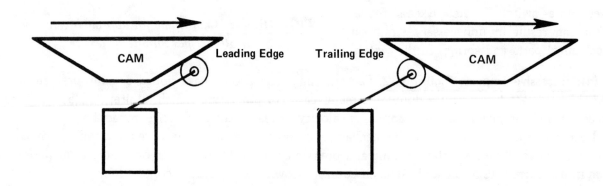

FIGURE 6-13. The trailing edge of an overriding cam should have a slope to prevent "snap-back" of the switch after the cam passes. A 30° angle between trailing edge and lever arm is usually sufficient.

121

and switch arm should be no greater than 30°. Remember, too, that the cam must pass back over the switch arm on its return stroke unless a 1-way actuator is used. Return speed of the cam should be considered in designing slope angle of the trailing edge.

<u>(6). Excessive Current.</u> Handling an excessive current will reduce switch life expectancy. Inrush current to an A-C solenoid valve can be 5 times higher than its normal, steady state current after its armature has seated. For simplicity, circuits in this book show solenoid valve coils directly operated with limit switches. This is all right for normal or average applications, but if a system is being designed for maximum service-free life, extended switch life can be obtained by interposing relays between limit switches and solenoid valve coils. This modification is applicable for any circuit shown in this book.

<u>(7). Other Switching Devices.</u> Where a switching signal must be picked up by a fast moving cam from a switch mounted at mid stroke of the cylinder, a proximity switch or photoelectric sensor will be more reliable than a limit switch and has an unlimited life.

On hydraulic cylinder applications, the cylinder can be purchased with a built-in cushion to reduce speed at about one inch before impact. This not only protects the limit switch mounted at the end of the stroke, but will protect the cylinder from impact damage.

PRODUCING ONE-WAY ACTUATION OF A LIMIT SWITCH

"One-Way" actuation of a limit switch is that condition of operation where a moving cam actuates and overrides a limit switch when approaching from one direction, but will pass by it on the return stroke without actuating the switch contacts. There are several ways of producing this one-way actuation:

<u>(1). Knee-Joint Actuator. Figure 6-14.</u> Most standard industrial limit switches can be furnished with some kind of "knee-joint" actuator. The joint is stiff against a cam approaching from one direction, and the switch mechanism is actuated. The joint collapses against a cam approaching from the opposite direction without actuating the switch contacts. This type of switch is briefly described on Page 19.

The knee-joint actuator should only be used at low cam speeds, 50 feet per minute or less; if used against cams moving at high speed, operation may be unreliable, the switch contacts may bounce, and switch life expectancy reduced. Cams for knee-joint actuation should be shaped similar to Figure 6-11 on both leading and trailing edges.

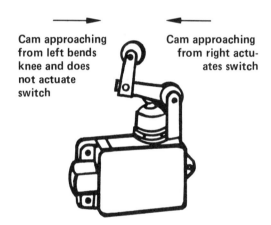

FIGURE 6-14. "Knee Action" Switch.

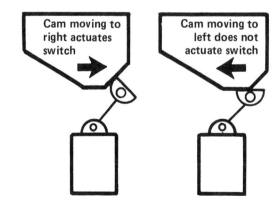

FIGURE 6-15. Partial Roller Mounted on Standard Limit Switch.

(2). Partial Roller. Figure 6-15. For high speed 1-way actuation, a standard limit switch fitted with a partial roller will give better response and will work better at higher cam approach speeds than either of the other methods shown in this section. This actuator is available on most industrial limit switches. The roller is flattened on one side, and has a torque spring to return it to initial angular position after it has been deflected by a machine cam passing by it in the reverse direction. This is shown in the right view of Figure 6-15. Design recommendations on preceding pages should be followed in shaping leading and trailing edges of the actuating cam.

(3). Hinged Trip Dog. An inexpensive trip dog can be suitably mounted on the moving machine member. This requires no springs for its operation, as it is hinged at a point where it will return to normal position by gravity. Trip dogs can be mounted in other positions, for example on vertically moving members by varying shape and location of hinge point to provide gravity return. Return springs can be added if necessary. Trip dogs are limited to cam speeds of 50 feet per minute or less, and leading and trailing edges of hinged dog can be designed as in Figure 6-11.

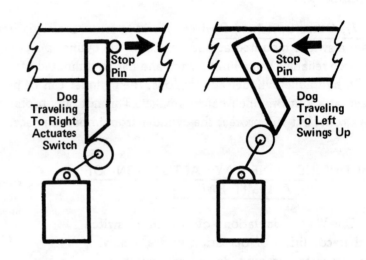

FIGURE 6-16. Hinged Trip Dog With Standard Limit Switch.

CHAPTER 7

Miscellaneous Applications

PROGRAM TIMERS

In previous chapters cylinders have been programmed in an automatic cycle by using limit switches and pressure switches. Another way to set up an automatic cycle between any number of cylinders is with a program timer. This method should be considered: (1), on those machines where circuit simplification can be achieved by eliminating a large number of holding relays; (2), where limit switches if mounted on the machine, would have to operate with high impact or at an unfavorable cam angle; and (3), where it may be desirable to establish a constant production rate with an operator required to keep pace with the machine.

In a typical motor-driven program timer a self-starting synchronous electric motor drives a shaft on which are mounted a number of cams, one for each valve solenoid to be controlled, plus one or more extra for auxiliary functions required. The timer motor can be allowed to run continuously, starting another machine cycle as soon as one is completed. Or, it can be wired to make only one cycle and stop. If the 1-cycle feature is not built into the timer it can be added with one of the arrangements on Pages 131 and 132. Each cam must be adjusted individually for length of ON and OFF time.

A series of individual timers can be used instead of one program timer, with each timer starting the next one. This is especially suited to programmable controllers which have built-in electronic timers.

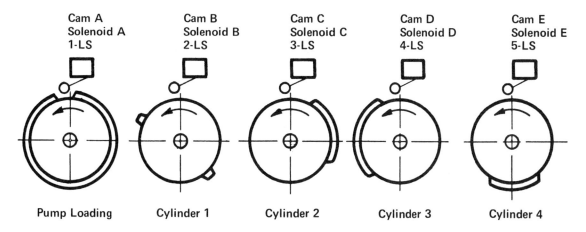

FIGURE 7-1A. *Example of cams on a motor-driven program timer to control movements of the cylinders shown in the hydraulic diagram on the next page. These five (or more) cams are mounted on a common shaft and driven with an electric motor.*

Figure 7-1A. This timer is set up with five cams to control the five solenoids in Figure 7-1B. Cam A, for example, controls the pump unloading Solenoid A. It is adjusted to load the pump at the start of each cycle and keep it loaded until the end of the cycle. It could also be arranged to load and unload the pump at intermediate points in the cycle.

Additional cams could be added for special functions such as pressure control — automatically reducing pressure during certain parts of the cycle. See Page 105. Other functions could include operation of automatic parts feeders, solenoid or hydraulic parts ejectors, chip blowing, coolant feed, opening and closing of safety doors or gates, and many other auxiliary functions.

Figure 7-1B. This hydraulic system operates from the program timer shown in Figure 7-1A. Pump unloading is accomplished by venting the pilot-operated relief valve with a small 2-way solenoid valve.

Single solenoid valves should be used in program timer circuits whenever possible to reduce the number of cams required. However, double solenoid valves may be required for cylinders which must stop and hold in mid stroke. A separate cam will be required for each solenoid. These separate cams must be accurately adjusted so both solenoids of a double solenoid valve will never be energized at the same time, even momentarily. In the electrical circuit of Figure 7-1A, Switch 1-LS energizes Solenoid A, Switch 2-LS energizes Solenoid B, etc.

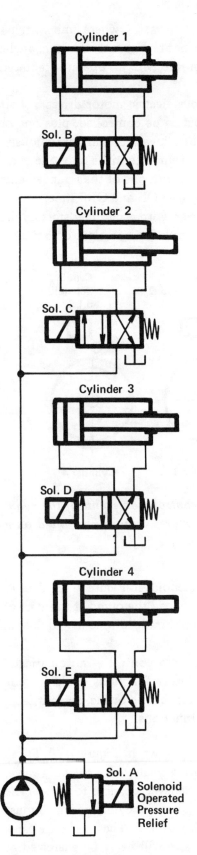

FIGURE 7-1B. Hydraulic circuit to operate from program timer.

As in all hydraulic circuits, when two cylinders operate at the same time from one pump, the available oil must be shared by both cylinders. Unless the cylinders are mechanically tied together, flow control valves or flow divider valves may have to be installed to prevent one cylinder from taking more than its share of oil.

CYLINDER DWELL

A cylinder driving a metal cutting tool is sometimes required to dwell for a short time at the end of its stroke to clean up the cut before retracting. Timing devices such as those on Page 117 can be used for setting the length of dwell time.

A positive stop should be placed at the dwell position. The cylinder should be allowed to stall against the stop for the duration of dwell with full pressure behind its piston. This holds the tool firmly in place while it cleans up the cut. A limit switch should be carefully positioned to actuate just as the cylinder reaches the stop. This switch starts the dwell timing. On hydraulic systems it may sometimes be possible to unload the pump during long dwell periods, but is not necessary for short periods.

Figure 7-2, Page 126. On this air cylinder application, the spindle is rotated by an electric motor. The drill feeds by compressed air. Circuit action is 1-cycle reciprocation, forward and reverse, each time the pushbutton is pressed. The drill must dwell before retracting when depth is reached as indicated by 1-LS limit switch.

Electrical action in Part B of Figure 7-2 is as follows: When the pushbutton is momentarily pressed, valve Solenoid A becomes energized and the drillhead starts down. When Switch 1-LS is actuated, timing relay Coil 1-TR becomes energized. At the end of the timing period, Contacts 1-TR-A close, causing valve Solenoid B to become energized and the drillhead to retract. On some applications a pressure switch could replace 1-LS. This would permit the positive stop to be re-positioned at will without also having to re-position a limit switch each time. Meter-in speed control works better than meter-out when a pressure switch is used, so the speed control valve shown in the figure could replace the regulator in the top cylinder port. It should be installed so its flow arrow points toward the cylinder.

A feature of the air circuit is the use of a pressure regulator to limit maximum drill thrust. This regulator

125

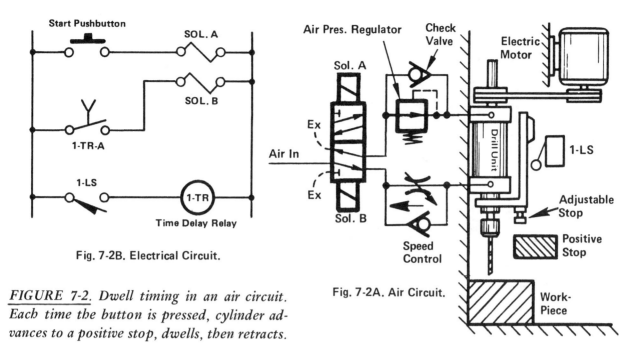

Fig. 7-2B. Electrical Circuit.

Fig. 7-2A. Air Circuit.

FIGURE 7-2. Dwell timing in an air circuit. Each time the button is pressed, cylinder advances to a positive stop, dwells, then retracts.

should be adjusted to suit the diameter of the drill bit in use, and will minimize drill breakage as a drill bit becomes dull. A needle or flow control valve will limit speed but will not limit thrust.

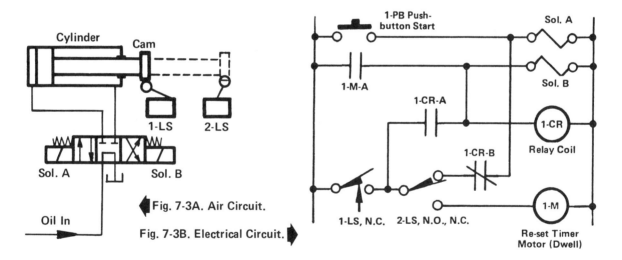

Fig. 7-3A. Air Circuit.

Fig. 7-3B. Electrical Circuit.

FIGURE 7-3. Dwell timing in a hydraulic circuit using a re-set timer (see Page 28). This cylinder has 1-cycle reciprocation each time the button is pressed. Pump unloads during dwell and between cycles.

Figure 7-3. Hydraulic Dwell. The operator presses and holds the pushbutton long enough for the cylinder to move a short distance and release Switch 1-LS. This switch then takes over for the pushbutton to keep the cylinder moving forward. When 2-LS is actuated, Solenoid A becomes de-energized while the re-set timer motor becomes energized. At the end of dwell time, Contacts 1-M-A close to energize Relay 1-CR coil. This relay locks in and energizes valve Solenoid B. The cylinder retracts to home position and actuates 1-LS. This de-energizes the entire circuit, centering the valve spool, and this unloads the pump.

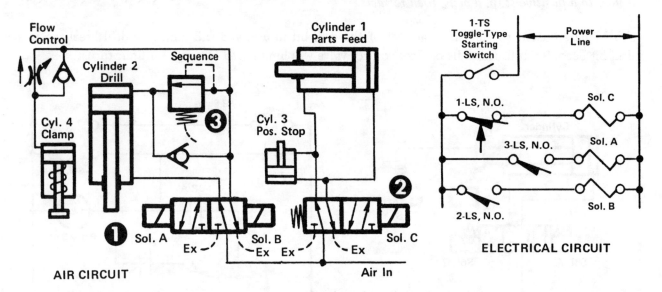

AUTOMATIC FEED AND DRILL

Figure 7-4. A good example of automation in which parts are continuously processed without operator attention except to keep the machine supplied with parts, and to replace drill bits when necessary.

Parts are fed from a hopper, pushed under a drill against a positive stop, clamped and drilled, then pushed off into a receiving bin by a new part being fed in.

FIGURE 7-4. Automatic and Continuous Feeding and Drilling Operation.

Circuit Operation. When starting Switch 1-TS is closed, valve Solenoid C becomes energized. This shifts Valve 2, causing Cylinder 3 (positive stop) to extend a positive stop into the path of the feeding parts, and causes Cylinder 1 (parts feed) to start pushing the line of parts under the drill. When limit Switch 3-LS is actuated by advancing Cylinder 1, valve Solenoid A becomes energized. This shifts Valve 1, causing Cylinder 4 (clamp) to act first, and when it stalls against the work, sequence Valve 3 opens to allow the drill (Cylinder 2) to start downward. When the cam on the drill structure moves off of 1-LS, Solenoid C becomes de-energized, which retracts both Cylinder 1 (parts feed) and Cylinder 3 (positive stop). Drilling continues to depth, when 2-LS is actuated. This energizes Solenoid B to shift Valve 1. The clamp (Cylinder 4) and the drill (Cylinder 2) are both retracted but a flow control valve delays release of the clamp, giving the drill time to withdraw from the work. At home position of the drill 1-LS is actuated to start the next cycle in this automatic operation.

PECK DRILLING WITH COMPRESSED AIR

"Peck drilling" is a term for deep hole drilling in which the drill bit must be temporarily withdrawn from the hole several times during drilling in order to clear chips. After receiving a starting signal, the machine should operate automatically through the pecking cycles and final withdrawal of the drill. A build-up of chips could be detected by sensing the current on the electric motor which rotates the drill, but for most applications it is quite satisfactory and much easier to set the pecking on a regular time interval by using a re-set electrical timer.

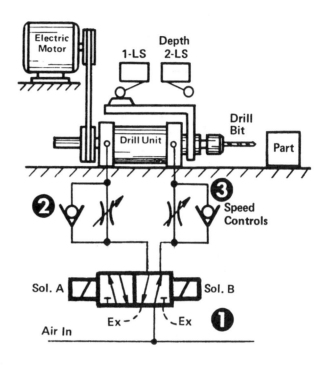

Figure 7-5. Usually, on peck drilling fed with compressed air, no attempt is made to reduce approach speed before the drill contacts the work. Speed control Valve 3 should be set slow enough that the bit will not be damaged by impacting the work. Limit Switch 2-LS is adjusted to actuate when final depth is reached. Switch 1-LS starts the drill forward again after each pecking operation. A hydraulic checking cylinder is used if the drill is to break through the work.

Electrical Circuit. An adjustable re-set timer controls length of time the drill remains in the hole. It can be set experimentally to withdraw the drill every (so many) seconds. The drill is returned to the hole by Switch 1-LS. Symbols 1-M and 1-M-A indicate the re-set timer electric motor and contacts respectively. See Page 28.

Circuit operation is as follows: When an operator presses the pushbutton, 1-CR relay coil is energized. Contacts 1-CR-A lock the relay closed. Valve Solenoid A is energized through 1-CR-B and Switch 1-LS (which is held actuated at this time by a cam on the retracted drill unit). The cylinder starts forward, and when 1-LS is released by the cam, the timer motor is energized to start a timing cycle. The drill contacts the work and drills until Contacts 1-M-A on the timer close. This energizes valve Solenoid B to retract the drill. At home position, 1-LS switch is actuated, starting the drill forward into the hole to continue drilling. Pecking can be repeated a number of times until full depth is reached and Switch 2-LS is actuated. This energizes Solenoid B and releases Relay 1-CR. The drill retracts and with Contacts 1-CR-B open it cannot go forward again. The cycle is now complete.

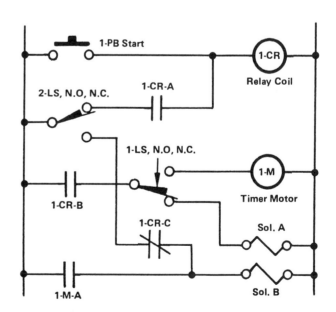

FIGURE 7-5. Compressed Air and Electrical Circuits for Peck Drilling.

PECK DRILLING WITH HYDRAULIC FEED

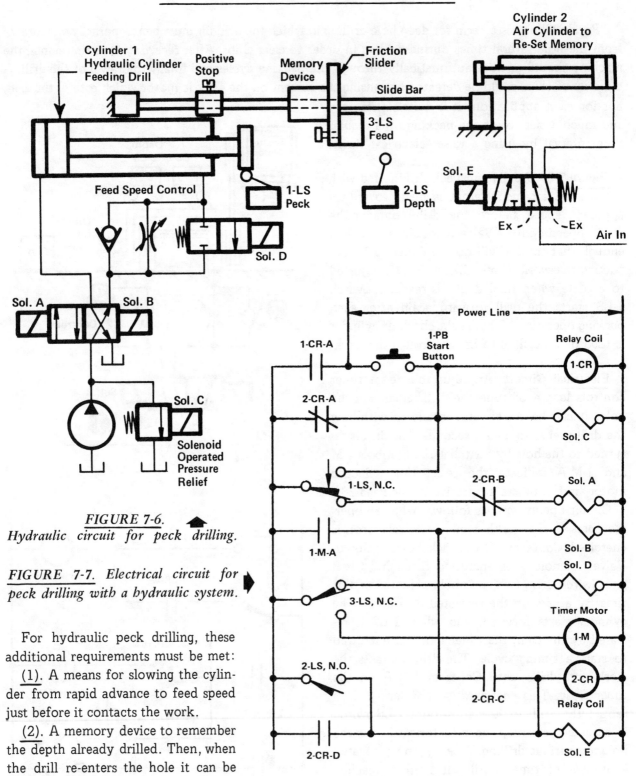

FIGURE 7-6.
Hydraulic circuit for peck drilling.

FIGURE 7-7. Electrical circuit for peck drilling with a hydraulic system.

For hydraulic peck drilling, these additional requirements must be met:

(1). A means for slowing the cylinder from rapid advance to feed speed just before it contacts the work.

(2). A memory device to remember the depth already drilled. Then, when the drill re-enters the hole it can be rapidly advanced to this depth before its speed is reduced to the proper feed rate.

(3). A means for unloading the pump after the hole is completely drilled and the drill retracted.

Note: An electric re-set timer is used to retract the drill at frequent intervals to allow chips to clear the hole. See timers on Page 28. Adjust re-set time according to drill size, hole depth, and work material.

(1). Reducing Cylinder Speed from Rapid Advance to Feed Rate. In Figure 7-6, Solenoid D, when energized, permits unrestricted oil flow for full cylinder speed. When de-energized, it routes return oil through a flow control valve which has been set for the desired feed rate. If Solenoid D burns out or control current is lost, the cylinder automatically drops back to the feed rate to protect the work.

(2). Memory Device. This is a special device constructed for the job. Its purpose is to remember the depth of penetration, so when the drill advances, after withdrawing to clear chips, it can rapidly advance up to this position before slowing to feed rate.

The memory system consists of a limit switch, 3-LS, mounted on a slider which is friction positioned on a stationary slide bar. During drilling the slider, with 3-LS, is pushed along by the advancing cylinder. When the feed cylinder retracts to clear chips, the slider remains in its advanced position. When the cylinder moves forward again, it can travel at full speed to the slider position. When 3-LS is actuated, Solenoid D is energized and the cylinder slows to its feed rate.

When full hole depth has been reached, Switch 2-LS retracts the feed cylinder for the final time. A small bore air cylinder, operated by Solenoid E, pushes the slider and 3-LS back to their starting position as set by a positive stop on the slide bar.

Note: Switch 3-LS should be mounted on a spring loaded bracket, not shown, so it will spring back slightly each time the cylinder backs away from it. Then, on its next advance, the cylinder will slow to feed speed slightly ahead of drilling position.

(3). Pump Unloading. The pump is loaded and unloaded by energizing Solenoid C which controls the vent line of the pilot-operated relief valve. Refer to Page 99 for details of solenoid vent unloading.

Directional control of the feed cylinder is with a double solenoid, 2-position hydraulic valve. Control of the re-set memory cylinder is with a single solenoid air valve.

Electrical Circuit Operation. Figure 7-7. When 1-PB button is pressed, Relay 1-CR locks in through 2-CR-A. It remains energized and keeps Solenoid C energized during the entire drilling operation to maintain pump pressure. It is released as the final action in the cycle after hole depth is reached and the hydraulic drill cylinder has retracted.

Solenoids A and D also become energized, Solenoid A through 2-CR-B, 1-LS, and 1-CR-A (to start the drill feed cylinder forward), Solenoid D through 3-LS and 1-CR-A (to give it rapid advance). The memory slider, carrying 3-LS, is positioned close to the work. When 3-LS is actuated, Solenoid D becomes de-energized and the cylinder slows to feed speed. Timer 1-M is started by closure of 3-LS. Drilling continues until timer Contacts 1-M-A close. Solenoid B becomes energized and the cylinder retracts, at full speed, to home position, leaving the slider and 3-LS to remember the depth already penetrated by the drill. The timer immediately re-sets as soon as 3-LS is released. At home position 1-LS is actuated. Valve Solenoid A becomes energized and starts the cylinder forward. It advances rapidly to the new drilling position before actuating 3-LS and slowing to feed speed. The timer is also energized by 3-LS and a new drilling operation starts.

Adjust pecking time according to the job. Pecking can be repeated any number of times. When 2-LS depth switch is actuated, Relay 2-CR is energized and locks in through 2-CR-D and 1-CR-A. Contacts 2-CR-C energize Solenoid B to retract the feed cylinder. Contacts 2-CR-A open and prepare the holding circuit of Relay 1-CR for unlocking as soon as the drill cylinder fully retracts. Contacts 2-CR-D energize Solenoid E to operate a single solenoid air valve to extend Cylinder 2. This cylinder pushes the slider, with 3-LS switch, back to starting position for the next drilling operation. When the drill cylinder reaches home and actuates 1-LS, this unlocks 1-CR relay, then Contacts 1-CR-A de-energize the rest of the circuit. Solenoid C becomes de-energized and unloads the pump. Solenoid E becomes de-energized and retracts the memory re-set cylinder.

ONE-CYCLE OR ONE-REVOLUTION CONTROL

The principle of "one-revolution" control can be used when a hydraulic, air, or electric motor is driving a load device which must, when signalled, make exactly one revolution and stop until signalled again. The load may also be rotated 1/2, 1/3, or 1/4 turn by using a control cam with 2, 3, or 4 lobes. This type of control is useful on such applications as 90°, 120°, 180° or 360° parts turnover, on control of hydraulic motors which rotate large index tables, on turning cam assemblies of specially built program timers, and other applications where a rotation of 1 turn or an even fraction thereof is required on each cycle. Although the load device, which also carries the control cam, makes one revolution, the driving motor can be a high speed type coupled through a speed reducer.

If the driving motor is hydraulic, a counterbalance valve at Point "x" will bring it to a rapid stop when Solenoid A is de-energized. See Volume 3 – Industrial Fluid Power for deceleration circuits.

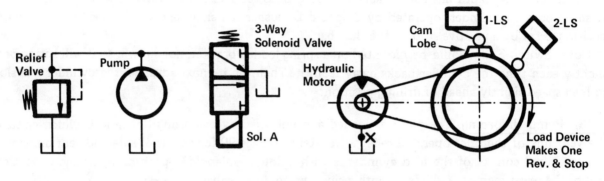

FIGURE 7-8. *The control cam operates on the same shaft with the load device and can have 1, 2, 3, or 4 lobes for 1, 1/2, 1/3, or 1/4 turn each cycle.*

Figure 7-8. A hydraulic motor is shown in this illustration driving a load device which has a control cam with one lobe. A 3-way solenoid valve is used to start and stop the hydraulic motor and to unload the pump when the motor is stopped. Two limit switches may be needed depending on the type of electric control circuit chosen. Switch 1-LS is mounted at the reference position, and 2-LS is mounted at any other convenient location around the cam so that it will not be actuated until the cam has passed 1-LS.

Simple Pushbutton Control. Figure 7-9. On applications where the starting signal is to be supplied by an operator using a momentary pushbutton, and where the load device is in plain view of the operator, this simple control circuit may be adequate.

Wiring to Switch 1-LS is to its COM and N.C. terminals. In reference position of the control cam, the cam lobe holds 1-LS in an open or actuated state.

The operator presses the pushbutton and must hold it long enough for the cam lobe to release 1-LS switch. Valve Solenoid A becomes energized and starts the hydraulic motor. Switch 1-LS takes over after the operator releases the button. The cam makes one revolution and stops when the cam lobe again actuates 1-LS. In the circuit of Figure 7-8, Switch 2-LS is not needed.

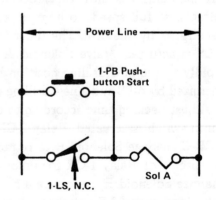

FIGURE 7-9. *Simple pushbutton control can be used if the load device is in view of the operator.*

Circuits on this page show alternate electrical control for one-cycle operation. The first one, Figure 7-10, is for use with a momentary starting signal of short duration, on those applications where the mechanism is out of view of the operator.

The second circuit, Figure 7-11 at the bottom of this page, is for control by a maintained starting signal or a steady signal from another machine or programming device. Even though the starting signal is maintained for a long time, the mechanism will stop after making one revolution. The starting signal must then be interrupted, at least momentarily, then re-applied to start the next revolution.

Figure 7-10. When a starting signal is received, either from a pushbutton or from some other source, Relay 1-CR becomes energized and locks in through Contacts 1-CR-A and 2-CR-A. Valve Solenoid A also becomes energized through 1-CR-B. The hydraulic motor starts and moves the cam lobe off of Switch 1-LS. Closure of this switch prepares the other relay to be locked in later in the cycle. The cam continues to rotate and its lobe actuates Switch 2-LS. This energizes Relay 2-CR, which locks in through Switch 1-LS and Contacts 2-CR-C. Contacts 2-CR-A, which are now open, release the holding circuit on Relay 1-CR, allowing it to open. Solenoid A is kept energized through 2-CR-B contacts. The motor continues to rotate until the cycle has been completed. When Switch 1-LS is actuated, Relay 2-CR is released. This causes Solenoid A to become de-energized and the motor will stop with the pump unloaded to tank through the hydraulic directional valve.

Figure 7-11. When toggle Switch 1-TS is closed or when a sustained signal is received from another source, valve Solenoid A becomes energized through Contacts 1-CR-A. The motor starts and the cam lobe releases Switch 1-LS to its closed state. When the lobe actuates Switch 2-LS, Relay 1-CR becomes energized and locks in through 1-CR-B contacts. The circuit through 1-CR-A is broken but Solenoid A remains energized through 1-LS. When the cam has made a full cycle, limit Switch 1-LS is again actuated. This de-energizes Solenoid A and the motor stops. Switch 1-TS must be opened, at least momentarily before another cycle can be initiated.

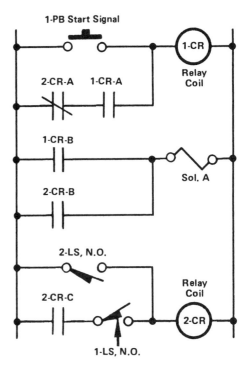

FIGURE 7-10. This circuit is for initiating a 1-cycle rotation from a momentary starting signal, especially if the machine is out of view of the operator.

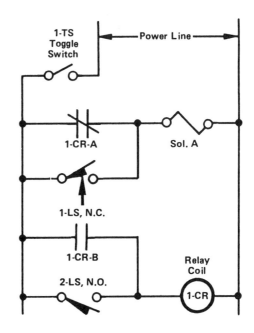

FIGURE 7-11. This circuit is for initiating a 1-cycle rotation from a maintained starting signal such as from a toggle switch.

132

MULTIPLE INDEXING

Multiple indexing is a method of joining two or more cylinders end-to-end to obtain an assembly which can be extended and retracted to several very precise indexing positions. The method shown is especially useful on compressed air because one long-stroke cylinder cannot be accurately stopped, and held, at selected positions in mid stroke. But several short-stroke air cylinders can be stacked in series to obtain accurate and rigidly-held pre-selected positions. By extending each cylinder singly or in combination with other cylinders in the string, the pin-to-pin length of the stack can be selected by electric control for applications such as moving the stroke lever of a variable volume pump to several pre-selected positions, for shifting workpieces in a fixture for drilling or machining operations, for moving a machine cross slide to select width of cut, etc.

To obtain equally spaced mid positions, on a 2-cylinder assembly one cylinder should have a stroke twice as long as the other (1:2 ratio) as shown in Figure 7-12. On a 3-cylinder assembly the stroke ratio must be 1:2:4, etc. One 4-way solenoid valve must be used for each cylinder in the assembly. Total force from the assembly is no more than obtained from one cylinder of the same bore since the cylinders are effectively in series. Either single or double solenoid valves can be used according to the type of control desired. Circuits shown are for compressed air but can be adapted to hydraulics for applications requiring higher power. Caution! The tolerance error on each cylinder stroke may add up to an unacceptable value when all are extended. For greater positional accuracy, special cylinders can be ordered from the manufacturer built to very close tolerance on the length of stroke.

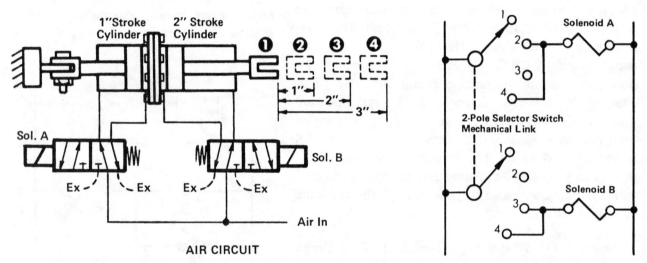

FIGURE 7-12. *Example of a 2-cylinder stack-up controlled with a rotary selector switch.*

Figure 7-12. To illustrate the principle, two cylinders are bolted back-to-back, one having a 1-inch stroke, the other a 2-inch stroke. This combination gives 4 fixed positions spaced one inch apart. Position 1 is obtained with both cylinders retracted; Position 2 with the short cylinder extended, the other retracted; Position 3 with the short cylinder retracted, the other extended; and Position 4 is obtained with both cylinders extended. If both cylinders have equal stroke, only one mid position is possible.

<u>Electrical Circuit.</u> A 2-pole, 4-position rotary selector switch controls the two cylinders. Positions 1, 2, 3, and 4 on the switch represent corresponding rod extension positions on the air diagram. An important rule to remember in electrical circuitry is that the same number of poles is needed on the rotary switch as the number of solenoid valves and cylinders in the string.

Figure 7-13. This circuit is similar to the one on the preceding page except that double solenoid, 2-position air valves are used instead of single solenoid valves. Double solenoid valves can be more easily adapted to pushbutton control. They can be controlled with one of the circuits below.

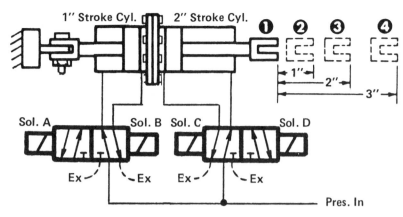

FIGURE 7-13. *Air Circuit Adaptable for Pushbutton Control, Giving Four Positions.*

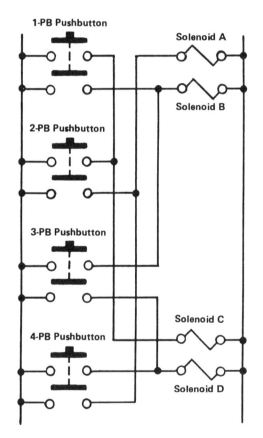

FIGURE 7-15. *Four-Pushbutton Circuit Can be Controlled from Several Locations.*

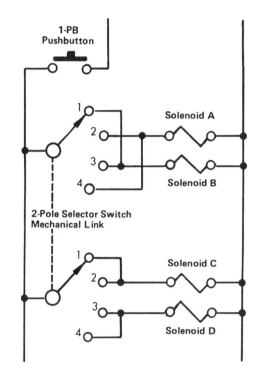

FIGURE 7-14. *Electric Circuit Using Selector Switch With Pushbutton Start.*

Figure 7-14. Symbols on this circuit refer to the air circuit above. To select a cylinder position, the selector switch must first be rotated to the desired index position, then the button pressed.

Current is maintained on the valve solenoids only while the button is held. For some applications this could have an advantage over the selector switch circuit shown on the preceding page, in which current must be maintained on one or both valves while the cylinder string is in Positions 2, 3, or 4.

Figure 7-15. Four pushbuttons of the momentary type are used. Symbols refer to the air circuit above. This circuit is the only one shown which can be remotely controlled from several operator positions.

COUNTING AND STACKING

On packaging applications, circuits must sometimes be included for counting and stacking production items, boxes, bottles, packages, etc., into groups. The usual method is for one cylinder to make (so many) strokes, picking up one (or more) items on each stroke. At the end of the required count, a switching signal is generated which causes a second cylinder to carry the stack away.

Counting can be done with one of these two methods: (1), by sensing thickness of pieces stacked together; this method is the simpler if practical for the job but is accurate only for relatively thick pieces heavy enough to actuate a limit switch. The electric circuit of Figure 7-17 can be used. Or, (2), counting with a memory device such as an electrically operated mechanical counter, a solid state counter, or some type of stepping switch. Refer to Page 30. Counters must be used when handling very thin pieces or those of irregular or varying shape or size, or with pieces too soft, fragile, or flexible to be physically contacted with a switch actuator. The circuit of Figure 7-18 can be used for these applications.

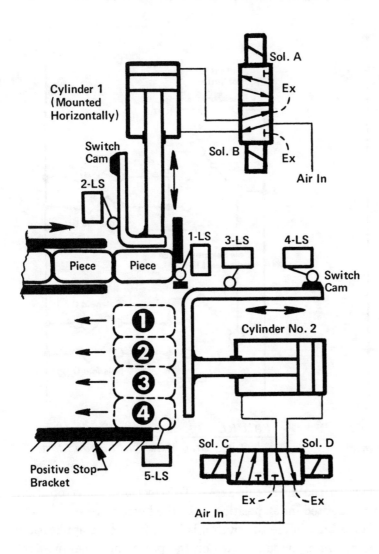

FIGURE 7-16. Top view of layout with cylinders operating in a horizontal plane. When once started, this machine will continue to work indefinitely without an operator as long as workpieces are supplied to it.

Figure 7-16. This is a top view of an arrangement of two cylinders working in a horizontal plane. It illustrates one of the endless variations in physical layout that is possible, and shows the working principles. It is set up to accept a single line of parts delivered from a conveyor, and count them out in groups. Although shown for a group of four, this may be varied to suit the requirement. It works automatically, without an operator, and will accept pieces coming at spaced intervals or with no space between.

When an entering piece moves in front of Cylinder 1, this cylinder makes a forward and return stroke, pushing the piece to Position 1. The action continues to repeat, stacking piece on piece, until the first piece to enter has reached Position 4. Cylinder 2 then makes a forward and return stroke to push the stack out of the way.

Figure 7-17. Electrical Circuit. This simple control circuit is adequate if counting is done by sensing thickness as in Figure 7-16.

The solenoid valves are 2-position models which remain shifted after being momentarily energized.

Starting with Cylinder 1 retracted, when a piece is pushed under the cylinder and against 1-LS by movement of the feed conveyor, this energizes Solenoid A, causing Cylinder 1 to start its forward stroke. A guard attached to the cylinder rod holds back other pieces from the conveyor until the cylinder has retracted.

At the end of the forward stroke of Cylinder 1, limit Switch 2-LS is actuated. This energizes Solenoid B to retract the cylinder to starting position where it stops. Another piece can now be fed in by the conveyor and the process is repeated. The stacking action continues until the first piece actuates 5-LS. This energizes Solenoid C to extend Cylinder 2. A guard on the rod of this cylinder prevents the entry of other pieces into the stacking area until Cylinder 2 has retracted.

At the end of the forward stroke of Cylinder 2, limit Switch 3-LS is actuated. This energizes Solenoid D to retract Cylinder 2.

Note that limit Switch 4-LS is in series with 1-LS to prevent Solenoid A from being energized until Cylinder 2 has completely retracted.

Figure 7-18. Electric Counters. For counting pieces too thin or too delicate for the count to be sensed with a limit switch as in Figure 7-16, or where the count exceeds a few pieces, a counter must be used. It can be either an electro-mechanical or a solid state model. Programmable controllers contain a number of solid state counters, and if a controller is used, one of its internal counters can be used. But the count can only be changed by re-programming. If the count must be changed from time to time, an external model as pictured on Page 30 can be used, and mounted on the operator's console where the count can be easily changed. A solid state counter can count faster; it can count to higher numbers, and has a longer life expectancy than an electro-mechanical model.

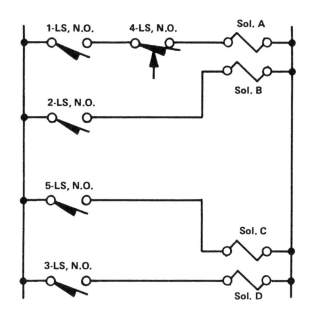

FIGURE 7-17. If parts can be counted by thickness stack-up, this circuit can be used.

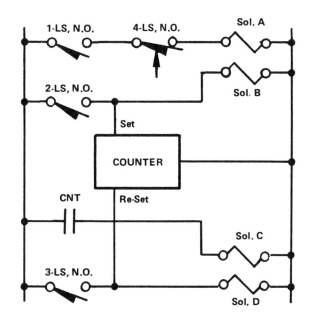

FIGURE 7-18. Counters must be used for counting thin pieces or to high numbers.

A counter will have one terminal on which to receive impulse signals to be counted. It will have another terminal on which a momentary impulse can be applied to re-set the count to zero. It will also have switching terminals, a COM, a N.O. and a N.C. terminal. For use with programmable controllers, only the COM and N.O. terminals are used.

The same physical layout can be used as shown in Figure 7-16 except limit Switch 5-LS must be removed. Its function is served by the contacts in a timer.

INDEX TABLE OPERATION

Index tables are usually rotated with compressed air rather than hydraulic cylinders except on very large and heavy tables. The rotating power is relatively low and air cylinders give faster rotation. Two cylinders are used, one for rotating the table, the other to move a locking pin, dog, or wedge into position for very positive alignment as well as to prevent table drift while work is being performed.

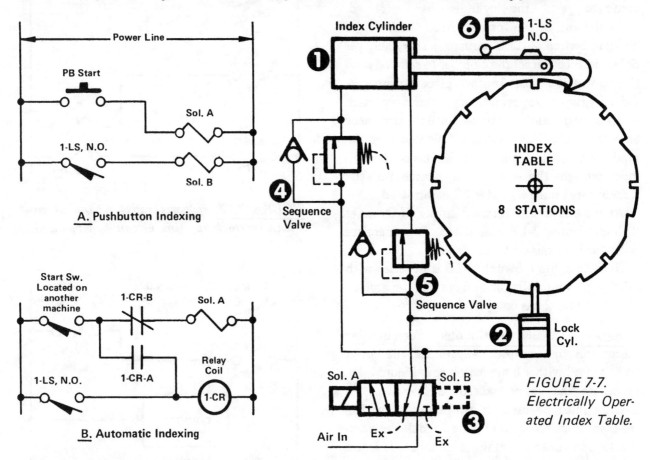

A. Pushbutton Indexing

B. Automatic Indexing

FIGURE 7-7.
Electrically Operated Index Table.

Figure 7-19. Air Circuit. The index cylinder is normally at rest in its extended position. When a starting signal is received, it retracts to rotate the table, actuates 1-LS limit switch, returns to extended position and stops. Sequence Valves 4 and 5 cause the lock cylinder to withdraw before indexing starts and to lock the table before the indexing cylinder returns to starting position.

Pushbutton Indexing. Figure 7-19, Part A. If indexing is started by an operator, a double solenoid, 2-position air valve, 3, is used. When the pushbutton is pressed, valve Solenoid A becomes energized. The lock cylinder first retracts, then the index cylinder rotates the table. At the new indexed position, 1-LS is actuated and valve Solenoid B becomes energized. The lock cylinder extends first, then the index cylinder extends to its home position and stops.

Automatic Indexing. Figure 7-19, Part B. If the indexing signal is taken from a computer or from a switch on another machine, it will usually be a maintained signal. On this application, a single solenoid 4-way valve should be used. On receipt of the maintained signal, the valve becomes energized and indexing takes place as above. When 1-LS is actuated, Relay 1-CR is energized and locks in. Contacts 1-CR-B de-energize the valve solenoid causing both cylinders to return to their home positions and stop. The starting signal must be interrupted and re-applied before another indexing can start.

TURNOVER OF PARTS

Workpieces on an assembly or production line can be turned 90 degrees with one cylinder or 180 degrees with two cylinders. Air cylinders are usually preferred to hydraulic cylinders for loads within their capacity; the reasons being that control is simpler and turnover speed is usually faster. The application shown here is especially suitable for workpieces on a gravity powered or powered roller conveyor.

The first cylinder should carry the load just beyond the overcenter point which may be beyond the 90° position. Guards should be provided to keep a piece from entering the turnover station while a preceding piece is being turned. Limit switches should be mounted at the positions indicated in the diagram below.

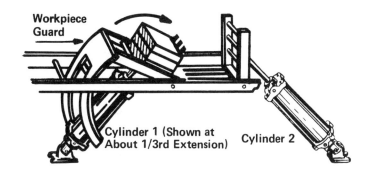

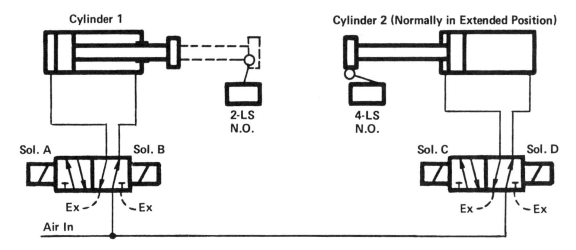

FIGURE 7-20. Air circuit for turnover is controlled with circuit below.

Figure 7-20. Complete automatic action without operator attention. Limit Switch 1-LS (not shown on fluid diagram) is actuated by a workpiece entering the turnover area. Limit Switch 3-LS, also not shown on fluid diagram, is actuated by the workpiece after it leaves, completely turned over. Cylinder 1 extends when 1-LS is actuated, carrying the load halfway over. Cylinder 2 retracts when 2-LS is actuated, carrying the load to complete turnover. When the workpiece has moved clear of the cylinders, 3-LS is actuated which returns both cylinders to their starting positions. Limit Switch 4-LS is for safety, to prevent Cylinder 1 from starting another turnover until Cylinder 2 has reached fully extended position.

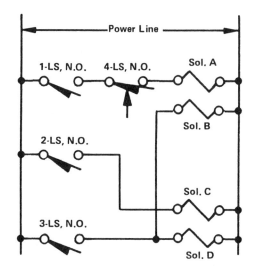

DECOMPRESSION OF HIGH PRESSURE CYLINDERS

Decompression of the oil may be a serious problem on cylinders of large bore or long stroke, particularly when operating at very high pressure. A severe shock is produced in the fluid system at the moment oil pressure is released. This is partly the result of sudden expansion of compressed oil, and partly due to spring-back of mechanical parts in the press which have been highly stressed by high oil pressure. Decompression may not be a serious problem on ordinary applications operating at a moderate pressure with cylinders of medium to small bore and stroke.

Decompression shock is sometimes solved with non-electrical means such as pilot-operated check valves (those with built-in pressure breaker), with speed control on shift of 4-way valve spool, etc. We are concerned in this book with electrical circuitry to deal with the problem, and the circuit on this page is an easy solution, applicable to most hydraulic systems with electrical control.

Remember, there may be more than one source of shock in the system. For example, decompression circuits will not eliminate shifting shock produced in high power systems by shifting tandem center 4-way valves. This problem is discussed separately on Pages 49 to 51.

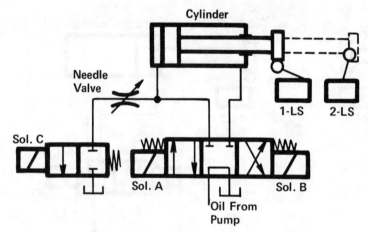

FIGURE 7-21, Part A. Hydraulic Circuit.

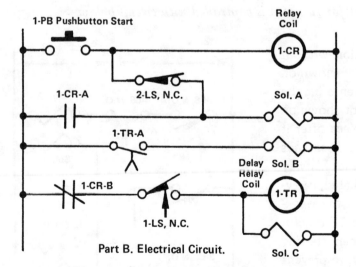

Part B. Electrical Circuit.

FIGURE 7-21. Most hydraulic systems using electrical control can use this decompression system.

Figure 7-21, Part A. Hydraulic Circuit. In this 1-cycle reciprocating circuit the cylinder is started on its forward stroke by an operator with a pushbutton. It automatically reverses when Switch 2-LS is actuated. This is a modification of Figure 3-15 on Page 50 to which decompression components have been added. Solenoid C is a 2-way, N.C. valve to bleed off compressed oil, and a needle valve is included to adjust decompression rate. At the end of the forward stroke, Solenoid C is energized first, and after a short delay, timed with a delay Relay 1-TR, Solenoid B is energized to retract the cylinder.

Figure 7-21, Part B. Electrical Circuit. The delay before retraction is produced by any kind of a delayed action device, the simplest being an industrial relay with dashpot to delay closing of the contacts after the coil is energized. The delay should be adjusted for the shortest time which gives acceptable results, to avoid prolonging cycle time more than necessary.

Detailed action of the hydraulic and electrical circuits of Figure 7-21: When the pushbutton is pressed, Relay 1-CR and valve Solenoid A become energized. The relay locks in through 1-CR-A contacts and 2-LS. The cylinder makes a forward stroke and actuates 2-LS. This releases Relay 1-CR which also de-energizes Solenoid A. The 4-way valve spool centers. The coil of delay Relay 1-TR and Solenoid C become energized through Contacts 1-CR-B and 1-LS as Relay 1-CR drops out. Solenoid C bleeds off high pressure oil during the short delay period. When Contacts 1-TR-A close (after the delay period) Solenoid B becomes energized and the cylinder retracts. At home position, 1-LS is pushed open, de-energizing Solenoid C and Relay 1-TR. In turn, Solenoid B becomes de-energized, the 4-way valve spool centers, and the pump becomes un-loaded. Delay Relay 1-TR automatically re-sets each time it is de-energized.

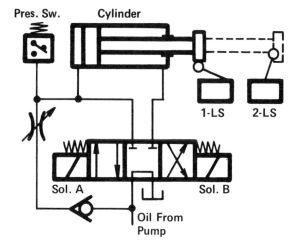

A. Hydraulic Circuit

Figure 7-22. This alternate decompression method interposes a pressure switch to delay complete reversal of the 4-way valve until pressure behind the piston has dropped to a pre-set level which is considered safe against damaging shock.

This, again, is a modification of the circuit on Page 50, to which decompression components have been added in the blind end of the cylinder. The pressure switch is a "break-on-rise" or N.C. type. The needle valve permits the rate of decompression to be adjusted, and the check valve prevents loss of pump oil during the retraction stroke.

Circuit action is the same as described for Figure 3-15 except that when 2-LS is actuated, and Relay 1-CR releases, Solenoid B is not immediately energized, since the circuit is still open through 1-PS pressure switch. Valve Solenoid A becomes de-energized when the relay releases, and the 4-way valve spool goes to center position. High pressure oil bleeds out of the cylinder, through the needle and check valves, and through the tandem center spool to tank. When pressure has dropped to pressure setting, the pressure switch closes, energizing Solenoid B and the cylinder retracts. At home position Switch 1-LS is pushed open, de-energizing Solenoid B. The valve spool centers and the pump becomes unloaded.

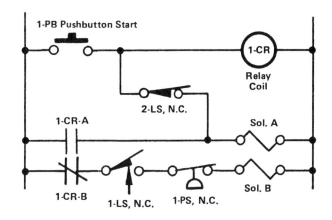

B. Electrical Circuit

FIGURE 7-22. Alternate decompression circuit using a pressure switch.

This circuit has limitations to which the circuit on the preceding page is not subject. If the cylinder is stopped in mid stroke for any reason, the system decompresses. This may or may not be acceptable on a given application. The 4-way valve must have tandem center or open center porting; a closed center valve cannot be used. A pilot-operated check valve is another means of decompression. These valves are described in the Womack book "Industrial Fluid Power — Volume 2".

ADDING PILOT LIGHTS TO SOLENOID VALVE COILS

On some machines it may be desirable to mount indicator lamps on the operator's control panel to indicate the position or energized state of each solenoid valve. To be of greatest value, the lamps should show which valve coils are energized at every moment during the cycle, or which solenoid was last energized. This is a simple matter with 4-way valves having return springs or centering springs. Each lamp can be wired across the corresponding solenoid coil to indicate when the coil is energized. But the solution is not as easy with 2-position double solenoid valves. These valves are often energized only momentarily and current is not maintained, or is maintained for only a part of the time the valve spool remains in the same position. Indicator lamps wired across such a valve would be of little value.

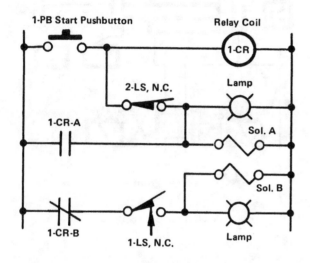

FIGURE 7-23. *When using spring centered or spring return valves, indicator lamps can be wired directly across solenoid coils.*

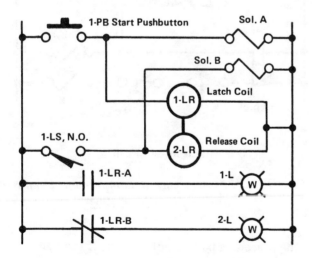

FIGURE 7-24. *When using 2-position double solenoid valves which are momentarily energized, current must be maintained on indicator lamps with a latching relay or similar device.*

Figure 7-23. This is the hydraulic reciprocation circuit of Figure 3-15, modified to include panel indicator lamps. Circuit action is described on Page 50. Solenoids A and B are on a 3-position double solenoid valve. Current must be continually maintained on such a solenoid valve to keep the spool shifted. Therefore, lamps may be wired directly across each solenoid coil.

Figure 7-24. A latching relay is used to solve the problem of indicator lamps on 2-position double solenoid valves. This is the reciprocation circuit of Figure 3-1. Circuit action is described on Page 40.

The latching relay used here is one having a latching magnet, 1-LR, and a release magnet, 2-LR. Two sets of contacts, 1-LR-A and 1-LR-B, are mounted on the armature of the latching magnet. When the latching magnet is energized, even momentarily, the relay armature and contacts pull in and mechanically latch in the actuated position. They remain in this state until the release magnet is momentarily energized, allowing them to return by spring action to their original state.

When Solenoid A is momentarily energized, the latching magnet is also energized and latches closed. Even though the pushbutton is released, Lamp 1-L remains energized through Contacts 1-LR-A. When solenoid B is momentarily energized, release Magnet 2-LR also becomes energized. This unlatches the relay, Lamp 2-L becomes energized and Lamp 1-L becomes de-energized.

JOGGING

The purpose of "jogging" is to move a cylinder forward or backward in small increments while the machine is being set up for a job. Momentary pushbuttons can be used for jogging, and the machine is set for its slowest speed. (Refer to "slow" circuit, Page 102). Jog buttons should be rendered inoperative after the set-up work has been completed, to avoid machine malfunction if one of them should accidentally be pressed during a production cycle.

Figure 7-25. This is the reciprocation circuit of Figure 3-15, Page 50, adapted for jogging.

A 2-position or 3-position selector, 1-SW, switches incoming control voltage from the automatic circuit to the jog pushbuttons. This disconnects the buttons during normal machine cycling.

The jog buttons can usually be wired directly to the terminals of the solenoid valve which controls the cylinder to be jogged, although the complete circuit should always be carefully examined to make certain this will not

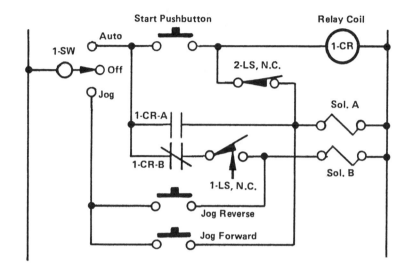

FIGURE 7-25. This jogging arrangement is one that can be used on most hydraulically powered machines.

cause unwanted operation of another valve solenoid at the same time. If it will, then additional contacts must be added to the jog buttons to disconnect the valve solenoids completely from the rest of the circuit while jogging. Not shown but recommended is to cross wire the jog buttons as shown on Page 149, making it impossible to energize two valve solenoids at the same time.

Figure 7-26. Jogging circuits are not often used for compressed air cylinders, but if required, the above circuit can be adapted easily for this use. A more practical arrangement usually is simply to operate the air cylinder at a very slow speed. This can be done with a 1/4" needle valve by-passing the main shut-off air valve. This valve can be

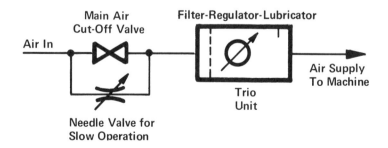

FIGURE 7-26. Slowing a cylinder with a needle valve rather than jogging is usually preferred for an air cylinder.

used to move the cylinder slowly, stopping it whenever required. The needle valve should not be placed in series with the main air flow since it has restricted internal porting even when wide open, and might introduce too much restriction to air flow during normal operation of the cylinder at high speed.

DECELERATION OF FAST-MOVING CYLINDERS

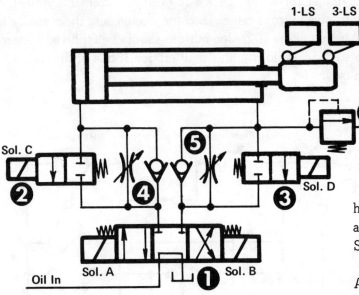

1-LS 3-LS 4-LS 2-LS

Sol. C
Sol. D
Oil In Sol. A Sol. B

FIGURE 7-27.
Electrical Deceleration at
Both Ends of the Stroke.

Figure 7-27. The circuit of Figure 3-15 has here been modified to include deceleration at both ends of the cylinder stroke. See Page 50 for further circuit details.

This is a 1-cycle reciprocation circuit. After being started with a pushbutton, the cylinder makes a complete cycle, forward and back, and stops with the pump unloaded.

Limit Switches 3-LS and 4-LS are adjusted to positions where the deceleration should start at each end of the stroke. Cams on the moving cylinder must be long enough to keep these switches actuated for the remainder of the stroke. They energize solenoid Valves 2 and 3 which on closing direct fluid discharge from the cylinder through deceleration flow control Valves 4 and 5.

If oil flow from the rod end is too highly restricted or closed off, pressure intensification can damage the cylinder, especially cylinders with oversize piston rods. Relief Valve 6 should be connected to the rod end and adjusted for about 400 PSI higher than the main relief valve back at the pump. In some circuits where cylinders are traveling unusually fast, a second relief valve, connected to the blind end of the cylinder may be desirable.

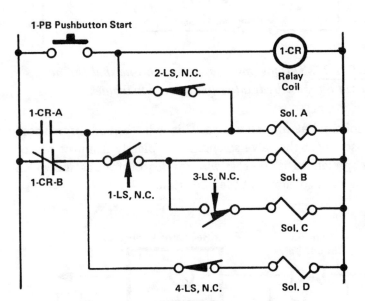

1-PB Pushbutton Start

1-CR
Relay
Coil

2-LS, N.C.

1-CR-A
Sol. A

1-CR-B
Sol. B
1-LS, N.C. 3-LS, N.C.

Sol. C

4-LS, N.C. Sol. D

FIGURE 7-28. The electrical circuit on Page 50
is here modified to include deceleration compo-
nents 3-LS, 4-LS, and Solenoids C and D.

Figure 7-28. Electrical Circuit. Circuit action is the same as described for Figure 3-15, Page 50, except for deceleration solenoids C and D. To make certain one of these solenoids will not be left in an energized condition at the end of the cycle, they should obtain operating current, not directly from the main power line, but from the same circuit serving the valve solenoid which is being kept energized at the time they are actuated to start deceleration. Since Solenoid A is the one energized on the forward travel, 4-LS should be wired to the same circuit supplying this solenoid.

CHAPTER 8

Safety Circuits

TWO-HAND OPERATION

Where cylinders are operating mechanisms which might present a safety hazard to the operator, dual controls can be provided. These require the use of both hands to start the cylinder and keep it in motion. Dual controls are also used on large presses which require two operators. One control is provided for each operator; then, neither operator can start the press until the other one is ready. Usually, only one direction of cylinder motion is hazardous, so most dual control circuits work only in one direction.

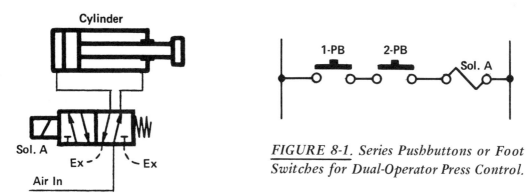

FIGURE 8-1. Series Pushbuttons or Foot Switches for Dual-Operator Press Control.

Figure 8-1. Series pushbuttons or series contacts on relays are simple to install and may give sufficient protection on presses where two operators are stationed on opposite sides of a press. Both buttons must be actuated before the valve solenoid can become energized. If the two pushbuttons are for two-hand actuation by just one operator, series buttons or contacts are not safe. It is relatively easy for the operator to tie down or weight down one button. To make tie-down more difficult, flush-type buttons can be used and mounted in a vertical plane and well above any horizontal surface.

Figure 8-2. When operating a double solenoid, 2-position valve, air or hydraulic, two buttons, each having one N.O. and one N.C. set of contacts can be wired with their N.O. contacts in series and their N.C. contacts in parallel. Both buttons must be pressed to energize valve Solenoid A and start the cylinder forward. If either button is released, valve Solenoid B becomes energized and the cylinder immediately starts to retract. At home position, current is removed from Solenoid B by 1-LS.

Figure 8-3. The N.O. contacts of the buttons are wired in series to Solenoid A. The two N.C. button contacts are wired in series to Solenoid B. Both buttons must be pressed to start the cylinder. If either button is released during forward travel, both solenoids become de-energized, the valve spool

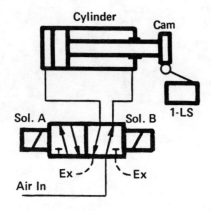

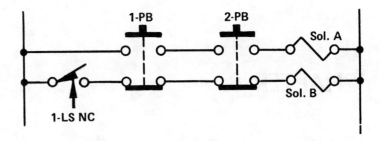

FIGURE 8-2. Two-position double solenoid valves, air or hydraulic, can use this circuit.

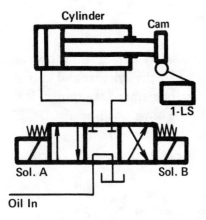

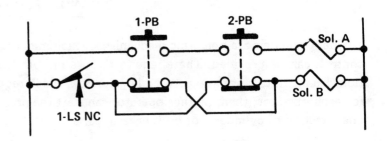

FIGURE 8-3. Three-position double solenoid valves, air or hydraulic, can use this circuit.

centers and the cylinder stops. When both buttons are released, Solenoid B becomes energized and the cylinder retracts. At home, 1-LS de-energizes both solenoids. The valve centers, unloading the pump.

Figure 8-4. Unbeatable Circuit. This circuit uses two time delay relays of the kind described on Page 117, set for a delay of one second for opening of their N.C. contacts after their coils are energized. It is designed for control of one valve solenoid coil, or the forward coil of a double solenoid valve.

If one pushbutton should be tied down, or if both buttons are not pressed within a 1-second interval, relay Coil 1-CR may momentarily pull in but immediately drop out. After a false operation, to restore the circuit, both pushbuttons must be released. If either or both pushbuttons are released during operation, the solenoid coil will be de-energized, and this de-energizes the solenoid valve coil.

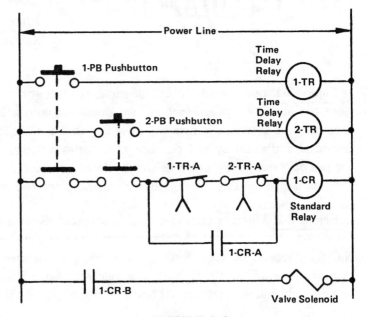

FIGURE 8-4.

Unbeatable, non-tie-down circuit for a single solenoid valve using time delay relays.

EMERGENCY OR "PANIC" BUTTONS

It is a wise precaution, on all electrically controlled fluid power machines, to place an emergency button within easy reach of the operator. Sometimes it might be a good idea to place several of these buttons at various positions on the machine so one of them will always be handy. This emergency button, popularly called a "panic" button, is usually a normally closed hand switch fitted with a large diameter, red mushroom button. On some applications a foot switch may be more appropriate.

The circuit action produced when the panic button is actuated will vary on each application according to the electric control circuit used, type of work performed, physical layout of the machine, and the type of action judged to best minimize the hazard or which will produce the safest condition. Sometimes a cylinder should be stopped but not retracted. On other machines it may be best to instantly reverse the cylinder. Or, one cylinder, only, should be stopped or retracted while other cylinders on the same machine should not be affected. It becomes the job of a designer to decide what kind of safety reaction should be initiated when the panic button is pressed, and to find a way to include this action in the electrical circuit.

As a general rule, on compressed air operated machines, the moving cylinder should be instantly reversed, since an air cylinder cannot be instantly stopped simply by shutting off the air or centering a neutral position valve. The cylinder will continue to move after the air has been shut off until a balance is reached between air pressure and the load. A hydraulic cylinder can be instantly stopped, and the designer must decide whether stopping it or reversing would produce the safest action.

Keep in mind that to conform to JIC electrical standards, a solenoid valve should be de-energized rather than energized to put the circuit into a safe condition. (See Page 99). This guards against an unsafe condition if a solenoid coil or relay coil should burn out, or if the control current should fail. This rule should always be observed if the potential hazard is to an operator but is sometimes disregarded, in the interest of simpler circuitry, if the hazard is to inexpensive tooling or to workpieces of small value. A spring offset or spring centered solenoid 4-way valve, rather than a double solenoid, 2-position model, is usually desirable and should be connected so it stops or retracts the cylinder if a solenoid coil burns out or if control current fails.

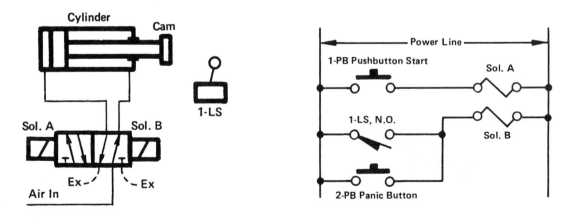

FIGURE 8-5. A momentary pushbutton circuit protected with "panic" or override button.

Figure 8-5. The air circuit, on the left above, is the same as the one in Figure 3-1, Part A, Page 40. When operated with the simple electrical circuit shown beside it on Page 40, it is potentially hazardous because, when once started forward, the cylinder is out of control of the operator. To make it safer, a "panic" button can be connected into the electric circuit as shown above. The operator, by pressing the panic button, can instantly reverse the cylinder during its forward stroke if a hazardous situation should develop. This button, 2-PB, can serve not only as a panic button but also as an override control if the operator should want to reverse the cylinder in mid stroke for reasons other than safety.

Note: Figure 8-5 does not conform to JIC recommendations because it depends on energizing rather than de-energizing a valve coil to reach a safe condition. However, in cases where the operator's safety would not be in jeopardy if the override circuit fails to function, this simple circuit may be adequate.

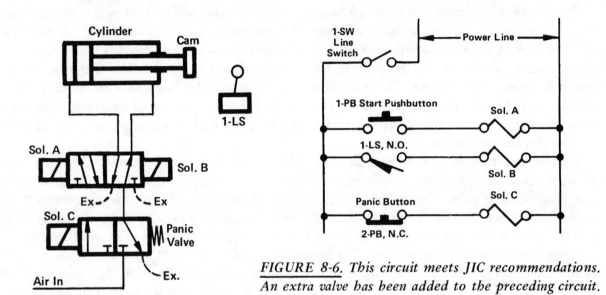

FIGURE 8-6. This circuit meets JIC recommendations. An extra valve has been added to the preceding circuit.

Figure 8-6. This is a modification of the preceding circuit which retains the simplicity of operation from momentary signals on a 2-position double solenoid valve, and has the added feature of conforming to JIC recommendations for "fail-safe" operation.

A single solenoid, 3-way, normally closed, air valve is added ahead of the main 4-way valve. Solenoid C (on the 3-way valve), shuts off inlet air and vents the cylinder to atmosphere when 2-PB panic button is actuated, stopping the cylinder very quickly. When the panic button is released, the cylinder resumes travel in the same direction. This panic circuit works to quickly stop the cylinder when traveling in either direction. Solenoid C normally is energized when the machine is first turned on in the morning and remains energized until the machine is shut down for the day by opening Switch 1-SW.

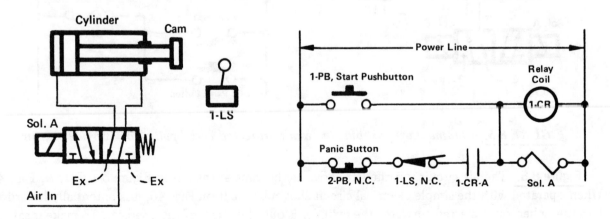

FIGURE 8-7. A single solenoid valve adapts more easily to "fail-safe" operation.

Figure 8-7. This air circuit, using a single solenoid valve, lends itself quite easily to JIC "fail-safe" operation. For details of circuit operation, please refer to Figure 3-3, Page 41. A panic pushbutton, with one set of N.C. contacts is wired in series with the relay holding circuit. During forward travel of the cylinder, the relay is locked closed. Pressing the panic button, 2-PB, releases the holding circuit, de-energizing valve Solenoid A, and causing the cylinder to instantly reverse its travel.

Figure 8-8. A simple panic button control on a double solenoid *spring centered*, 4-way hydraulic valve is to disconnect the normal wiring from each solenoid and to wire the panic button N.C. contacts in series with the solenoids. Both sets of contacts are operated from one button.

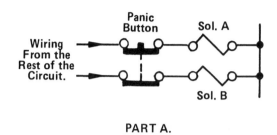

PART A.

Figure 8-8, Part A. Pressing the panic button de-energizes both valve solenoids, causing the valve spool to center and the cylinder to stop. When the button is released, the cylinder should resume its travel in the same direction. If panic buttons are installed in series with solenoid coils only, as shown, usually the rest of the circuit will not be disturbed when the button is actuated. Holding relays which are locked in at the time should remain holding. The system works in both directions of cylinder travel.

Figure 8-8, Part B. The panic button, when pressed, de-energizes both valve solenoids but connects one of them directly to the control voltage source, and the cylinder retracts. In a 1-cylinder system, if the button is held until the cylinder completely retracts, the system should be ready to start another cycle when the button is released. In a multiple-cylinder system, additional contacts may be needed on the panic button to de-activate any limit switches that would be actuated when the retracting cylinder reaches home position, in order to prevent the automatic cycle from resuming.

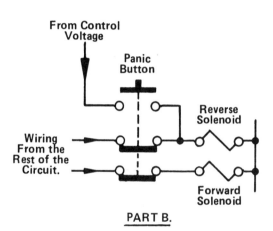

PART B.

FIGURE 8-8. Panic buttons installed on a 3-position double solenoid hydraulic valve.

Figure 8-9. A very simple method of stopping a cylinder in mid travel is to de-energize the solenoid which vents its relief valve. This method works on any hydraulic circuit in this book which uses solenoid vent pump unloading, by wiring a N.C. panic button in series with the existing circuit to the venting solenoid valve. It can also be added to tandem center valve circuits which use a pilot-operated relief valve.

One Caution! Venting reduces pump pressure to about 75 PSI. Lightly loaded cylinders may drift with as little as 75 PSI. Be sure your cylinder will completely stop when its pressure is reduced to 75 PSI.

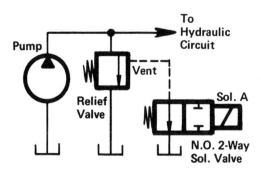

FIGURE 8-9. Stopping a Cylinder by Venting the Pump Relief Valve.

DE-ACTIVATING PUSHBUTTONS FOR ACCIDENT PREVENTION

Many optional features such as safety interlocks, manual/automatic control, slow speed operation, jog, emergency buttons, indicator lamps, manual override, etc., can be added to circuits in this book. This chapter deals only with safety features to protect operator or equipment. Other optional features will be found in other chapters. See additional safety material on Page 74 for JIC circuits and on Page 179 for programmable controllers.

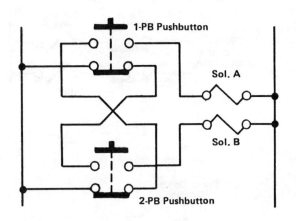

FIGURE 8-10. Interlocking Through Push-buttons to Prevent Solenoid Valve Burnout.

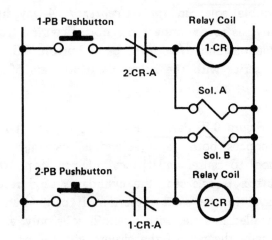

FIGURE 8-11. Priority-type Interlocking Through Relay Contacts.

Figure 8-10. Applicable to double solenoid valve circuits operated with momentary pushbuttons. The two buttons can be cross wired so each one de-activates the other. If 1-PB has already been pressed and is being held, and the cycle has started, then if 2-PB should be pressed, current would be removed from both solenoids. In a spring centered valve the spool would return to center and the action would stop. If both buttons were pressed at exactly the same time, neither solenoid would be energized.

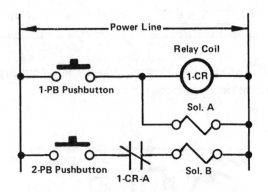

FIGURE 8-12. Another Form of Priority Interlocking.

Figure 8-11. Priority-Type Interlocking. The action is different from the preceding figure. Instead of having the cylinder action stop if both buttons are pressed, the button which was pressed first, and held, will keep control and keep the cylinder moving even if the other button should also be pressed, and will keep the opposite solenoid from being energized.

Figure 8-12. Still another kind of priority is obtained with this circuit. Pushbutton 1-PB always has priority over the other one. If 2-PB is pressed, and held, then if 1-PB is also pressed, 1-PB will take over control, de-energizing Solenoid B and energizing Solenoid A.

De-activating Pushbuttons. Circuits on the next page show several ways of disconnecting pushbuttons after the cycle starts. For increased safety, all limit switches which could be accidentally actuated manually should also be disconnected during standby periods. This nearly always requires a limit switch mounted at the home position of the first cylinder to start.

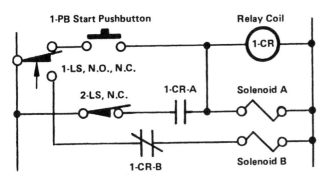

FIGURE 8-13A. Start Button De-activated on Both Forward and Return Strokes.

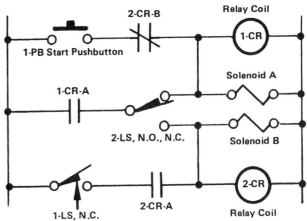

FIGURE 8-13B. Variation of Figure 8-13A.

Figure 8-13A. This is a re-arrangement of Figure 3-15 on Page 50. Refer to that page for circuit action. Switch 1-LS has been re-wired so it disconnects the pushbutton as soon as the cylinder has moved a short distance.

Figure 8-13B. Another re-arrangement of Figure 3-15 in which the pushbutton is disconnected only on the cylinder return stroke.

Figure 8-14. For air circuits using a 2-position double solenoid valve.

When 1-PB is pressed, Solenoid A is energized and the cylinder starts to move. Switch 1-LS is quickly released and disconnects the pushbutton for the rest of the cycle. During its advance, the cylinder can be reversed with pushbutton 2-PB before it reaches the forward end of its stroke.

Figure 8-15. This is a partial circuit, a feature to be added to a complete circuit which uses holding relays.

When 1-PB is pressed, Relay 1-CR and Solenoid A become energized. The relay locks in through 1-CR-A to keep Solenoid A energized after the pushbutton has been released or disconnected. A second relay, 2-CR, has been added for the sole purpose of disconnecting the pushbutton after Solenoid A has been energized. Note: It is important that a separate relay be used for this purpose instead of using another set of contacts on 1-CR. Relay 1-CR would probably be dropped out during transfer of its

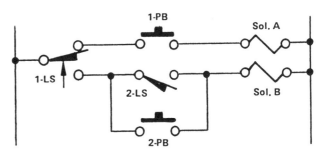

FIGURE 8-14. For Air Circuits.

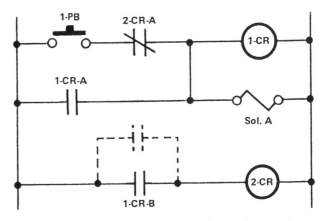

FIGURE 8-15. For Circuits With Holding Relays.

own contacts. The slight delay between actuation of 1-CR and 2-CR will prevent this dropout.

If 1-CR will not remain energized through the complete cycle, it may be necessary to parallel another set of contacts from another relay (shown in dotted lines) to guarantee that Relay 2-CR will remain energized and the pushbutton disconnected until the end of the cycle.

AUTOMATIC DISCHARGE OF AN ACCUMULATOR

An accumulator contains a highly compressed gas and is a potentially hazardous device in a hydraulic system. When connected to hydraulic circuits using closed center 4-way valves it will hold its charge for a long time after the system has been shut down. A maintenance or service man may not be aware of the presence of an accumulator, and could be injured by a piercing jet of oil if he loosens a fitting anywhere in the high pressure line. Many companies demand that the system be designed so all accumulators will automatically discharge when the system is shut down. An application where high pressure oil must be stored in an accumulator to start the system is an exception to the rule.

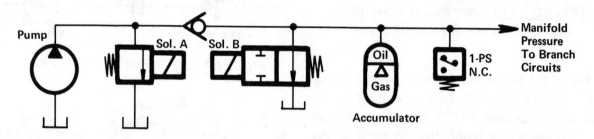

FIGURE 8-16. Manifold Hydraulic System With an Accumulator for Oil Storage.

Figure 8-16. In a pressure manifold system the accumulator can be bled down with Solenoid B after the pump has been stopped. Valve solenoid B can be a N.O., 1/4'' size 2-way valve. When energized, it closes the bleed-off and permits the accumulator to be charged by the pump. To make the bleed-off automatic, Solenoid B can be tied to the control circuit of the motor starter. See below.

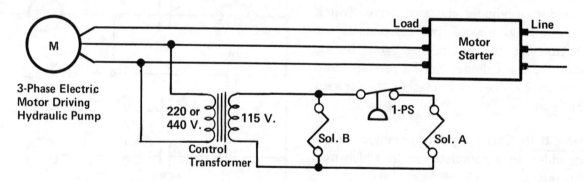

FIGURE 8-17. Electric Circuit for Accumulator System Shown Above.

Figure 8-17. Automatic bleed-down is effected by connecting Solenoid B to the power source supplying the electric motor. Usually the motor will be operating from a 3-phase power line at 220 or 440 volts. Current to energize Solenoid B must be obtained by tapping into the power wiring between motor junction box and motor starter. Connections can be made to any two of the three power wires, and this circuit may have to be run through a control transformer to reduce its voltage to match coil voltage, usually 115 volts. The 115-volt circuit from the transformer can also be used as a source of power for operation of other solenoid valves in the circuit such as Solenoid A in Figure 8-16 which unloads the pump when the accumulator has become fully charged. When the accumulator pressure drops to the setting on the pressure switch, Solenoid A again loads the pump.

WARNING SIGNALS

Pump Cavitation. Pump manufacturers allow a vacuum of 2'' to 5'' mercury on pump inlets depending on pump type and construction. When pump suction strainers become dirty, vacuum builds up and pump wear increases. Suction strainers are available which have visual indicators to show when an abnormally high vacuum has developed, but these indicators are not always within easy view of the operator. Even when they are, they may go unnoticed. Warning lights on the operator's control panel draw more attention to cavitation conditions, and they can be operated either by electric switches built into the suction strainer or by an external vacuum switch as shown in this diagram. Panel lamps operated through a flasher draw more attention to cavitation conditions.

Figure 8-18, Part A. A vacuum switch, 1-VS, can be teed into the pump inlet and connected to a red lamp on the operator's panel. Switch contacts close on an increase of vacuum, and the panel lamp becomes energized.

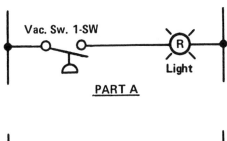

Part B. Flashing Signal. The lamp signal is more effective if connected to a flasher. Relay 1-TR is a thermal type relay having one set of N.C. contacts and a contact delay of about two seconds after its coil is energized. The relay makes and breaks its own circuit to produce a flashing signal from the panel lamp.

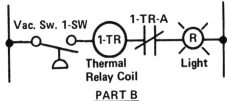

Part C, Figure 8-18. The red lamp remains lighted when operating conditions are normal. If cavitation develops, vacuum Switch 1-VS closes, transferring the lamp to a flasher circuit through thermal delay Relay 1-TR and its N.C. contacts. This circuit is "fail-safe" in the sense that burn-out of the lamp will be noticed. Note: In cold weather the hydraulic pump will pull more vacuum than normal until the oil warms up to operating temperature.

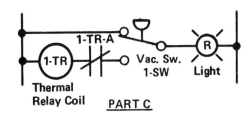

FIGURE 8-18.
Three Circuits for Warning Lights.

High Oil Temperature. Oil temperature is usually sensed inside the reservoir with a sensing bulb immersed below the oil level and connected through a capillary tube to a switch element. As a rule, high temperature switches should not be wired into the motor starter to stop the electric motor. This could be objectionable because it might be preferable to continue to run with hot oil than to shut down the machine. Temperature switches should operate warning signals in one of the circuits shown above.

Low Oil Temperature. A hydraulic system should not be started if its oil has cooled to a temperature which would cavitate the pump. Systems installed in cold climates should have means of keeping the oil up to a minimum temperature overnight or should have some means of warming it, usually with an electric immersion heater in the reservoir. The oil should be heated to an acceptable temperature before starting the pump. Temperature switches installed to measure oil temperature can be attached with good thermal contact to the outside wall of the reservoir. However, a more accurate way is to use a switch with remote sensing bulb, and to immerse the bulb under the oil level inside the reservoir.

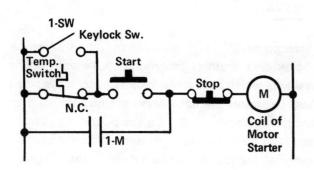

FIGURE 8-19. Temperature Switch
Wired Into the Motor Starter.

Figure 8-19. A temperature switch can be wired in series with the cycle "Start" button, or with Coil M of the motor starter to prevent starting at low temperatures. The diagram shows a temperature switch connected into a 3-wire starter control circuit. Starter control diagrams are covered in more detail in Chapter 9. The switch will keep the starter coil from being energized until oil temperature has risen to a required minimum. To enable authorized persons to start the motor even when the oil is cold, a key lock switch, 1-SW, can be wired in parallel with the temperature switch.

Low Oil Level. A float switch can be used to signal a dangerously low level of oil in the reservoir. This switch can be wired to an indicator lamp on the operator's panel. Oil level normally rises and falls each cycle as cylinders retract and extend. If the oil level should fluctuate below and above the actuation point of the float switch, this would produce a flashing warning signal to the operator.

UNLOADING THE PUMP WHILE STARTING THE ELECTRIC MOTOR

Most hydraulic systems will have the hydraulic pump in an unloaded state before its electric driving motor is started. But for those systems where the motor must start against the resistance of a dead-headed pump, the starting current can be greatly reduced, and in some cases a smaller size motor starter can be used if the pump is unloaded prior to starting the motor. A simple circuit is shown below.

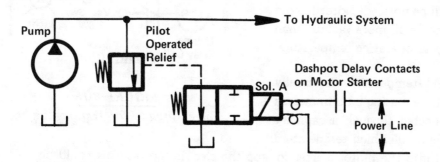

FIGURE 8-20. Dashpot delayed auxiliary contacts on the motor starter keep the pump unloaded until the motor can get up to speed.

Figure 8-20. Automatic electric unloading is a great advantage on systems of more than 40 HP in which the motor must start under full load. The venting principle can be applied to any hydraulic system which uses a pilot-operated relief valve on the pump. Solenoid Valve A is a 1/4" size, single solenoid, 2-way N.C. valve installed in series with the relief valve vent port and tank. See Page 99 for relief valve venting. Its coil is energized from auxiliary dashpot contacts on the magnetic motor starter which give a 3 to 5 second delay before the contacts close after the starter is energized. This should allow the motor time to come up to full speed before the load is applied. Solenoid Valve A is kept energized as long as the electric motor is running and maintains full pump pressure. When the motor is shut off, Solenoid Valve A vents the relief valve and unloads the pump.

CHAPTER 9

Electric Motors
and Motor Starters

THE NATIONAL ELECTRICAL CODE

In most localities, power wiring and equipment installation must conform to recommendations of the National Electrical Code, and in some localities to local ordnances as well.

The National Electrical Code (NEC) was originally formulated in 1897 through the united efforts of various electrical, insurance, architectural, and allied interests. Since that time it has been revised, enlarged, updated, and supplemented several times. Since 1911 it has been sponsored by the National Fire Prevention Association (NFPA), and this organization is the present copyright owner.

The National Electrical Code as a set of standards is purely advisory but is widely used as a basis of law and for regulatory purposes. The code is administered by various local inspection agencies, whose decisions govern the actual application of the code to individual installations. Local inspectors are for the most part members of the International Association of Electrical Inspectors with head office in Chicago. This organization, together with the National Electrical Manufacturers Association (NEMA), the Edison Electrical Institute, the Underwriters Laboratories (UL), and other governmental groups and independent experts are all involved in the development, updating, and application of the National Electrical Code. It is a nationally accepted guide to the safe installation of wiring and equipment.

The National Electrical Code is primarily intended for use by trained electrical people. Copies can be ordered through your bookstore, either the basic code book or an amplified version with copious notes as published by McGraw-Hill. Copies of the JIC Electrical Code for machine tools can be purchased from the National Machine Tool Builders Association. Inquire for their current address from the National Fluid Power Association, 3333 N. Mayfair Rd., Milwaukee, WI 53222.

Notice: Design and installation of power circuits external to the fluid power machine must be done by qualified electrical engineers and licensed electricians in accordance with local ordnances and subject to official inspection. In some states, even the power wiring inside the fluid power machine, if it is over 24 volts, is subject to the same rigid rules governing external wiring. Our study will be limited to motor starter control which may have to be integrated into an overall machine control circuit. Diagrams and text material in this book are for information and study, and are not intended to be at variance with local restrictions nor with any recommendations of the National Electrical Code.

START/STOP CONTROL OF ELECTRIC MOTORS

The following is a brief summary of the National Electrical Code recommendations for power wiring to an electric motor. Horsepower and current carrying and interrupting capacity must be sized to NEC recommendations. For specific details, see NEC Handbook.

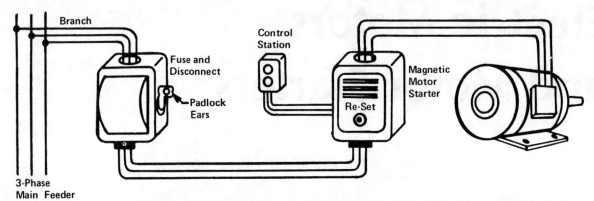

FIGURE 9-1. General Layout of Motor Control Equipment.

Fuse and Disconnect Switch. Shall be located within view or not more than 25 feet from motor and starter. May use either fuses or circuit breakers correctly sized for stall current of motor and provided with instantaneous protection against short circuits and ground faults. Must have means so a workman can padlock handle in open position and keep the key in his possession while working on equipment. Must have sufficient poles to equal the number of ungrounded conductors. A disconnect switch is not normally used for starting the motor, only for disconnecting it from the line when necessary.

Motor Starters. All electric motors must have some kind of switching equipment. Fractional horsepower motors are sometimes controlled with a simple starting switch but integral horsepower motors are nearly always controlled with a "motor starter" having a built-in overload protective device.

(1). Manual Motor Starters. For simple and economical installations. A manual lever operates the switch contacts. They are primarily used on low power systems of less than 3 HP, although available up to 10 HP (at 440 volts). Since they cannot be remotely controlled or tied into an automatic control system they will not be discussed further in this book.

(2). Magnetic Motor Starters. A solenoid operates the switch contacts and can be controlled either with a toggle switch or set of momentary pushbuttons mounted in the cover. They can also be remotely controlled or tied in with an automatic machine circuit through 2-wire or 3-wire remote control systems to be described. They have a built-in overload protective device with a manual re-set button.

Motor starters should be located near the motor. If out of view or more than 25 feet distant, another disconnect switch must be installed at the motor. The starter must be able to interrupt all ungrounded conductors, and can have several sets of auxiliary contacts, either with instantaneous or delayed action, and usually of low current rating, for operating pilot devices or auxiliary equipment.

Starter assemblies also include overload coils in series with at least two of the conductors on a 3-phase system. These are shown as Symbol OL on diagrams to follow. The set of contacts operated by the overload coils are also designated OL and are wired in series with the operating solenoid, 1-M. At untended locations, all three ungrounded conductors on a 3-phase system must be wired through overload coils. Contacts operated by the overload coils are N.C. and have a delayed opening action to permit the motor to accelerate to full speed or to be momentarily overloaded without tripping. They do not protect against short circuits and ground faults (the fuse and disconnect box does this); their purpose is to protect motor windings against excessive heat build-up due to overload running conditions. Since the overload coils are heat sensitive, a sufficient time must elapse for them to cool after tripping before they can be re-set.

Coil 1-M rating must be the same as the main line voltage. It can be operated at a reduced voltage of 115 volts from a 220 or 440 volt line by interposing a step down transformer. This transformer can be sized with sufficient ampere capacity to also operate 115 volt solenoid valves in the electrical system.

Figure 9-2. This figure shows operating buttons as part of the assembly. They have momentary action, a N.O. "Start" button and a N.C. "Stop" button. They are usually mounted in the starter cover together with a manual re-set button for the overload coils. The starter can be operated remotely with another set of buttons by disregarding or omitting the ones in the cover. (Fig. 9-3).

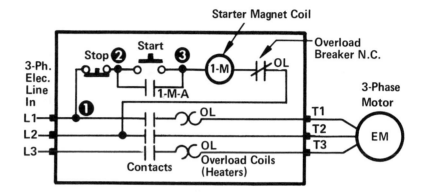

FIGURE 9-2. Internal Circuit of a Magnetic Motor Starter With Self-Contained Operating Pushbuttons.

Pressing the "Start" button momentarily energizes the starter magnet, 1-M. The contacts close and power is connected to the motor. The solenoid magnet, 1-M, locks closed electrically through a set of auxiliary contacts, 1-M-A, and the operator may then release the "Start" button. To stop the motor, the "Stop" button must be momentarily pressed. This breaks the holding circuit to Magnet 1-M, and the contacts are released.

Motor starter circuits given here are for full voltage across-the-line starting. For motors of 50 HP and larger, power companies may require the use of reduced voltage starting equipment. This is to limit the magnitude of current draw while the motor is coming up to speed.

Remote Operation of Magnetic Motor Starters. Wiring diagrams inside the starter cover show connections for remote operation. Several types of remote control are illustrated in the following diagrams.

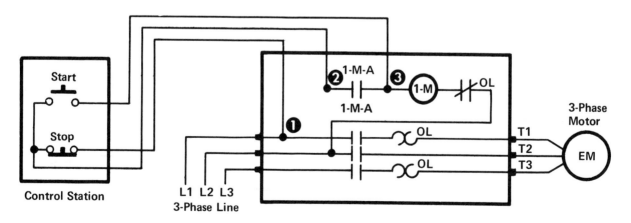

FIGURE 9-3. 3-Wire Remote Control of a Magnetic Motor Starter.

Figure 9-3. The term "3-wire" control is derived from the fact that three wires are required to connect between the remote control location and the motor starter.

Momentary pushbuttons or similar pilot devices are used to energize the main magnet, 1-M. This type of control permits remote operation from two or more locations. It also provides low voltage protection, to prevent unexpected re-starting after a power interruption which could cause personnel injury or damage to machinery. The motor will not re-start until the "Start" button is actuated.

The starter is energized by pressing the "Start" button. An auxiliary "holding" contact set, 1-M-A on the starter forms a parallel circuit around the "Start" button, keeping Coil 1-M energized after the button is released. The N.C. contacts of the "Stop" button break the holding circuit to release Coil 1-M.

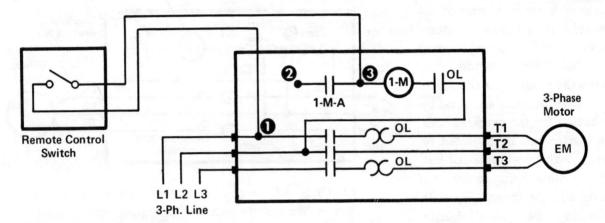

FIGURE 9-4. *Two-Wire Remote Control of Magnetic Motor Starter.*

Figure 9-4. The term "2-wire" control is applied to this system because only two wires are required to control the starter remotely. This type of control is used when the starter is required to function without attention from the operator. If there should be a power failure while the remote switch is closed, the starter will drop out. When the power is restored, the starter will pick up automatically through the closed contacts of the remote switch.

The remote control switch can be any type with maintained action as a toggle switch, a rotary selector, etc. This control system does not lend itself well to control from more than one location. In the diagram, auxiliary contacts on the starter are not used, and Point 2 is left unconnected.

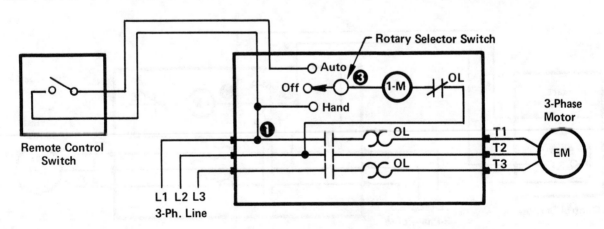

FIGURE 9-5. *Two-Wire Remote Control of Magnetic Motor Starter with the Addition of a Selector Switch on the Starter Cover.*

Figure 9-5. A 3-position rotary selector switch is mounted in the starter cover. With this switch in center OFF, the motor cannot be started from the remote location. It can be started locally by rotating the switch to the HAND position. With the selector switch in the AUTO position, the motor can be started and stopped from the remote location.

A 2-wire remote control is shown in the diagram. A 3-wire control can also be used by following the wiring shown in Figure 9-3, and using an auxiliary "holding" contact set on the starter.

Multiple Remote Control Stations. By using a 3-wire control with momentary pushbuttons, a motor can be started and stopped from several control locations. The general rule is that "Start" buttons at all locations must be wired in parallel, and all "Stop" buttons wired in series.

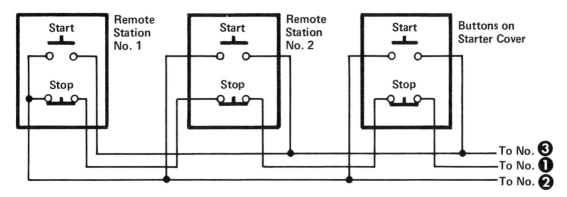

FIGURE 9-6. *Multiple Control Stations for Electric Motor.*

Figure 9-6. A common design practice is to have control buttons mounted in the starter cover for use while setting up and testing the system, and to have one or more sets of pushbuttons on an operator's control panel for permanent use. In this diagram, remote control Stations 1 and 2 may be located at a distance, and the third station is the one shown in Figure 9-3 with buttons in the starter cover or mounted adjacent to the starter box. Connections 1, 2, and 3 are made to corresponding terminal points as shown in Figure 9-3.

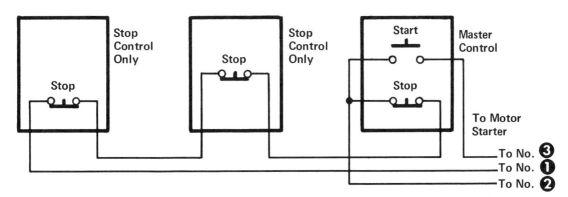

FIGURE 9-7. *Master Control and Several Emergency Stop Stations.*

Figure 9-7. An alternate arrangement is to have one master control station with both "Start" and "Stop" buttons, and to have several "Stop" buttons mounted at convenient locations around the machine for emergency use. The master control buttons can be either in the starter cover or on a master control panel.

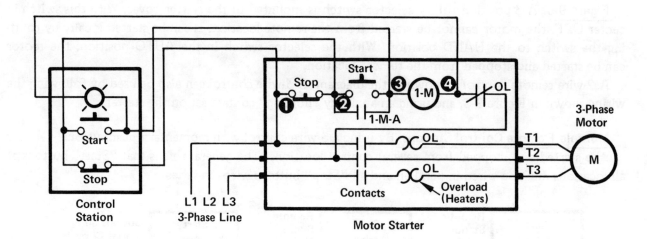

FIGURE 9-8. Adding a pilot light requires a fourth wire.

Figure 9-8. Pilot Lights to Show Motor is Running. If the operator control station is not within view of the motor, a pilot lamp should be installed on the panel to show if motor is running. This requires one extra wire connecting to Point 4 as shown in this figure.

Sequence Starting of Several Motors. Several motors on the same machine should be started one at a time to avoid excessive current peaks on the power line. This operation can be made automatic from one starting switch by energizing their starter coils in a timed sequence. This circuit is suggested:

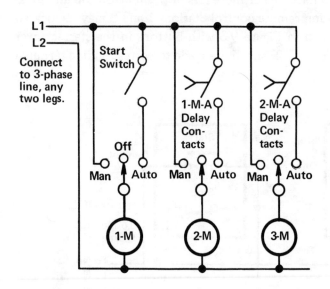

FIGURE 9-9. Sequence Starting of Three Motors.

Figure 9-9. Each starter should be ordered with 3-position rotary switch, "Man-Off-Auto", mounted in its cover, and with one extra set of auxiliary contacts having dashpot action, with a delay on closing after the starter coil is energized. A maintained type (toggle) switch should be installed for operator control and connected to the first starter with a 2-wire control per Figure 9-5, or a 3-wire control with pushbuttons can be used if preferred.

In this figure, 1-M, 2-M, and 3-M are coils in Motor Starters 1, 2, and 3. Dashpot delay Contacts 1-M-A of the first starter are wired into the "Auto" line of Starter 2 and will energize Coil 2-M after a delay interval from the time Coil 1-M is energized. Delay Contacts 2-M-A are wired into the starting circuit of the third starter to energize its coil, 3-M, a short time later.

When all selector switches are set to "Auto", the motors will start in sequence from one starting switch. Set dashpots for time delay needed for each motor, usually 5 seconds on small motors to 20 seconds on large motors. Each motor can be individually started and stopped with its own selector switch.

ELECTRIC MOTOR SELECTION

The chart on Page 254 of the Appendix can be used to determine the electric motor drive HP to a pump with assumed 85% efficiency to produce a desired PSI pressure and a GPM flow. Caution! This is not the HP which a cylinder needs to produce a desired force and speed. There are system power losses between the pump output and the cylinder, and additional pressure must be produced by the pump to make up these flow losses. For suggested method of estimating system losses between pump and cylinder, please refer to Appendix A of "Industrial Fluid Power — Volume 1".

NEMA Electric Motor Designs . . .

There are several kinds of NEMA motor designs available, each one preferred for certain kinds of applications. For hydraulic pump drive, the 3-phase squirrel cage induction motor, Designs A, B, C, or D are most often used. It has a rotor made up of iron laminations but does not have a winding on the rotor; therefore, it has no brushes, commutator, or slip rings. All windings are on the stator which is also constructed of iron laminations with various numbers of north and south poles (in pairs). The motor runs at a constant speed determined by the line frequency (Hertz) and by the number of pairs of poles. The rotor and stator are laminated instead of being solid iron to reduce eddy current losses. The speed on this kind of motor cannot be varied, but it will slow down slightly as load is increased.

Design B, Squirrel Cage Induction Motor.

This is the design most often used for pump drive but does have some limitations. Starting torque required by the load, for frequent starting, should not exceed 50% of the motor rated torque at full speed. This means that on hydraulic systems where the pump is dead-headed before the motor is started, the pump may have to be unloaded long enough to permit the motor to reach full speed. See information on Page 153.

The load reaction should have as little torque pulsation as possible.

Load inertia should be no greater than the inertia of the motor rotor.

The motor should work against a fairly steady load, variations in the load during a cycle excepted.

	60 Hz Motors		50 Hz Motors	
No. of Pairs of Poles	Synchr. RPM*	Full Load RPM	Synchr. RPM*	Full Load RPM
1	3600	3490	3000	2900
2	1800	1745	1500	1450
3	1200	1160	1000	970
4	900	875	750	725

Design B Electric Motor Speeds

Synchronous RPM is the theoretical speed with no slip. The full load RPM has been calculated with a 3% slip from synchronous.

The motor should not be stopped and started frequently; it should be left running and the load removed by unloading the pump.

Design D, Induction Motor.
This design may be preferred if starting torque is greater than 50% of rated motor full speed torque. Also if there may be frequent and severe changes in the torque load.

There are several variations of Design D motors, but all of them have a slip in speed of more than 5% as compared to less than 3% on a Design B motor. This means the pump flow will be slightly less. Those with a 5 to 8% slip are reasonably obtainable, but those having a higher slip, up to 13% should be considered as special order items and may require extended delivery time.

Design D motors are sometimes used to "peak out" a hydraulic pump at a pressure which would severely overload and possibly damage a Design B motor. The "slip" in speed under full load or overload reduces input HP and line current.

Designs A and C, Induction Motor. These are seldom used for pump drives. They are capable of starting full torque loads but the line current may be extremely high, requiring special and expensive starting equipment.

Current and Voltage Characteristics, Design B Motors . . .

Motor Current. Torque is produced by current flow; the higher the current the greater the torque output. Current is also responsible for temperature rise in the windings. Any operating condition such as low voltage, wrong frequency, or torque overload, will cause an abnormal temperature rise.

Design B motors (most often used on pump drives) are capable of starting under full load. But if they are to be started frequently, starting load should be reduced to 50% to prevent overheating.

Effects of Low Voltage. Nameplate HP rating is based on full voltage being available. HP output is a combination of voltage times current. If the voltage is too low, then to produce rated HP the current becomes too high, and this causes an abnormal temperature rise. Motors can usually accommodate as low as 90% of rated voltage and still produce rated HP although temperature rise in the windings will be greater than rated rise, but not so great as to damage windings. For permanent operation on a voltage source known to be low, the HP load should be limited, and reduced by the same percentage that the voltage is low.

Example: A 25 HP, 220-volt motor on a 208-volt line has only 94½% of its rated voltage. Therefore, it should be de-rated to .945 x 25 = 23.6 HP (plus service factor if applicable).

Effects of High Voltage. If the motor load does not exceed nameplate HP, full load current will be lower than rating and the motor will run cooler than rating. However, its starting and breakdown current (at stall) will be higher than normal. The wiring, fusing, and thermal overload protection will have to be sized accordingly. Also, the motor noise will increase and could be objectionable.

Voltage Test. On installations where the motor is running at or near full HP, an unbalance of as little as 3½% between the highest voltage on any phase and the average voltage of all three phases can cause a temperature rise of about 25% above the normal rated temperature rise, and can cause damage to insulation. If the fuse should go out on one phase, the current will increase on the other phases. The motor will be unable to deliver full HP and if the operation is continued, a winding may burn out.

If the voltage, at full load, is unbalanced between phases, either the motor is defective or the power line is unbalanced. To determine the cause of the fault, first measure the voltage to all three phases at the motor, when the motor is operating under load. Then, advance all line wires by one phase by re-connection and repeat the measurements. If the higher voltage advances with the re-connection, the power line is unbalanced. Corrective measures can be taken as follows:

Check for voltage unbalance *where the power line enters the building*. If unbalanced more than 3½% at that point, call the utility company for an inspection and corrective measures.

With the motor running at or near full load, compare the voltage of each phase *at the motor*, with voltage readings taken *at the power line entrance*. If the voltage loss in any phase is more than 3% between these two readings, check for high resistance in wiring, connections, fuses, circuit breaker, or disconnect switch.

Polyphase induction motors should not be operated on more than a 10% voltage variation, higher or lower, than the nominal voltage stamped on the nameplate. Over-voltage can be tolerated better than under-voltage provided motor HP output is limited to keep line current within nameplate rating.

Effects of Incorrect Frequency.
Most hydraulic systems are operated from a utility company power line on which the frequency (Hz) is closely controlled. If the operation is from a small, isolated power source, the frequency should be accurate to within 5% of the motor rating to obtain full performance.

If a 60 Hz motor is to be operated from a 50 Hz power source or vice versa, significant sacrifices may have to be made in motor performance. In any event, to keep the motor from overheating the current must be kept to rated value even at the sacrifice of horsepower.

	60 Hz Motor on 50 Hz Line	50 Hz Motor on 60 Hz Line
HP will be:	16-2/3 less	20% more
Adjust voltage to:†	16-2/3 less	20% more
Full load torque	Same	Same
Breakdown torque	Same	Same
Locked rotor torque	Same	Same
Locked rotor current	5% less	6% more
Speed, RPM	16-2/3 less	20% more
Max. service factor	1.00	1.00
Noise level	less	more

†Voltage adjustment is to maintain current at rated value, to produce rated shaft torque. Motor current is always a limiting factor on a variation in rated frequency or voltage.

Effects of Oversizing or Undersizing an Electric Motor ...

This information is specifically for 3-phase induction motors. Optimum results will be obtained if motor HP rating closely matches load HP requirements, being neither too far oversize nor undersize. Some effects of HP mismatch are:

Oversize Motor. Using a 20 HP motor on a system which requires only 10 HP, for example, will give good results as far as running the pump is concerned, but will consume a little more electric power than a 10 HP motor and will cause the power factor of the electric system in the plant to become poorer, especially during periods when the motor is idling. Idling current of a 20 HP motor is about half the full load current of a 10 HP motor, so a great deal of power is wasted during periods in the cycle when the motor is idling.

Undersize Motor. Using a 20 HP motor on a system which requires 25 HP for short peak periods is quite possible, but during overload periods the line current of such a motor may be about twice the line current of a 25 HP motor. Again, there may be a waste of power during peak periods in the cycle. But the smaller motor could save power during periods it is working at less than full rating.

In view of the above factors, on a hydraulic system where peak consumption occurs less than 10% of the total running time, it may be good design to use a slightly undersize motor provided it will not be overloaded by more than 25% during momentary peaks in the cycle.

Power companies charge for power by the number of kilowatt-hours used. But in some plants, the rate at which each kW-hr is charged is based on the maximum current flow at any moment during the metering period. A poor power factor in the plant electric system increases the rate of current flow without producing additional HP. Therefore, either oversizing or undersizing of electric motors can increase the cost of power to run the hydraulic system.

Measuring HP Load on an Electric Motor . . .

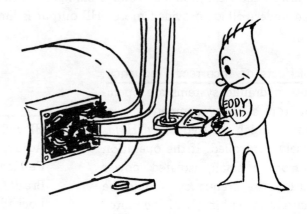

It is the line current which causes heating in the motor windings. Line current can be measured with a loop ammeter without disconnecting any wires, to see whether the motor is working at more or less than its nameplate rating. The ammeter loop can be clipped around any one of the 3-phase feeder wires any place in the circuit, in the motor junction box, in the motor starter, or the fuse and disconnect box. The reading can be compared to the rating on the nameplate. Line current is not strictly proportional to HP output of the motor. At 0 HP out (idling) line current will be about 16% of full load current. At 50% rated HP out, line current will be about 55% of full load current.

Miscellaneous Information on Induction-Type Electric Motors . . .

Starting. For starting under no load, motors of any size, up to about 50 HP, can be connected directly across the line at full voltage. Normally a Design B motor should not be required to start under more than 50% of its full speed torque rating. Starting frequently under full load may damage the motor. Line current, during starting, may become excessive, possibly overloading the power line, or producing high peak current resulting in a higher power rate from the utility company. This means that hydraulic circuits should be designed so the pump is in an unloaded state at the time the motor is started. This is a normal condition for most hydraulic systems but in pressure manifold or accumulator systems an unloading device may be needed. Refer to Page 153.

Local power companies have restrictions on peak current draw. High power motors (50 HP and over) if connected directly across the power line at full voltage, may cause a momentary voltage drop which might adversely affect power company equipment or that of other customers on the line. Although high power motors are not damaged by occasionally connecting them directly across full voltage, reduced voltage starters are usually required to reduce line current and to protect other equipment.

If the motor must start a pump under full load, your motor supplier may recommend a NEMA Design C or D motor. These designs produce more starting torque at less line current. They are not as readily available as the Design B and may be considerably more expensive.

Environmental Conditions. Motors should be operated at full power or above only under normal environmental conditions summarized below. For adverse environmental conditions the precise amount of reduction in power rating should be determined and specified by the manufacturer.

(1). Ambient air temperature should be in the range 50 to 104° F. Outside this range, motor may have to be de-rated or a special motor may be required. Get manufacturers recommendations.

(2). Motors are designed for operation at low altitudes, up to 3300 feet. They may overheat at higher elevations unless operated at less than nameplate rated HP. Get manufacturers recommendations.

(3). They should be installed in a location which allows free and unrestricted circulation of clean, dry air for cooling. They may overheat if operated at full HP in confined locations.

(4). They should be installed on a rigid surface and in a location which provides convenient access for periodic inspection, lubrication, and maintenance.

Motor Speed. Induction motors are rated for "synchronous" speed. This is the maximum theoretical speed of the motor which could be attained on that line frequency if there were no losses. A Design B motor will usually run at about 4% less than synchronous speed when fully loaded. The chart on Page 160 shows the speeds which may be expected on 60 Hz and 50 Hz power lines. Induction motors are limited to these speeds, and to drive a pump at some intermediate speed, a belt, chain, or gear drive must be used between motor and pump.

To operate a motor on a line frequency other than that for which it was designed, it must be de-rated in HP. The motor supplier must be consulted on such a problem. Synchronous speed on other frequencies is proportional to frequency. For example a 60 Hz motor run on a 50 Hz line will run at 5/6ths of its rated synchronous speed.

Service Factor. This is a multiplier usually shown on the nameplate of general purpose motors. For most integral HP induction motors up to 200 HP this factor is 1.15. This means that if the motor is operated under ideal conditions of ambient temperature, elevation, and free air circulation, at rated line frequency, and with full terminal voltage, it can be operated at 15% above rated horsepower, and the additional heat generated will not harm the insulation on the windings. Since current is what causes heat in the windings, this really means that it will handle up to 15% more line current without damage. If operating conditions deviate from those stated above, the motor must be limited to nameplate current and HP, or may even have to be de-rated below these values. Explosion proof and TEFC motors should not be operated continuously above nameplate rating. They do not have the built-in air circulation of an open frame motor.

If a motor is to be operated at an average HP above nameplate rating by using the service factor, the heater coils in its magnetic motor starter will have to be selected to operate on the increased current without tripping the breaker mechanism.

Peak Overload. A NEMA Design B induction motor can be operated for short periods without damage on peak overloads provided the average load over an extended period does not exceed nameplate rating. As a general rule, these peak periods should be evenly spaced and not to exceed 5 to 10% of the total running time. A Design B motor can usually produce 200 to 250% of full load torque while running, just before stalling. But because the line current (and consequent heating) increases at a rate far out of proportion to the increase in torque, NEMA recommends that peak torque be limited to 125% of full load rating to prevent line current from skyrocketing.

Direction of Rotation. Most 3-phase motors are made with symmetrical parts so rotation is equally efficient in either rotation. However, certain large sizes of 3600 RPM motors have uni-directional cooling fans, and these models must be run in a specified rotation to get maximum cooling. A direction arrow is prominently displayed on the end bell or frame.

There is no standard direction of rotation because the phase sequence of the incoming power line is not known, and there is no standard method of specifying this phase sequence. When a 3-phase motor is first connected, it may run in either rotation. If rotation is wrong, it can be reversed by interchanging connections to any two of the three power wires. Rotation is specified as "clockwise" (CW) or "counter-clockwise" (CCW) *when viewing the end opposite the shaft.*

Since most hydraulic pumps must be rotated in a specified direction, it is important to check rotation of the motor when first connected and to reverse rotation if necessary.

Safety. In addition to the usual protections against electric shock, the motor frame should be earth grounded. If ground is not carried in with the power wiring a separate ground wire, connected to the motor frame should be run to an outside ground rod. It is poor practice to ground to a water pipe and against all code regulations to ground to a gas pipe.

Guards should be placed over rotating parts such as couplings, sheaves, or gears connected to the motor shaft, to prevent clothing or hair of personnel from entanglement.

Troubleshooting. If a motor winding burns out, it is the current through the windings which causes the temperature rise. Motor will not overheat even if run on abnormally high voltage or an incorrect frequency if current does not exceed motor nameplate rating. This means that if voltage and/or frequency is not within specified limits, the HP load must be reduced as much as necessary to reduce current to nameplate value. Excessive current can also be caused by a mechanical overload on the shaft or from environmental conditions such as high ambient temperature or from lack of free air circulation around the motor frame.

Motor may overheat over a period of time from being started too frequently, or "plugged" too often for quick stop or reversal.

Mechanical problems are usually related to shaft bearings. Motors with sleeve or roller bearings should be mounted with shaft horizontal to within 5 or 10 degrees. Motors to be mounted with shaft vertical should have ball bearings capable of supporting shaft end thrust. Unusually heavy side loads, such as those caused by the use of very small diameter gears or sheaves, will reduce bearing life. Sleeve bearings, size for size, will carry more side load than ball or roller bearings but usually have to be lubricated periodically.

Heaters for Magnetic Motor Starters. For normal motor service choose the standard heater coil closest to the motor nameplate current rating. If motor operates in a cold environment, the coil with the next lower rating may be preferred. If motor operates in a hot environment, the heater with next higher current rating may work better.

Metric Equivalent of Horsepower. Sometime in the future, the SI unit of power, the kilowatt, abbreviated kW will become the standard unit for measurement of all kinds of power — electrical, fluid, and mechanical. In mechanical power kW = T x RPM ÷ 9543, where torque, T, is in nm (Newton-metres). In electrical power, 1 HP = 0.746 kW, or 1 kW = 1.34 HP.

Single-Phase Induction-Type Electric Motors . . .

Single-phase motors are built to 20 HP or more, but are seldom used to drive pumps except on fractional HP systems of 1½ HP or less which can be operated from a standard wall outlet. When up to speed they will deliver about the same torque as 3-phase motors, but have less starting torque and some means must be built in to distort the induction field to produce torque for starting. Three-phase motors are preferred if 3-phase power is available.

Common types of single-phase motors are: split-phase induction, capacitor-start induction, permanent split capacitor induction, shaded pole induction, and universal brush-type motors. Of these, the capacitor start is usually preferred for hydraulic pump drive. When up to speed its torque and overload characteristics are similar to a 3-phase induction motor, but a capacitor must be used to distort the induction field to produce a starting torque. It may not be able to start a hydraulic pump unless that pump is unloaded before start-up.

A capacitor-start motor can be set up to run in either rotation. Unlike a squirrel cage 3-phase induction motor, there are windings on both rotor and stator. To reverse rotation, one of these windings must be reversed in polarity with respect to the other. Instructions for reversal will usually be found inside the junction box cover.

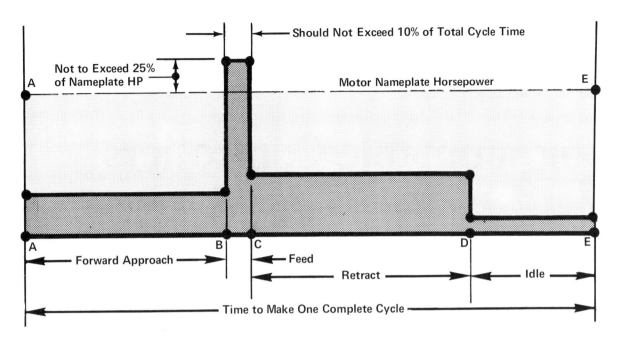

FIGURE 9-10. Block diagram of horsepower requirements during a cylinder cycle.

Duty Cycle on a 3-Phase Induction-Type Electric Motor . . .

Figure 9-10. The diagram above is plotted to illustrate typical power (and electric motor power) required during one cycle of a hydraulically powered machine. The relative time the cylinder is in various parts of the machine cycle — fast forward, feed, retract, and idle — is shown along the base line. The HP level relative to motor nameplate rating is shown by the vertical height during each part of the cycle.

A 3-phase induction-type motor can be overloaded to a limited degree during part of the cycle provided the *average* power over a complete cycle does not exceed the continuous HP rating of the motor as defined by Points A, A', E', and E and provided the momentary peak power does not exceed the limitations shown on the diagram, and provided overload time does not exceed 10% of total running time. On the diagram the darker gray area shows HP required during each part of the cycle. The lighter gray area shows continuous HP which the motor can deliver without exceeding its nameplate rating. If the service factor is applicable, slightly more power can be produced without overheating.

Remember, this graph may not apply to every hydraulic application but does show a very common machine cycle. From Point A to Point B, forward approach, the motor is most likely working at a fraction of its nameplate HP. From Point B to Point C, feed, if this period does not extend over more than 10% of the total cycle time including idle and re-loading periods, it may be good design to allow the motor to work slightly above nameplate HP but not to exceed 25% overload. From Point C to Point D, retract, the motor again is usually working at a fraction of its maximum power. At home position, the pump is unloaded and the motor is also idling at about 16% of its rated power from Points D to E.

Caution! The degree of overloading suggested by the graph is typical of good design on many hydraulic systems, and depends on environmental conditions in which the motor is operated. We suggest the motor manufacturer be consulted to verify that this is a safe operating condition for the kind of motor and the environmental conditions in which it is operated.

CHAPTER 10

Programmable Controllers

Earlier chapters in this book have described "hard wired" electrical circuits in which components such as relays, timers, and counters have been mounted in a closed metal cabinet. A technician connects these components together with a wiring harness, working from a ladder or wiring diagram. Terminal blocks are provided inside the cabinet for connecting wires to switches mounted on the machine and to solenoid valve coils in the fluid circuit. Other items such as pilot lights, pushbuttons, selector switches, and adjustable timers and counters are usually installed either on the cabinet door where they can be accessed without opening the door, or they may be mounted on an operator's console. Wiring from these components connects to terminal boards inside the metal cabinet.

Today, solid state programmable controllers have been developed to replace the older methods of hard wiring on some of these applications because of certain advantages they may offer. Since there are dozens of controller models available from many manufacturers, our discussion in this chapter will necessarily be limited to principles which apply in general, and we will relate them to the control of fluid powered machines.

WHAT IS A PROGRAMMABLE CONTROLLER?

A programmable controller is a solid state electrical device which will duplicate the action of "hard wired" electric logic components, and can be programmed into an almost infinite variety of electrical circuit combinations. At any time the existing program can be erased and a new program entered.

There are two basic units to a controller system. The CPU (Central Processing Unit) consists of a cabinet housing a large number of solid state relays, counters, and timers. It has a memory bank for "remembering" in what order these components must operate. An operator, working from a ladder diagram which has been developed for the circuit action desired, "connects" these components together. But instead of connecting them together with a wiring harness (hard wiring), he uses a small console with a keyboard. These two units together form the essential components of a PC (Programmable Controller). After the desired program has been played into the memory bank of the CPU, the CPU can be connected to limit switches and solenoid valves on the machine and will exercise complete control. For example, on fluid power applications, a PC can be used for electrical control of machines where a series of manufacturing operations must be performed in sequence, cycle after cycle. It can be programmed to cause any number of air or hydraulic cylinders or motors, for example, to extend and retract (or reverse) in a specific sequence on every cycle.

On many applications a programmable controller may offer some or all of the following advantages over control of the same machine with conventional hard wiring:

(1). Most of the hand wiring is eliminated. The only loose wiring is from components mounted on the machine to input and output terminals on the CPU, and from operator control devices such as start/stop pushbuttons, manual/automatic or jog pushbuttons, and pilot lights. These must also be connected to terminals on the CPU. Entering a program into the CPU memory may require only 10 minutes compared to several man-weeks of labor in hard wiring an equivalent system. At any future time, if a change or correction is required, it can be done in a few minutes usually without changes in wiring. The CPU can be used on another application or machine at any time by erasing the memory and re-programming. The memory chip can be erased and re-programmed an unlimited number of times.

(2). The CPU contains a large number of solid state components, and as many as required can be used. The small model we will describe has 40 solid state relays for internal circuitry plus a large number of other components including timers and counters. Larger CPU systems may have many times this number of components. The contacts on each component can be used an unlimited number of times, either as N.O. or N.C. contacts. An important advantage of a PC system is that a circuit designer does not have to economize on the number of contacts operated by each relay "coil". The same number of conventional components would require a control cabinet of very large size.

(3). These internal components can be programmed (connected) together, by an operator, using a keyboard, into any kind of circuit. The program can be corrected, modified, or completely changed at any time, usually without wiring changes.

(4). After a program has been stored in the memory bank of the CPU it can, if desired, be duplicated (copied) into an audio cassette or into a non-volatile electronic chip for storage. Later, it can be copied back into the CPU memory bank. A number of different programs or variations can be originated and stored. A desired program can be plugged into the CPU and will take over control.

(5). Most CPU's have no moving parts and are therefore less likely to develop service problems. But some models do have output relays with mechanical action for directly switching the current of solenoid valves without the use of additional external relays.

(6). In case of a breakdown in the electrical circuit, a CPU is easier to troubleshoot. It has built-in circuits and displays to help a technician quickly find the source of trouble. It monitors itself on every machine cycle and will instantly stop the machine if any of the electrical components should fail.

FIGURE 10-1. Programmable controllers come in many shapes and sizes. Some are completely self-contained, some are in modular form. Capacities up to 24K bytes and 512 I/O points, and even higher, are available.

(7). The initial cost of a PC system is sometimes higher than the cost of individual components for a hard wired system, but the saving in hard wiring labor cost will usually make the PC system less expensive in the end, even on machines where the control circuit is relatively simple.

(8). Since solid state components and circuitry are used, programmable controllers are much smaller and lighter than equivalent hard wired systems. In many cases they can be mounted directly on the machine to be controlled. The model described in this book will mount on standard DIN rails.

TYPICAL PROGRAMMABLE CONTROLLER

There are several manufacturers of PC's and each offers a choice of several models. But all of them work on similar principles using solid state switching, but different models may vary greatly in size and appearance. Some may have extra features, or a different number of internal components, or may have a different input and/output capacity.

For the purpose of illustration we have selected one of the smaller models, produced by a prominent manufacturer, and this model will be identified in this book as a Model S-6. It has sufficient capacity, with add-on modules, for simple to moderately intricate circuits, and will handle most electrically controlled fluid powered machines.

The Model S-6 happens to be built in stackable modules as illustrated below. Other models may have all individual units combined in one housing. Some models have built-in power supplies, others may use an external power supply.

The Model S-6 includes the basic unit called the CPU (Central Processing Unit), a separate power supply to operate it, and a keyboard console (called a programming console) for entering a program into the CPU memory. Maximum capacity of the Model S-6 is obtained by using add-on modules up to a total system capacity of 64 assorted input and/or output (I/O) channels. Each unit will be described. Other optional accessories are available for copying a finished program out of the CPU memory into either an audio cassette or a non-volatile (permanent) electronic chip for storage.

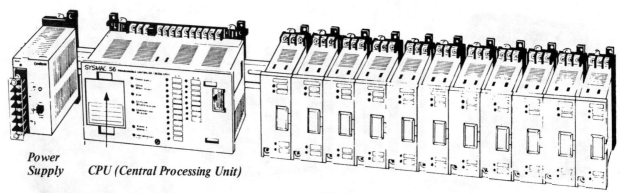

Power Supply   *CPU (Central Processing Unit)*

Add-on units to increase system capacity

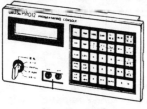

Programming Console

FIGURE 10-2. The Model S-6 happens to be built in separate modules which include the basic unit called the CPU (central processing unit), a separate 24v D-C power supply, and a programming console. This forms a complete system. If additional capacity is needed, either more input channels or more output channels, modules can be added to increase capacity up to 64 assorted input or output channels.

TERMS AND ABBREVIATIONS USED WITH PROGRAMMABLE CONTROLLERS

PC Programmable Controller. This term includes all units — central processing unit, power supply, and auxiliary and add-on modules.

CPU Central Processing Unit. This is the section which contains memory chips, solid state components for circuitry, input and output processing components, program scanning and error detection circuits, and temporary storage registers. In the Model S-6, the CPU is housed in a separate cabinet from its power supply, programming console, and auxiliary add-on units for increasing system capacity.

RAM Random Access Memory. This is the part of the memory circuits in the CPU where a program is stored by an operator using the programming console. There are many kinds of memory units. A RAM memory will accept instructions, bit by bit, up to its capacity. After programming, individual bits can be erased and re-programmed without affecting the rest of the memory, or the entire memory can be wiped out and re-programmed an unlimited number of times. The RAM memory is volatile, meaning it will be lost during a power failure. CPU's have a battery back-up or a large capacitor for maintaining power on the memory in case of a power failure.

ROM Read Only Memory. The CPU also has a ROM memory section. A ROM memory is permanent. It is programmed during fabrication according to the user's requirement and cannot be re-programmed. It determines how the CPU functions, data format, what control signals mean and what they do, terminal numbers for specific functions, the meaning and priority of various messages, etc. It cannot be altered in the field, and only certain parts of it are accessible to the user. It is regarded as a throw-away item if it should fail.

EPROM Erasable, Programmable, Read-Only Memory. This kind of memory is non-volatile, but can be erased by ultra-violet radiation and re-used. It is the kind of memory used in a small module for permanently storing a program which has been originated in the RAM memory of the CPU.

BIT One binary digit which has a value of either "1" or "0" (on or off). It is the smallest unit of information which is used in programming a CPU RAM memory. A group of 4 bits is called a "nibble"; a group of 8 bits is usually called a "byte".

BYTE A group of adjacent bits usually operated on as a unit, such as when moving data to and from memory. There are 8 bits per byte.

WORD A word is a group of bits consisting of one (or more) bytes, and is operated on as a group by the CPU. In the Model S-6 described in this chapter, the capacity is 512 words. This means that up to 512 circuit contact instructions can be entered into the CPU RAM memory.

I/O Abbreviation for input/output. This specifies the number of input and output circuits which can be handled by the CPU. In the Model S-6, there are 12 input and 8 output circuits. This capacity can be increased up to a random total of 64 input and output circuits by using add-on modules.

ADDRESS An identifying or reference number assigned to each memory location. Each memory location has an address and each address has a memory location.

PROGRAM A planned set of instructions (usually derived from an electrical ladder diagram) stored in the RAM memory and executed in an orderly fashion by the CPU.

HARDWARE Includes all the physical components of the programmable controller system, including all peripherals and optional or auxiliary equipment, as contrasted to the software components which control its operation.

SOFTWARE Any written documents associated with the system hardware, such as ladder diagrams, program instructions, assignment of input and output terminals, and the stored instructions.

VOLATILE A volatile memory is one in which the stored program will be lost if power is lost. A non-volatile memory is one in which the stored program is retained without power applied.

WRITE This is the process of burning information into the memory. A "write" key on the programming console, when pressed, will burn displayed data into the RAM memory.

LED Light emitting diode. A semi-conductor diode which emits light when passing a current. Commonly used as pilot light indicators on the CPU or other hardware.

LCD Liquid Crystal Display. Usually consists of black letters displayed against a white background. Consumes an infinitesimal current and is used as a data display where current must be minimal.

LADDER A ladder diagram is an industrry standard method of diagramming electrical control circuits. Most programmable controllers are designed for ladder diagram logic.

170

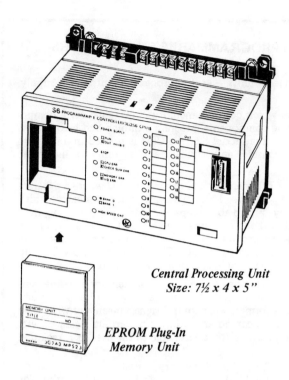

Central Processing Unit
Size: 7½ x 4 x 5"

EPROM Plug-In
Memory Unit

FIGURE 10-3. *Central processing unit, shown above, will control a fluid power machine from its own built-in RAM memory or from the EPROM memory of a plug-in memory unit.*

SYSTEM COMPONENTS

Central Processing Unit (CPU). This is the main unit of the system. In the Model S-6 which we are using as an example, dimensions are about 7½" wide x 4" high x 5" deep. This small model has the capacity to accept up to 12 input switching signals from sources such as pushbuttons, limit switches, rotary or toggle switches, and from other sources such as photo-electric sensors, proximity switches, accoustical sensors, etc. If the system needs more than 12 switching inputs its capacity can be increased with add-on modules as described later.

It has a capacity to control up to 8 output devices. On a fluid power system these would be solenoid valve coils, indicator lights, etc. If more than 8 outputs are needed, its capacity can be increased with add-on modules.

The program source for the CPU can be either from its own built-in RAM memory which has previously been programmed to the desired operating sequence of the controlled machine, or it can come from an EPROM memory chip which contains the desired program and which can be plugged into the CPU.

The program memory in the CPU is of the RAM (random access memory) type. Individual bits of information can be entered, changed, or deleted without affecting other information stored in the memory. Additional bits of information can be inserted anywhere in a stored program without affecting information already stored. However, the RAM memory is volatile, meaning that it will be lost unless power is maintained on it. In the Model S-6, a large built-in capacitor is charged during normal operation. If incoming power should fail, the capacitor will feed back power to maintain RAM memory for a week or more. Or, a plug-in battery will maintain the memory for more than a year.

In setting up a new system, an operator, working from an electrical ladder diagram or a program instruction chart, keys the electrical circuit, one contact at a time, into the RAM memory by using the keyboard of a small programming console. This console is attached to the CPU by a short cable. After programming is complete, the keyboard can be detached and set aside. After the program has been completed and checked, it can be copied into an audio cassette or into the non-volatile EPROM memory of a memory unit for safe keeping. An EPROM memory is permanently retained without power. If for any reason the program in the RAM memory should be damaged or lost, it can be restored by playing back from the cassette or the memory unit.

The Model S-6 has a capacity of 512 words or "slots" where information about the contacts can be stored. Larger models have a greater capacity. These slots are called "addresses". Each slot will hold complete instructions for one set of contacts in the electrical circuit including its identification number as shown on the ladder diagram, whether it is N.O. or N.C., and how it is combined (in series or in parallel), with previously entered contacts.

The CPU of the Model S-6 has 40 solid state relays, 8 electronic timers, 8 counters, 8 latching relays, 1 reversible counter, and 1 high speed counter. As many of these components can be used as needed,

171

the remaining ones disregarded. The set of contacts on each component can be used as many times as desired, either N.O. or N.C., in any part of the program. In addition to these solid state components there are 8 mechanical relays connected to the 8 output terminals. These have a contact capacity sufficient to switch the solenoids of fluid power valves.

The EPROM memory unit can plug into a recess on the front panel of the CPU, and will override any existing program which may be in the CPU memory. On machines where the program must be changed from time to time to manufacture parts of different sizes or kinds, each program can be entered into the CPU then transferred to a memory unit. It is then simply a matter of plugging the desired memory unit into the CPU. Memory units can be erased with ultra-violet light and re-used, but are considered to be a permanent storage medium.

The front panel of the Model S-6 contains LED pilot lights to indicate input and output circuits which are in operation. If the program should stop, a troubleshooter can see which circuit was in operation when the failure occurred.

Programming Console. On the Model S-6 the programming keyboard (called a programming console) is a small unit about 7" wide x 4" high x 1¼" deep. It will attach directly to the front panel of the CPU or can be connected to it by a cable and operated from a few feet away.

This is the keyboard which an operator uses to play an electrical program into the CPU memory. The operator works from an electrical ladder diagram and enters switch and relay contacts, one at a time, into memory. Instead of hard wiring, the operator "connects" internal components together in the desired circuit. Thus, changes, additions, or corrections are very easy to make or change without any re-wiring.

On the Model S-6, the console can also be used to run diagnostic checks to discover errors in the program or can serve as a troubleshooting tool for finding the source of a fault.

A switch on the console will place the system in a choice of several modes including the programming mode, a run mode, a monitor mode, and into modes for duplicating a stored program into an audio cassette or an EPROM memory chip.

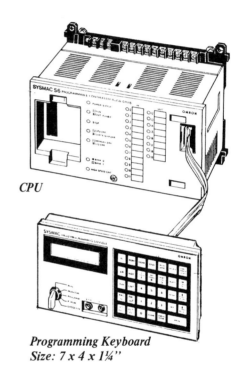

CPU

Programming Keyboard
Size: 7 x 4 x 1¼"

FIGURE 10-4. The programming console or keyboard will plug into the controller and is used for storing a program or monitoring machine operation.

Power Supply. In the Model S-6, operating power for the CPU comes from a peripheral unit which can be mounted alongside the CPU. On some programmable controllers the power supply is built into the same cabinet with the other components.

Peripheral Components. Depending on the brand and model, auxiliary and optional components can be added to the system as desired. These may include modules for increasing input or output capacity, back-up battery, EPROM memory units, extra patch cords, DIN mounting rails, fuses, and equipment for duplicating a stored program into a memory unit. Tape recorders are obtained locally and are not furnished by the controller supplier.

172

ELECTRICAL CONNECTIONS TO A PROGRAMMABLE CONTROLLER

Remember we are illustrating a typical small programmable controller which is identified as a Model S-6. Details of the wiring may vary when using other brands or models.

Controllers are usually designed to operate at a low D-C voltage, 12 or 24 volts. Power can be obtained from batteries or from a 110 or 220 volt A-C line through either a built-in power supply or from a separate module as in the Model S-6.

Input switching devices will include limit switches mounted on the machine at designated points along or at the ends of cylinder strokes. Other switches may include start, stop, jog, and panic pushbuttons, manual/automatic and mode selector switches, etc. There may be other sensor switches such as proximity, heat sensing, and photoelectric sensors. Each switch must be hard wired to an input terminal on the CPU, with switch COM connected to input COM terminal. The wire from either

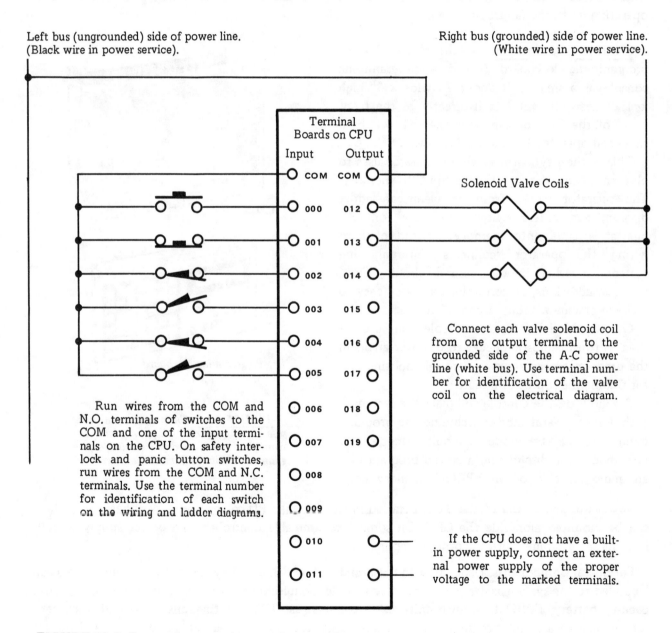

Left bus (ungrounded) side of power line. (Black wire in power service).

Right bus (grounded) side of power line. (White wire in power service).

Solenoid Valve Coils

Connect each valve solenoid coil from one output terminal to the grounded side of the A-C power line (white bus). Use terminal number for identification of the valve coil on the electrical diagram.

Run wires from the COM and N.O. terminals of switches to the COM and one of the input terminals on the CPU. On safety interlock and panic button switches, run wires from the COM and N.C. terminals. Use the terminal number for identification of each switch on the wiring and ladder diagrams.

If the CPU does not have a built-in power supply, connect an external power supply of the proper voltage to the marked terminals.

FIGURE 10-5. External connections to the central processing unit (CPU) input and output terminals.

the N.O. or the N.C. switch terminal must be connected to one input terminal, Terminals 000 through 011 on the Model S-6. These terminal numbers become identifying numbers for each switch and should be recorded on the ladder or wiring diagram and the programming chart.

Run only two wires from each switch even though both the N.O. and N.C. terminals are available. A rule-of-thumb is to connect from COM and N.O. terminals of all except safety switches, regardless of what their action is. If N.C. action is required, this can be programmed by the keyboard console without actually running a wire from the N.C. switch terminal. On safety switches such as operator panic button, safety interlock switches on gates, doors, and other parts of the machine, run wires from the COM and N.C. switch terminals. This keeps the terminal on the CPU in an activated condition during normal running. If a switch contact should fail, a wire should come loose or break, this will de-activate the CPU input terminal and stop the cycle. If a N.O. action is required from a safety switch, this can be programmed by the keyboard without actually running a wire from the switch N.O. terminal. The diagram on the preceding page shows how input switches should be wired.

Connect load devices to output terminals on the CPU. These will include solenoid valve coils, pilot lights, alarm devices, etc. On the Model S-6, Terminals 012 through 019 are for load devices. Note: the controller does not provide operating voltage for the loads. Output terminals provide only switching circuits. Operating voltage must be provided externally from the 110 or 220 volt power line or other source. Connections for load devices are shown on the preceding page. Connect each solenoid coil, for example, between one of the output terminals and the white or grounded side of the A-C power line. Connect the black or ungrounded side of the A-C power line to the COM output terminal on the CPU. Check the current rating of each load device to be sure it is within the rating of the relay contacts in the CPU. Terminal numbers to which load devices are connected become the identification numbers for the devices and should be recorded on the ladder or wiring diagram and the programming chart.

If the machine has an operator console, all switches on the console must be wired to input terminals on the CPU. All pilot lights must be wired to output terminals.

When running A-C power wiring, observe polarity. The white wire is at earth ground potential and the black wire is the "hot" side. An earth ground should be connected to the white side of the line.

On the Model S-6, if there are more than 12 input switches or more than 8 output devices, add-on modules must be used to increase system capacity.

ELECTRICAL LADDER DIAGRAM FORMAT

Although a ladder diagram is not the only way information can be presented to a programmable controller, it seems to be the most popular method and probably the simplest and easiest. A designer works from the fluid diagram and job specifications to produce an electrical diagram which can then be entered into the RAM memory of a controller by an operator using a keyboard. Rules for construction of a ladder diagram must be scrupulously followed. Any deviation from the rules will end up with a program which will not run correctly.

Ladder Diagram Format . . .

Refer to Figure 10-6 on the next page. The diagram is started with two vertical lines spaced several inches apart. These are the uprights of the ladder. The left line or "power bus" represents the "hot" or ungrounded side of the power line. All switching devices must be connected to this line. The right line is the grounded side of the power line. All load devices must be connected to this line. The rungs are drawn horizontally between the uprights, starting at the top and working down. Each rung is a segment or unit of information to the controller and must include the complete switching circuit to one of the load devices (valve solenoids, etc.). Each rung must serve only one load, but all the switches on the machine which influence conductivity or non-conductivity through the rung to the load must be connected in series, in parallel, or series/parallel on the left side of the rung. How the switches are connected is determined by the electrical action required.

Rungs can be drawn in any order, but usually should be drawn in the approximate order in which each load is energized in the cycle. In the time frame of each machine cycle, when the switching circuit ahead of an output relay coil has been closed, the solenoid valve coil connected to that output terminal becomes energized.

Construction of the diagram proceeds, rung by rung, until all load devices have been assigned to a rung and the switches which operate them have been drawn.

Circuits for hard wired JIC electrical systems, as shown in earlier chapters, are also drawn in a ladder format but the rules are slightly different. Seldom is a JIC ladder diagram suitable for programming a controller. A later section in this chapter will show how to modify a JIC diagram for programming a controller.

Drawing a workable ladder diagram does require certain skills. The designer must be familiar with operation of the fluid circuit, and he must have enough electrical knowledge to know whether to connect switch contacts in series or in parallel in a ladder rung. But a non-electrical person, after a workable diagram has been produced, can program a controller in a few minutes after he understands its operation. A similar application designed for JIC hard wiring might require many hours or days to design and construct wiring harnesses and install them.

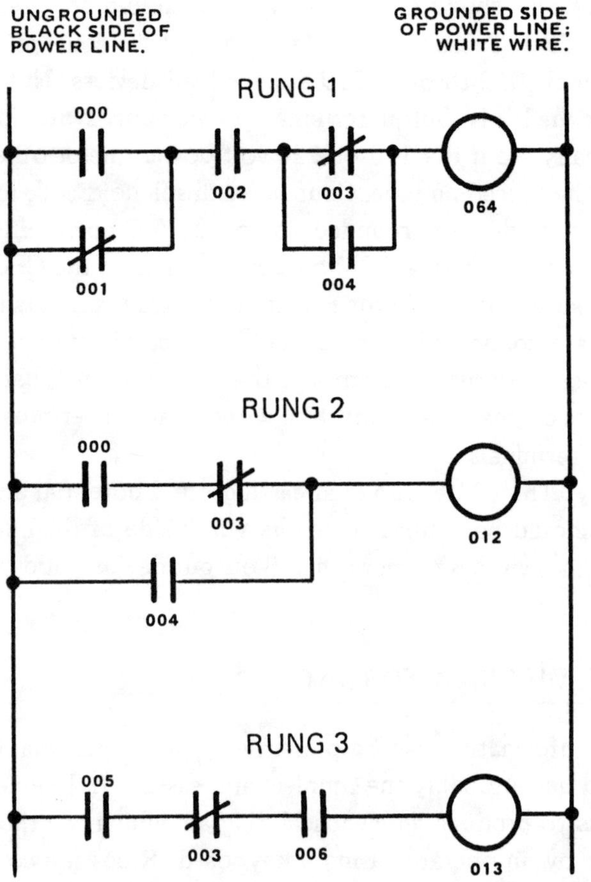

Example of Ladder Diagram . . .

Figure 10-6. This diagram shows the general appearance of a ladder diagram. The symbols and their meaning will be covered in detail in the next section.

In Rung 1, 000 could be the terminal to which the starting pushbutton has been connected. Load 064 is one of the 40 circuit relays in the Model S-6. All switches which influence closure of Relay 064 are drawn in the same rung. In Rung 2, all contacts which influence energization of valve Solenoid 012 connected to output Terminal 012 are shown.

FIGURE 10-6.

The format in which ladder diagrams for programmable controllers are usually drawn.

Symbols Used in Controller Ladder Diagrams . . .

The four symbols shown on the next page are the only ones used on most controller ladder diagrams. Each one must be identified with the 3-digit code symbol showing the controller input or output terminal to which it has been assigned.

Circle. A circle is used to show the relay "coils" in the controller. It could be one of the 40 solid state relays or one of the 8 output relays. Any relays added externally should not appear on the ladder diagram; this diagram is solely for the logic system in the controller. For example, a power relay connected to an output terminal to handle the high current required by an external load should not appear on the ladder diagram.

Circle (Relay)

Note that the 40 internal relays are not relays in the usual sense. Actually, they are solid state switching junctions. See information on Page 183. Those relays in the controller which are connected to output terminals are true relays, electro-mechanical or solid state.

Normally Open (N.O.) Contacts. This symbol, when used on a JIC electrical circuit, always means a state of non-conductivity at that point in the circuit. But in a controller diagram the meaning can be different. Symbols are always drawn, not in reference to the state of the external switch but to the state of the input terminal to which the switch is connected. N.O. means the state of conductivity is the same as the input terminal. N.C. means it is opposite to the state of the input terminal. See Pages 178, 179, and 184 for details.

N.O. Contact

When a N.O. symbol is used for contacts on an internal relay, it means the same as on a JIC circuit — non-conductivity at that point at that time.

Normally Closed (N.C.) Contacts. On a JIC diagram this symbol always represents a state of conductivity. But when used on a controller diagram it represents the opposite state of conductivity as referenced to the input terminal to which the external switch is connected. See pages referenced above.

N.C. Contact

Square (Misc.)

Square. A miscellaneous symbol which can be used for components in the controller such as timers, counters, and latching relays. It cannot be used for extra components added to the system; they should not appear on the ladder diagram. For information, refer to your Operation Manual.

Note: On a JIC diagram where a 2-position SPDT or DPDT switch is used, when converting to a controller, all circuits, both N.O. and N.C. can be controlled by wiring the switch COM and N.O. terminals to the controller, leaving all other switch terminals unconnected. On 3-position switches, connect switch COM and each active terminal to the controller.

On a multi-position rotary selector switch, regardless of the number of sections, banks, or decks, connect a wire from the switch rotor to COM on the input terminal board and a wire from each selector point on one of the banks to input terminals. All terminals on all other banks can be left unconnected.

Controllers have built-in memory circuits called latching relays. These are shown with the square symbol on the diagram. The relay can be locked closed by a signal coming from an input terminal or from contacts on an internal relay. It will remain locked closed until released by another signal coming from another source. Details of programming these latching relays are in your Operation Manual.

How to Combine Switch or Relay Contacts. (Contact Logic) . . .

There may be several relay and switch contacts, or combinations of both, in a rung which influence energization of the relay coil in that rung. These contacts must be properly combined in series, parallel, or series/parallel. Two contacts placed in series are called AND logic because continuity through them is possible only when there is continuity through the first one AND the second one.

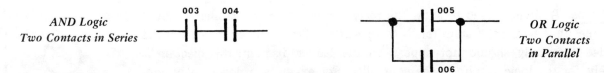

AND Logic
Two Contacts in Series

OR Logic
Two Contacts in Parallel

Two contacts placed in parallel are called OR logic because continuity through them is possible if either the first one OR the second one is closed.

Several contacts or groups of contacts can be placed in various combinations of series and parallel depending on which ones must be closed to provide continuity to the relay coil.

Detailed Rules for Drawing Ladder Diagrams for Controllers . . .

Anyone who has been accustomed to drawing ladder diagrams for JIC hard wired circuits will have to change his thinking to some degree. Symbols on controller ladder diagrams do not necessarily have the same meaning although they look similar. A ladder format is simply an easy way to graphically show which switches on the machine must be closed (or opened) to produce conductivity through each rung to a relay coil in the output.

The coil of an internal relay is not a wire-wound coil on a magnetic structure. It can be considered as a solid state switching junction. When all contacts on a rung have been closed, the relay "coil" becomes energized and provides conductivity to its output terminal. This also provides the opportunity to add changes in conductivity in other rungs of the diagram by simply drawing in contacts bearing the same 3-digit code number as the relay coil. Each relay (or switch) contact can be used an unlimited number of times anywhere in the diagram. This is more versatile than a JIC circuit in which each switch or relay has a limited number of independent contact sets. The following rules are basic for a programmable controller ladder diagram:

Rule 1. Every relay coil, whether one of the 40 internal relays in the Model S-6 or one of those connected to an output terminal for switching solenoid valve coils, must be drawn on an individual rung. A circular symbol is used and is marked with a 3-digit identification number of one of the 40 internal relays or one of the 8 output relays. Contacts operated by each relay coil must be marked with the same number as the coil.

Rule 2. All external switching devices of whatever nature must be connected to input terminals and this terminal number becomes their identification wherever they are used in the circuit. All switches are connected to the left power bus. Switches must never be connected directly to the right bus.

Rule 3. All relay coils, whether for internal or output relays, must be connected to the right bus. Relays must never be directly connected to the left power bus.

Rule 4. Each rung should start at the left bus and progress through relay and switch contacts to the relay coil connected to the right bus. All switch or relay contacts which influence conductivity through the rung must be connected in series, parallel, or series/parallel ahead of the relay coil, and must be drawn either N.O. or N.C. according to the rules on Pages 178, 179, and 184. The switch network may consist of a combination of several switch or relay contacts in one or more legs.

During running of the machine to which the controller is connected, when the CPU scanner (see Page 182) has determined that the group of contacts preceding the relay coil in any rung has become conductive, that relay coil becomes energized. If it is a relay connected to an output terminal, a switching signal is delivered to the solenoid valve coil connected to that terminal. If it the coil of an internal relay, all contacts throughout the diagram bearing the same number as the coil change their state of conductivity. Those drawn N.C. become non-conductive; those drawn N.O. become conductive.

Rule 5. Contacts on all relays should be drawn N.O. or N.C. exactly as they would for a JIC diagram. But contacts on external switches must be drawn in relation to the state of activity of the input terminals to which they are connected. Study carefully the information on Pages 178, 179, and 184.

Rule 6. There must never be any connection from an intermediate point on one rung to a point on another rung. This is common practice on a JIC diagram but is unacceptable to a controller. Each rung must be isolated from other rungs. There may be several legs but only one load device per rung.

Rule 7. Load devices (valve solenoids, etc.) never appear on a controller ladder diagram. The output relays which produce switching signals for them are shown on the diagram. For reference, the output terminal which switches a solenoid valve coil can be shown on the fluid diagram.

Rule 8. Where both a solenoid valve coil and a relay coil are energized at the same time, they are drawn in parallel on a JIC diagram. But on a controller diagram they should be separated to individual rungs. The network of contacts which energize them should be placed in the rung with the relay. Then, one of the relay contacts can be used to energize the solenoid coil in the next rung. This will often conserve the number of addresses used, and has other advantages.

Other rules and suggestions for circuit building will be added in following sections, and will be illustrated by examples later in the chapter.

How to Draw Relay and Switch Contacts . . .

Important! The symbol $\not\mid\mid$ for a N.C. and $\dashv\vdash$ for a N.O. contact, when used to represent the contacts on a relay, have the same meaning they do on a JIC hard wired circuit. But when these symbols are used to represent open or closed external switches mounted on the machine, they have a *different* meaning. The N.O. switch symbol on a controller diagram *does not* necessarily mean there is non-conductivity at that point. It means that state of conductity is the *same as* the state of the input terminal to which the switch is connected. The N.C. switch symbol means that conductivity at that

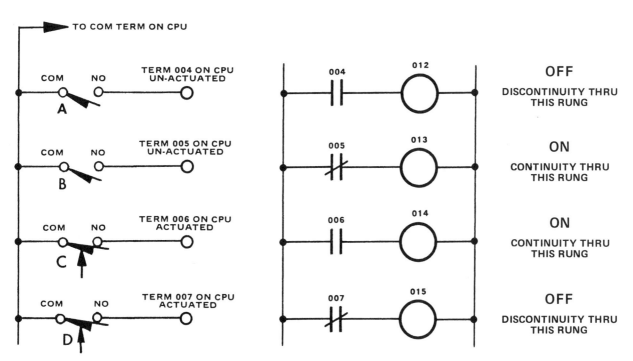

FIGURE 10-7. Examples of programming external limit switch contacts into a ladder diagram.

point is *opposite* to the state of activity of the input terminal. Study carefully Figures 10-7 and 10-8 for the correct way of drawing switch symbols.

Standard Limit Switches and Pushbuttons. When wiring the machine, run only *two* wires between a 2-position external switch and input terminals on the controller. Run switch COM to COM on the input terminal board. Run a wire from the N.O. switch terminal to one of the active terminals numbered from 000 through 011 on the Model S-6. (See exception for safety switches in the next section). Leave the N.C. switch terminal unconnected even though a N.C. action is needed in the circuit. It can be programmed in the controller. Running wires from both the N.O. and N.C. terminals is not only unnecessary but is wasteful of controller capacity.

The Symbols N.O. and N.C. for switch contacts have no meaning except to indicate whether continuity at that point is the same or opposite to the state of activity on the input terminal. On a machine converted from hard wired to programmable control, it is desirable to remove all wires from N.C. switch terminals, or to move them to the N.O. terminals.

Figure 10-7. Four standard limit switches or pushbuttons are shown, A, B, C, and D. Wiring from all switches is from their COM and N.O. terminals to Terminals 004, 005, 006, and 007 on the controller. Switch A is in its normal, unactuated state. Terminal 004 to which it is connected is de-activated at this time and 004 is drawn on the ladder diagram as a N.O. contact. This gives it the same state of continuity as the external switch. At this time there is no continuity to Relay 012 through the ladder rung.

Switch B is identical to A but connected to Terminal 005. This keeps 005 de-activated at this time. On the ladder diagram 005 has been drawn N.C. This gives continuity through the rung opposite to that of the input terminal. There will be continuity through 005 to Relay 013 while the external switch is open, and discontinuity when the external switch is closed.

Switch C is identical to A and B but is being forcibly held actuated. This causes Terminal 006 to which it is connected to be maintained in an activated state. If contacts on Switch C are drawn N.O. in the ladder diagram, continuity through the rung will be the same as the state of the input terminal. In this case Relay 014 will be maintained in an energized state.

Switch D is also an identical switch and is being forcibly held actuated. Terminal 007 to which it is connected is maintained in an activated state. If 007 is drawn N.C., continuity through the rung will be opposite to the state of the input terminal, and Relay 015 will be de-energized.

When looking at a ladder diagram, to determine if a N.O. contact is open or closed at the time, it is necessary to look at the state of the input terminal of the same number, to see whether it is being activated or de-activated by an external switch. Whether there is continuity or discontinuity through a N.C. contact on the ladder diagram can be determined in the same way.

Safety Switches and Pushbuttons. On safety switches provided for operator panic buttons, interlocks on gates and doors, on fixtures which must be in a safe position before the machine is started, wiring should be from the COM and the switch terminal which is normally closed during machine operation. This keeps the input terminal activated during normal running. Then, if the external connection between machine and controller should break or become disconnected for any reason, the controller terminal will become de-activated and the machine will stop or will not start. Figure 10-8 shows whether contacts on a safety switch should be drawn N.O. or N.C. on a ladder diagram.

Figure 10-8. The N.C. terminal of Switch E is connected to controller input Terminal 009 and is keeping that terminal activated. On the ladder diagram if a state of continuity is desired, the switch contact should be drawn N.O. If a state of discontinuity is desired, it should be drawn N.C. In this case, even though the contacts are drawn N.O., there will be continuity to Relay 016.

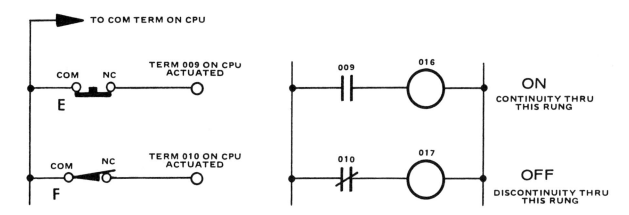

FIGURE 10-8. Examples of programming external safety switch contacts into a ladder diagram.

Switch F can be the same or a different kind of safety switch, also connected with its N.C. terminal wired to controller Terminal 010. If 010 is drawn N.C., there will be the opposite state of continuity as the input terminal and external switch, discontinuity even though the contacts are shown closed.

Note: Non-emergency STOP pushbuttons or those used for such functions as START, REVERSE, JOG, etc., should be treated the same way as other operating pushbuttons, with their N.O. terminal connected to the controller even though a N.C. action may be desired.

Application Example . . .

For programmable controller operation the same limit switches are used on the machine as would be used on a hard wired circuit. They must be connected to input terminals. The same operator pushbuttons and switches are required and are also connected to input terminals. On the small Model S-6 which we are using for illustration, all input switching must be digital (ON-OFF). Analog input signals, as from a rheostat, cannot be accommodated in this model but can be accepted by some of the larger models. A ladder diagram for a circuit may look similar to one drawn for a hard wired circuit having the same electrical action but the rules are different.

Input terminals on a controller can be regarded as "information points". Each terminal can be changed from an activated to non-activated state, or vice versa, when the external switch connected to it is actuated. The assigned 3-digit number of that input terminal can then

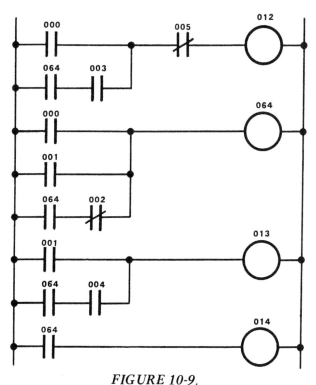

FIGURE 10-9.
Demonstration of Circuit Building Techniques.

be drawn anywhere in the diagram, in as many rungs, and as many times as desired, even in unrelated parts of the diagram, to change the state of conductivity when the external switch connected to that terminal is actuated.

Figure 10-9. The purpose of this circuit is to show how external switches should be drawn on a controller ladder diagram, N.O. or N.C. Please refer to the hydraulic circuit on Page 56 and the JIC electrical diagram on Page 57. Figure 10-9 is a conversion of the JIC electrical diagram into a controller diagram. Conversion rules are covered in later sections of this chapter. Figure 10-9 illustrates several important points of diagram construction as well as the correct way to draw switch contacts.

There are three solenoid coils and one relay. This will require four rungs in the controller diagram. One of the 40 internal relays in the Model S-6 can be used and we have selected at random, Relay 064. One contact of the same number (064) is used for relay Contact 1-CR-A.

Switch 3-LS is a safety switch on a gate or door which must be closed before the machine will start. We must connect the N.C. terminal of this switch to keep its assigned Terminal 005 activated before the cycle starts. But we want discontinuity to Solenoid A at this time, so 005 must be drawn N.C. on the controller diagram. When the safety gate has been closed, Terminal 005 becomes de-activated which produces continuity to Solenoid A. The operator can now energize Solenoid A with the Forward pushbutton. Please note that when using a 2-position 4-way air valve operated from a momentary pushbutton signal, there is nothing to prevent the operator from opening the safety gate after Solenoid A has been energized. Another circuit can be added using a N.O. 005 contact in series with Solenoid B which would automatically energize Solenoid B to reverse the cylinder if the gate should be opened.

The N.O. terminal of Switch 1-LS has been assigned to input Terminal 003. The switch is being held actuated before the cycle starts. This keeps 003 activated. Since we want continuity through 1-LS at this time, 1-LS (003) should be drawn N.O. in Rung 1.

The Forward pushbutton has been assigned to input Terminal 000. Only one of its N.O. contacts should be used. Activation and de-activation of Terminal 000 can serve both circuits in the controller. The same is true of the Reverse pushbutton which has been assigned to input Terminal 001.

The Stop pushbutton in this application is considered a working switch and not a safety switch. Its N.O. terminal is assigned to input Terminal 002, and this terminal remains de-activated at this time. Since this is opposite to the state of continuity required, 002 should be drawn N.C. in Rung 2.

Anothe point in circuit building is illustrated with Solenoid C (014) and Relay 1-CR coil (064). On the JIC diagram they are connected in parallel. On a controller diagram they must be separated into two rungs. All switch contacts which influence the energization of these two coils should be shown only in Rung 2 for the relay. Then one 064 contact on the relay can be used in Rung 4 to energize Solenoid C.

SWITCHING ACTION IN A PROGRAMMABLE CONTROLLER

The concept of switching in a programmable controller is quite different than in a JIC hard wired system. In the JIC system, external switches are wired to relays with mechanical action. If two different circuits must be operated from the same switch or relay coil, two separate sets of contacts are required to keep one circuit isolated from the other. If six circuits must be operated, six sets of contacts must be available. This sometimes makes the job of drawing a JIC diagram difficult because of the limited number of contacts which can be put on one switch or relay. This problem does not exist when programming into the controller solid state circuitry.

Scanning Circuit. In the Model S-6 there is a maximum of 512 "addresses" or "slots" where information can be stored. As many of these addresses can be used as needed for a desired program.

(Text continues on Page 183)

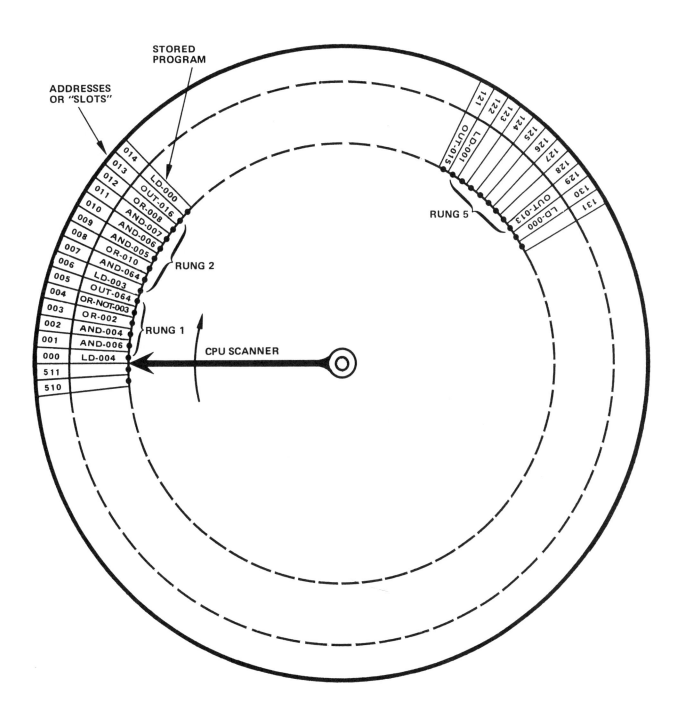

In the Model S-6 there are 512 addresses or "slots" at which program instructions can be stored. As many of these can be used as needed, the rest can be left unused. The scanner samples the state of continuity (or discontinuity) at each address at a rate of more than 100 complete scans per second. It detects the start of a rung where an LD instruction has been entered and detects the end of the same rung where an OUT instruction has been entered. It detects the end of the program where an END instruction has been entered.

FIGURE 10-10. Analogy to the electronic scanning circuit in a programmable controller.

The program is entered into the CPU memory by an operator working from an electrical diagram. When programming is complete and the CPU is in operation, a scanning circuit continuously "scans" each address, starting from Address 000 through 511. One scan requires about 10 milliseconds. When one scan is completed the next one immediately starts. If the CPU has been fully programmed with all 512 addresses, the scanner searches the program about 100 times a second looking for any change in continuity which has occurred at any address since the preceding scan.

Figure 10-10 is an analogy of the scanning principle. Imagine a rotating arm, pivoted in the center of the circle, rotating continuously and testing each address for continuity or discontinuity, starting with Address 000 on each scan. The scanner detects the start of a rung when it find a LD (Load) signal entered into an address, and detects the end of the same rung when it finds an OUT signal entered into an address. In each rung, between LD and OUT, when the scanner finds all contacts or groups of contacts in a closed state, the relay number associated with that particular OUT signal will become activated. For example, on Figure 10-10, the scanner starts at Address 000 where LD-004 has been entered, then proceeds to Address 001 where AND-006 has been entered, etc. When it reaches Address 005 where an OUT-064 has been entered, it knows this is the end of the rung. On any scan, when all contacts between LD-004 and OUT-064 have closed, Relay 064 will be energized. The scanner continues to scan all remaining addresses up to 511 or to the last one which has been used in the program, then starts the next scan at Address 000. If, in the meantime, one of the external switches has been actuated, this will change the state of continuity in any and all rungs of the ladder diagram where the input terminal to which the switch is connected has been programmed.

In a ladder diagram, each rung *must* contain only one relay "coil" which may be either one of the 8 output relays or one of the 40 internal relays. In the Model S-6, output relays are mechanical and provide a switching signal to one of the 8 output terminals. Internal relays are not relays in the usual sense. The "coil" is simply a "switching point". When the "coil" in any rung becomes activated, any N.O. contact bearing that same coil number and which has been programmed anywhere in the circuit becomes ON or conductive. Any N.C. contact bearing that coil number becomes OFF or non-conductive. Contacts, either N.O. or N.C., bearing the identification number of any internal relay can be placed anywhere in the ladder diagram to provide a change in continuity when the "coil" has become activated. N.O. and N.C. contacts of input terminals and relays are drawn on a solid state ladder diagram in the same way they are drawn on a JIC diagram, and are identified with the input terminal or internal relay to which they are connected.

Refer again to Figure 10-5. An external limit switch is connected, for example, between COM and Terminal 003 and is shown as N.O. When this external switch is actuated (as by a cylinder reaching the end of its stroke), Terminal 003 becomes conductive. Every place in the diagram where 003 has been programmed now becomes conductive. Every place where NOT-003 has been programmed (which up to this time has been conductive) now becomes non-conductive.

Primary switching points are those connected to input terminals. Their ON or OFF state is controlled by mechanical actuation of external switches connected to them. Secondary switching points are those inside the CPU in which continuity is controlled by the state of "contacts" bearing the same number and controlled by one of the 40 internal relays (or other internal component). Secondary switching points change state only when the relay "coil" bearing the same number becomes activated.

Most solid state controllers are designed to be programmed from the type of ladder diagram described in this chapter because it is an easy and familiar way of describing the action. Occasionally, another method of writing programming information is used.

Although the contacts of each external switch and internal relay can be used as many times as desired in the ladder diagram, one "slot" or address is required for each entry, so the number of times they are used is limited by the number of available addresses which can be spared to program them.

CREATING A LADDER DIAGRAM FOR A CONTROLLER

Just how does one go about originating a diagram which can be entered into a programmable controller? In this section we will use several fluid circuits from earlier chapters to illustrate some methods of circuit building. Prepare yourself for diagram drawing with these steps:

(1). A complete program should be *written* showing what the fluid power actuators should do — in what order should the actuators extend and retract, what safety devices should be added, where will the starting signal come from, whether from an operator pushbutton, from a switch on another machine, from a controller, computer, card reader, etc., and will it be momentary or maintained.

(2). The fluid circuit should be designed showing the actuators which will produce the kind of action required, and the solenoid valves that will control them. Other solenoid controlled components should be shown. For example, solenoid controlled relief, reducing, or flow control valves. Selection of pump, cylinder, and valve size is a fluid design problem and usually does not affect design of the electrical control circuit. Those limit switches actuated by cylinder movement should be shown in the approximate location where they will be mounted. This will help identify the switch which has been actuated. Other electrical devices such as pushbuttons, selector switches, timers, counters, relays, pilot lights, etc., usually cannot be shown on a fluid schematic but should appear on the components list.

(3). Limit switches and valve solenoids can be identified on the fluid schematic with regular JIC symbols. Later, when these components have been assigned terminal numbers on the controller, the terminal numbers can be added to the fluid schematic.

(4). Other functions required from the control circuit should be stated. This may include jog control, manual/automatic, forward/reverse, safety switches, etc.

(5). A complete list of components, both electrical and fluid, should be made with a brief statement of the function of each.

Electrical Circuit . . .

A switch of some kind is required at every place in the program where the action starts, stops, reverses, or changes. Wiring of switches to controller input terminals has been shown on Page 173. The input terminal number to which each switch has been connected will identify the switch on the electrical diagram, the fluid diagram, and the components list.

All load devices (valve solenoids, pilot lights, etc.) must be connected to output terminals. These 3-digit terminal numbers will identify them on the diagrams and components list.

All relays required for circuitry are inside the controller. On the Model S-6, 40 of these relays are available and have 3-digit identification numbers assigned by the controller manufacturer. All that is needed to access any of these relays is simply to draw the coil and contacts on the ladder diagram. All contacts are identified with the number of the coil which operates them. No other relays are required with the possible exception of power relays or contactors connected to output terminals to switch loads which require more power than can be switched with the miniature relays inside the controller.

Switch Contacts.
Circuit building with a controller is easier than when using hard wired components because on a hard wired circuit each limit switch has only one set of contacts. These contacts can be used only in one part of the circuit. If switching is also required in another part of the circuit at the same time, the switch must energize a relay with multiple contacts. But on a controller, when a switch connected to an input terminal is actuated, this terminal number can be used as many times as needed anywhere in the circuit to signal a state of conductivity or non-conductivity.

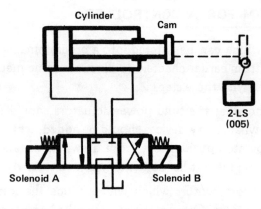

FIGURE 10-11, Part A. Hydraulic Diagram.

Figure 10-11. In Part A of this figure, the hydraulic cylinder actuates limit Switch 2-LS at the end of its forward stroke. This switch has been assigned to input Terminal 005 on the controller.

In Part B, 2-LS has been wired from its COM and N.O. terminals to input Terminals COM and 005. Closure of this switch will activate 005 and this terminal number can be used *anywhere* in as many places as desired in the ladder diagram whether or not those places are directly related to the movement of the hydraulic cylinder.

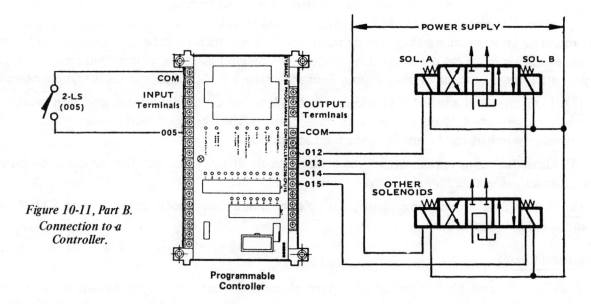

Figure 10-11, Part B. Connection to a Controller.

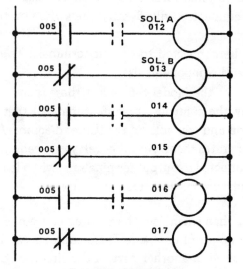

Part C. Ladder Diagram.

A partial ladder diagram is shown in Part C of this figure. The input terminal number 005 can be used separately in any rung or can be combined in series or parallel with other switch or relay contacts. Contact 005 should be drawn N.O. if continuity through it in the rung is to be the same as the state of input Terminal 005. It should be drawn N.C. if its state is opposite to that of the input Terminal 005.

As this ladder diagram is drawn, input Terminal 005 is de-activated at the start of the cycle. Therefore there is discontinuity through Rungs 1, 3, and 5, and continuity in Rungs 2, 4, and 6. When 2-LS switch is actuated, continuity will change in all rungs.

FIGURE 10-11. *Switching Action of an External Switch.*

185

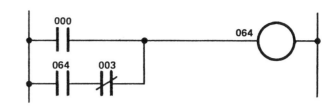

Control Relays. These can be used as holding relays. Holding relay action is described on Page 27. There are 40 relays in the Model S-6 numbered from 064 through 103. They are not connected to either input or output terminals.

A relay is a load device and is shown with a circle. Every relay must be on a separate rung preceded by contacts which open or close it. Almost any circuit problem can be solved by using one or more of these relays. Their action is very versatile: A relay can be energized when *any* input terminal is activated or de-activated by an external switch. A holding circuit can be set up through its own contacts to keep the relay coil energized. Contacts on the relays can be placed in any other rungs of the diagram. Then later, the relay can be released when *any* input terminal is activated or de-activated by its external switch.

In the diagram above, all switch and relay contacts which will cause the relay to become energized can be placed in series, parallel, or series/parallel. A holding circuit, if one is used, is shown in a separate leg, with those contacts which hold the relay closed and those which release it.

The six output relays in the Model S-6 are connected to output terminals. They provide a switching circuit to their terminal but do not supply power to operate a load connected to the terminal.

Procedure for Drawing a Ladder Diagram. Originating an electrical circuit may involve a certain amount of trial and error. When it becomes obvious that a change in circuit action cannot be accomplished with the limit switches on the machine, consider the addition of a holding relay. One way to start a diagram is to draw the two vertical uprights several inches apart. Then draw each electrical load device on a separate rung. Start with the first action which is usually the input or starting signal to the machine. This signal will energize a solenoid to start the first cylinder into action. When this cylinder actuates a limit switch, use these switch contacts to start the next action.

Each rung is handled separately, and should be completed, as nearly as possible, before starting the next rung. Add all switch and relay contacts which affect energization of the solenoid in that rung. Add these contacts in series (AND) or parallel (OR) as needed to satisfy circuitry requirements. If, for example, a cylinder actuates a switch then backs off of it, but the switch signal must hold, a relay can be added and locked in, then released at the right time later in the cycle.

Although the rungs can be drawn in any order, for sake of clarity it is better to arrange them in the approximate order in which the action progresses. Leave plenty of room between rungs so relay rungs can be added where necessary.

Be sure you understand all the rules given on Pages 177 and 178 for drawing diagrams, and the symbols and contact logic explained on Pages 175, 176, 185, etc.

EXAMPLES OF CIRCUIT BUILDING

EXAMPLE 1 – FIGURE 4-3A, PAGE 69

Please review the description of this application on Pages 69 and 70. The desired sequencing program between the two cylinders is shown in the box on Page 69.

This is an air circuit. The valves used to control the cylinders require only a short duration electrical impulse to shift the valve spool. A pushbutton will be used for starting. Limit switches must be placed as shown in the fluid circuit. Component description and controller terminal assignments are shown in this chart.

Component	Description	Controller Terminal
Cyl. 1	Clamp cylinder	- - - -
Cyl. 2	Work cylinder	- - - -
1-PB	Start pushbutton	000
1-LS	Limit switch to start Cylinder 2	001
2-LS	Limit switch to retract both cyls.	002
Sol. A	Solenoid to start Cylinder 1	012
Sol. B	Solenoid to retract Cylinder 1	013
Sol. C	Solenoid to extend Cylinder 2	014

186

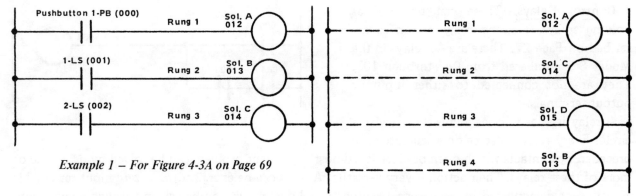

Example 1 – For Figure 4-3A on Page 69

Lay out the diagram by placing each solenoid in a separate rung. Start with Solenoid A in Rung 1. When Pushbutton 1-PB is pressed, Solenoid A becomes energized and Cylinder 1 starts forward. Draw 1-PB (000) contacts in series with Solenoid A (012) in this rung.

Solenoid C (014) is in Rung 2. When Switch 1-LS (001) is actuated, Solenoid 2 becomes energized and Cylinder 2 extends. Draw 1-LS (001) in series with (014) in this rung.

In Rung 3, when 2-LS (002) is actuated, Solenoid B (013) becomes energized and Cylinder 1 retracts.

As soon as Cylinder 1 withdraws from Switch 1-LS, Solenoid C becomes de-energized and Cylinder 2 retracts.

In this simple example it was not necessary to use any of the relays in the controller.

EXAMPLE 2 – FIGURE 4-5A, PAGE 71.

Please review the air circuit diagram and application description on Page 71, and the cycle sequence in the box on Page 72. In addition to those specifications we want to add safety features of disconnecting the pushbutton as soon as the first cylinder starts to move, and to disconnect limit Switches 1-LS and 2-LS as soon as the cycle ends. Component description and controller terminal assignments are shown in this chart. Further description of this circuit will refer to each component by its terminal number as shown in this chart.

Component	Description	Controller Terminal
Cyl. 1	Clamp cylinder	- - - -
Cyl. 2	Work cylinder	- - - -
1-PB	Start pushbutton	000
1-LS	Limit switch to start Cyl. 2	001
2-LS	Limit switch to retract Cyl. 2	002
3-LS	Limit switch to retract Cyl. 1	003
4-LS	Limit switch to disconnect pushbutton	004
Sol. A	Solenoid to start Cyl. 1	012
Sol. B	Solenoid to retract Cyl. 1	013
Sol. C	Solenoid to start Cyl. 2	014
Sol. D	Solenoid to retract Cyl. 2	015

DIAGRAM CONSTRUCTION. Lay out each of the four solenoids in a separate rung starting with Solenoid A (012) in the first rung, Solenoid C (014) in the second rung, Solenoid D (015) in the third rung, and Solenoid B (013) in the fourth rung.

We believe the way to most clearly explain the construction of the ladder diagram for this application is to

Example 2 – For Figure 4-5A on Page 71
Start with one ladder rung for each solenoid valve coil

show the finished diagram then go back, rung by rung, and explain why each contact was added to that rung. It was necessary, as will become apparent as we go through the diagram, to add one holding relay, and this is shown as Rung 5.

This circuit demonstrates the versatility and usefulness of holding relays. A relay can be set up by actuation of *any* external switch connected to the input terminal board. It can be locked in and then released at an appropriate time later in the cycle by actuation of *any* external switch. Any number of its N.O. or N.C. contacts can be added to *any* rung of the diagram wherever needed.

RUNG 1. Solenoid A is energized by pushbutton Contacts 000. Contacts 004 from Switch 4-LS are added to this rung to disconnect the pushbutton as soon as Cylinder 1 has released 4-LS. Switch 4-LS is wired from its N.O. terminal to 004 on the controller and, because it is held actuated by Cylinder 1, Terminal 004 is kept activated. Since this is the state of continuity desired in Rung 1 for the start of the cycle, 004 is drawn N.O. Cylinder 1 advances and actuates 1-LS (001).

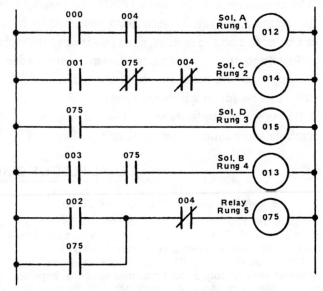

Example 2 – Finished Controller Ladder Diagram For Figure 4-5A on Page 71

187

RUNG 2. Contacts on 1-LS (001) actuate Solenoid C to start Cylinder 2 forward. A set of 4-LS (004) contacts is added to disconnect Switch 1-LS while the cycle is at rest. They are drawn N.C. because the input Terminal 004 is activated at this time and this is opposite to the state of continuity desired in Rung 1. It will be necessary to break the circuit through this rung later in the cycle so the valve spool can be reversed by Solenoid D. Contacts 075 (on a holding relay) are added for this purpose and they will be explained later. Cylinder 2 advances and actuates 2-LS (002).

RUNG 3. Normally, contacts from 2-LS (002) would (and still could) be used in this rung to energize Solenoid D. However, since a relay must be added to break the circuit to Solenoid C, it is better to use 2-LS to energize the relay coil, then contacts from the relay can be used several places in the circuit. From the 40 relays in the controller, 075 was selected at random. One set of N.C. 075 contacts is placed in Rung 2 to break the circuit to Solenoid C and a set of N.O. 075 placed in Rung 3 to energize Solenoid D for retracting Cylinder 2. The relay should be locked in during Cylinder 2 return so Solenoid C will not again be energized when 2-LS is released. The relay and its locking circuit are shown in Rung 5 to be described later.

RUNG 4. When Cylinder 2 retracts and actuates 3-LS (003) this energizes Solenoid B to retract Cylinder 1. However, to render 3-LS inactive until the proper time a set of N.O. contacts on the relay is added to this rung to prevent Solenoid B from becoming prematurely energized. Switch 3-LS does not become active until Cylinder 2 is away from home position and Relay 075 has closed.

RUNG 5. Relay 075 has been added to perform the several functions which have been described. It should be locked in while both cylinders are retracting and then released at the end of the cycle. When energized by closure of 2-LS (002), it locks in through 075, a N.O. set of its own contacts, and 4-LS (004). At the end of the cycle, when 4-LS is actuated this releases the relay. A set of N.O. 075 contacts is added to Rung 4 to complete continuity in that rung when 3-LS closes. A set of N.O. 075 contacts is added to Rung 3 to energize Solenoid D, and a set of N.C. 075 contacts added to Rung 2 to break the circuit to Solenoid C at the right time in the cycle. The set of 004 contacts in this rung also renders limit Switch 002 inactive, for safety, while the cycle is at rest.

EXAMPLE 3 – FIGURE 4-18, PAGE 86.

If you are just learning to draw diagrams and are at a loss on how to start, follow the procedure shown for this example. Your diagram may end up with having more contacts and relays than are strictly necessary but it will be workable. When you acquire a little experience you will learn how to simplify it by eliminating relays or contacts which perform duplicate functions or that are not necessary. This conserves controller capacity.

When working with spring return or spring centered solenoid valves, plan to use one of the internal relays as a holding relay for each solenoid coil. Usually there are many more relays in the controller than needed for most circuits, so they can be used lavishly.

When starting the ladder, forget about the solenoid

Component Description for Example 3

Compo-nent	Description	Controller Terminal
Cyl. 1	Hydraulic clamp cylinder	- - - -
Cyl. 2	Hydraulic work cylinder	- - - -
1-PB	Start pushbutton	000
1-LS	Limit switch at Cyl. 1 home position	001
2-LS	Limit switch at Cyl. 1 extended position	002
3-LS	Limit switch at Cyl. 2 extended position	003
4-LS	Limit switch at Cyl. 2 home position	004
Sol. A	Valve solenoid to start clamp cylinder	012
Sol. B	Valve solenoid to retract clamp cylinder	013
Sol. C	Valve solenoid to extend work cylinder	014
Sol. D	Valve solenoid to retract work cylinder	015
Sol. E	Valve solenoid to vent relief valve	016

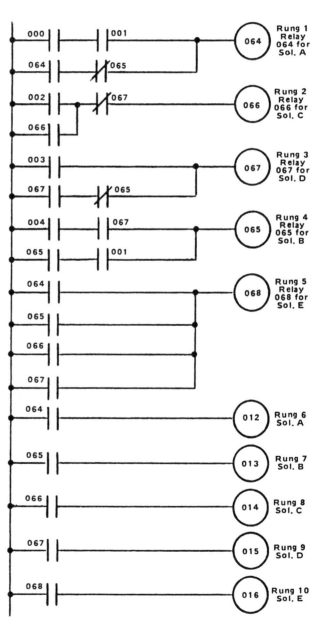

Example 3 – Ladder Diagram for Figure 4-18, Page 86

coils for the time being and use only the relays which energize them. In this example, Relay 064 has been assigned to Solenoid A, Relay 065 to Solenoid B, Relay 066 to Solenoid C, Relay 067 to Solenoid D, and Relay 068 to Solenoid E. When this part of the diagram has been conpleted, draw in the solenoid coils, each on a separate rung, energized by a contact on the relay assigned to it.

Please refer to the hydraulic diagram on Page 86 while constructing the ladder. This example is a demonstration of the construction of a ladder diagram acceptable to a controller which will control the hydraulic circuit of Figure 4-18. Input and output terminal numbers have been added alongside the JIC designations for limit switches and solenoid valves.

Since all solenoid valves are spring returned, a holding circuit will have to be set up in each relay rung to keep the relay closed during the time period its solenoid coil must remain energized.

Notice in this diagram the coil connections to the right bus are not shown. This is permissible to simplify the diagram since they all must connect directly to the bus.

STARTING THE DIAGRAM. Draw the first five rungs containing the relays which have been assigned to each solenoid coil. Rungs should be drawn in the approximate order in which the solenoid valves are energized.

RUNG 1. The pushbutton (000) will energize Relay 064 through the (now closed) contacts from 1-LS (001). Switch 1-LS is being held closed but as soon as Cylinder 1 moves far enough to release it, the pushbutton will become dead for the remainder of the cycle. The holding circuit for Relay 064 is through one of its own contacts in the lower leg of this rung. A contact 065 is inserted to break the holding circuit when Solenoid B (013) becomes energized later in the cycle by Relay 065.

RUNG 2. Cylinder 1 advances and actuates limit Switch 2-LS (002), and remains standing on this switch. Relay 066 (for Solenoid C) becomes energized through the (now closed) Contacts 067. A holding circuit is set up in the bottom leg of this rung through a set of 066 and the 067 contacts in the top leg. Later, when Relay 067 (and Solenoid D) become energized, the holding circuit to Relay 066 will be broken.

RUNG 3. Cylinder 2 advances and actuates 3-LS (003) limit switch. This energizes Relay 067 (and Solenoid D).

One set of 067 contacts releases Relay 066 (and Solenoid C) in Rung 2. A holding circuit is set up in the lower leg through Contacts 067 and (now closed) 065 contacts. Later, when Relay 065 (and Solenoid B) become energized, these 065 contacts will break the holding circuit to Relay 067 and release Solenoid D.

RUNG 4. Cylinder 2 retracts and actuates 4-LS (004). This energizes Relay 065 (and Solenoid B). Contacts on 065 also break the holding circuit to Relay 064 in Rung 1. Note: 4-LS (004) contacts are shown N.O. because this switch is being held actuated and is keeping input Terminal 004 activated. Since this is the same state of continuity required at the start of the cycle, it is drawn N.O.

This switch presents a problem which must be solved. To keep Relay 065 (and Solenoid B) from being prematurely energized, Switch 4-LS must be kept disconnected until Cylinder 2 is away from home position. This is done with a N.O. set of contacts on Relay 067. While Cylinder 2 is retracting, 004 has opened and 067 has closed. When Cylinder 2 reaches home and actuates 4-LS (004), Relay 065 in Rung 4 is energized.

One contact 001 (from Switch 1-LS) is added to Rung 4 to break the holding circuit to Relay 065 when Cylinder 1 reaches home position. Actuation of 1-LS also restores power to the pushbutton for starting another cycle. Contacts 1-LS (001) can also be used elsewhere in the diagram, if needed, to release any relays which may still be holding and to disconnect any limit switches on the machine which could accidentally be actuated while the machine is at rest, causing an accident.

Switch 1-LS (001) is being held actuated and is keeping input Terminal 001 activated. Since this is the same state of continuity required, it must be drawn N.O.

RUNG 5. Solenoid E vents the relief valve to unload the pump. It must be kept energized during the entire cycle. This can be done by placing one contact set from each of the other relays in parallel in Rung 5. However, the diagram can be simplified at this point by eliminating Relay 068 completely and energizing Solenoid E directly from the four relay contacts. This will eliminate Rung 10. It can be simplified further by eliminating legs 3 and 4 of Rung 5 because either Relay 064 or 065 will remain energized throughout the cycle.

RUNGS 6 THROUGH 10. The 4 (or 5) valve solenoid coils can now be added, each energized by its own relay.

Conserving Controller Capacity.

When working with relatively simple applications, the 512 addresses in the Model S-6 should be more than sufficient. But on more intricate circuits it may be necessary to use a larger model. Addresses can be conserved by eliminating those relay coils and contacts that are not really necessary, as was done in Example 3 above. If you find one relay becomes energized at the same time another one becomes de-energized, one of them can probably be eliminated and contacts on the one relay used for both functions.

On each rung, switch and relay contacts can be drawn in any sequential order. Sometimes, contacts can be arranged in an order which will economize on the number of addresses required. Connections cannot be made from one rung to a point on another rung but they can be made from a point on one leg to another leg of the *same* rung. An example in the first column of Page 191 illustrates this. Switch Contacts 002 and 005 are used in both top and bottom legs of Rung 1. By drawing a vertical line from 064 to the junction of 005 and 006, two contact entries are saved.

CONVERSION OF JIC TO CONTROLLER LADDER DIAGRAMS

Ladder diagrams made for JIC hard wired circuits must be converted to an equivalent form which a programmable controller can accept. All JIC diagrams in earlier chapters can be converted by using the procedure described here. Controller diagrams must follow the rules on Pages 177 and 178.

First, every electrical component in the JIC diagram must be assigned a terminal number on the controller. The 3-digit identification number of that terminal should be marked on the JIC diagram. Relays 064 through 103 (in the Model S-6 controller) are used to replace the electro-mechanical relays in the JIC circuit. Any of these 40 relays can be used at random by simply marking in the 3-digit number of their coil and all contacts operated by that coil. These internal relays are not connected to either input or output terminals.

A chart should be prepared listing all components, both fluid and electrical, with a brief statement of their function. The 3-digit terminal codes which have been assigned to electrical components should be included in this chart.

Remember that each valve solenoid and relay coil must be in a separate rung. Often a JIC diagram will have a relay coil and valve solenoid coil connected in parallel. On a controller diagram each one should be drawn on a separate rung. All contacts which energize them should be placed in the relay rung. Then, one contact from the relay can energize the solenoid in its rung.

The procedure is to start in Rung 1 with the relay coil or valve solenoid which is energized by the starting signal. From the left power bus, trace all possible pathways through switch and relay contacts leading to the coil. Place these contacts in series or parallel with one another according to the circuit. When one rung is completed, proceed with following rungs in the order they appear on the JIC diagram.

EXAMPLE 1 – FIGURE 5-10, PAGE 107.

Input and output terminals have been assigned and are marked on the fluid and electrical diagrams. There are four pushbuttons, each with three sets of N.O. contacts. Only one set of contacts on each pushbutton should be connected to an input terminal. When the button is pressed this terminal becomes activated. Its 3-digit number can be used to signal a change in conductivity in all three circuits connected to the pushbutton in the JIC diagram. So the remaining terminals on the pushbuttons should be left unconnected.

One set of contacts on 1-PB has been assigned to Terminal 001, one set on 2-PB to Terminal 002, one set on 3-PB to Terminal 003, and one set on 4-PB to Terminal 004. Solenoids A through F have been assigned to output Terminals 012 through 017.

Start with Solenoid A in Rung 1. Draw all pushbutton contacts which influence conductivity. This is 002 only. Draw Rung 2 with Solenoid B. Contacts which influence conductivity include 001, 003, and 004. They must be placed in parallel in an OR relationship because any one of them OR any other one will energize Solenoid B. The remaining rungs are drawn the same way.

EXAMPLE 2 – FIGURE 4-11, PAGE 78.

On the next page a reproduction of the JIC diagram for Figure 4-11 on Page 78 is shown for reference.

Since there are 6 valve solenoids and one relay, the controller diagram will have 7 rungs. Circuits to each coil can be traced either from the left bus to the coil or from the coil to the left bus.

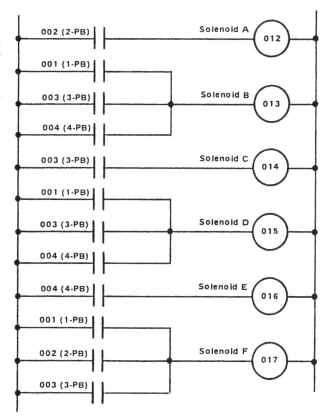

Ladder Diagram for Example 1

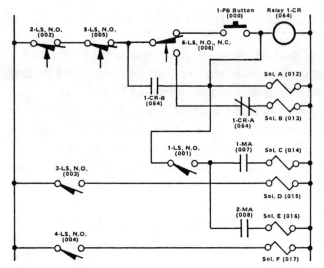

Reproduction of JIC Diagram of Figure 4-11 from Page 78.

Equivalent Controller Diagram – Example 2.

On the JIC diagram, 1-CR relay and Solenoid A are in parallel. On the controller diagram they will be placed in separate rungs.

For Rung 1, trace a circuit from the left bus through 2-LS (002), 5-LS (005), 6-LS (006), and 1-PB (000) to Relay 1-CR (064). These contacts are all in series. Another parallel switch path is through 2-LS, 5-LS, and 1-CR-B, all in series. Draw this as a bottom leg in the same rung in parallel with the top leg. Note: Contacts 002 and 005 do not have to be repeated in this leg if connections are made as shown here.

Switch 2-LS (002) is a N.O. type but is held in an actuated state before the cycle starts. This keeps Terminal 002 activated. Since this is the state of continuity desired, 002 should be drawn N.O. The same applies to 005.

Switch 6-LS (006) has both a N.O. and N.C. terminal, both of which are active on the JIC diagram. But for a controller, only the N.O. terminal should be assigned to an input terminal (006). The N.C. action can be programmed inside the controller. Terminal 006 is being kept activated. Since this is the state of continuity desired in Rung 1, 006 should be drawn N.O. even though it is shown closed on the JIC diagram. In Rung 7, since desired continuity is opposite to that of Terminal 006, draw 006 as N.C. in that rung.

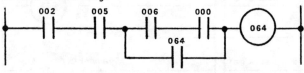

In Rung 2, the same two parallel pathways can be traced to Solenoid A, and it could be drawn the same way as Rung. But a better way is to use a set of contacts on 1-CR relay (064) to energize it.

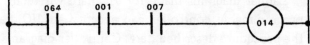

Solenoid C (014) is placed in Rung 3. Start at the left bus. From the bus to Point A the contacts are the same as

for 1-CR (064) relay. Therefore, one set of contacts on 064 can replace 002, 005, and 064. Then add 1-LS (001) and 1-MA (007) in series to complete the circuit to Solenoid A.

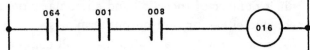

Rung 4 is for Solenoid E. Contacts 2-LS (002), 5-LS (005), and 1-CR-B (064) are the same as for 1-CR relay coil, so they can be replaced with one Contact 064. Then add 1-LS (001) and 2-MA (008) in series. This completes the circuit to Solenoid E.

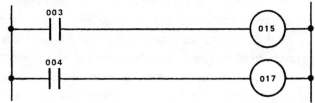

Rungs 5 and 6 are Solenoids D (015) and F (017). Solenoid D is actuated by 3-LS (003) and Solenoid F by 4-LS (004).

Rung 7 is for Solenoid B (013). It becomes actuated through 2-LS (002), 5-LS (005), 6-LS (006) and 1-CR-A

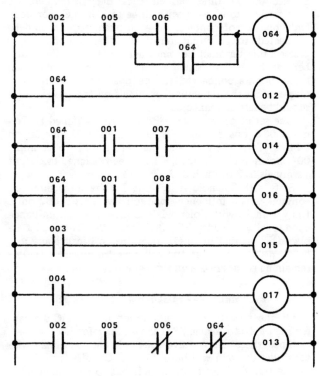

The Complete Ladder Diagram for Figure 4-11, Page 78.

191

EXAMPLE 3 – FIGURE 3-18, PAGE 54.

When converting the JIC diagram of Figure 3-18, use the N.O. terminals of all switches for assignment to input terminals. This includes 2-PB Stop pushbutton and 1-LS limit switch.

In this circuit there are two valve solenoids and two relays. The diagram will require four rungs.

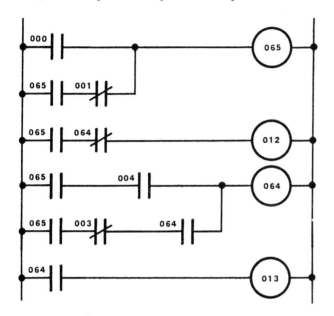

Example 3 – Figure 3-18, Page 54

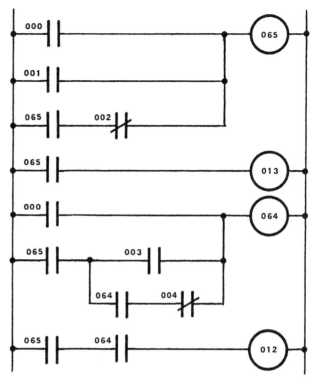

Example 4 – Figure 3-19B, Page 55

In Rung 1 there are two parallel pathways from the left bus to Relay 2-CR (065). Since the Stop button 2-PB (001) is not a safety switch in this application, its N.O. terminal should be assigned to input Terminal 001. This will keep 001 de-activated before the cycle starts. Since this is the same state of conductivity required in Rung 1, draw it N.O. (not N.C.).

In Rung 2 there is one pathway to Solenoid A (012), through 2-CR-A (065) and 1-CR-A (064).

In Rung 3 there is a path to Relay 1-CR (064) through 2-CR-A (065) and 2-LS (004). There is a parallel path through 2-CR-A, 1-LS (003), and 1-CR-C (064) and this is shown as a parallel leg in the rung. Switch 1-LS is a N.C. type but its N.O. terminal is assigned to input Terminal 003. This will keep 003 activated before the cycle starts. Since this is opposite to the state of continuity required in Rung 3, it should be drawn N.C. Note: One address on the controller can be saved by routing the lower leg to the upper one to eliminate one of the 065 contacts. This routing is shown by the dotted line.

The use of only one 064 contacts in Rung 4 to energize Solenoid B may be a little hard to see. When 1-CR coil (064) becomes energized, this gives continuity from the left bus to the left side of 1-CR-B. And since 1-CR-B is now closed, there is conductivity all the way to Solenoid B whenever Relay 1-CR (064) is energized.

EXAMPLE 4 – FIGURE 3-19B, PAGE 55.

The controller diagram will require four rungs, two for valve solenoids and two for relays.

Rungs can be drawn in any order and we have elected

in this case to draw Relay 2-CR (065) in the first rung, although any of the coils could have been in the first rung.

There are three continuity pathways from the left bus to 065. One is directly through 1-PB Forward pushbutton (000). Note that only one of the N.O. terminals on 1-PB should be assigned to an input terminal.

The second path is through 2-PB pushbutton, and this is drawn as a second leg parallel to the first.

The third path is through Contacts 2-CR-A (065), and Stop button 3-PB (002). This is not an emergency button in this application so its N.O. terminal should be assigned to input Terminal 002. This keeps 002 de-activated before the cycle starts. Since this is opposite to the state of conductivity required in Rung 1, draw 002 as N.C.

Solenoid B (013) is shown in Rung 2. It is in parallel with Relay 2-CR (065), and can be best energized with a single contact from the relay.

Relay 1-CR is shown in Rung 3. One path is directly through 1-PB (000) pushbutton.

The second path is through Contacts 2-CR-A (065) in series with 1-LS (003). Switch 1-LS is a N.O. switch and is held actuated. This keeps Terminal 003 activated. Since this is the state of conductivity required at the start of the cycle, 003 is drawn N.O. (not N.C.) in this rung.

The third path is through 2-CR-A (065), 1-CR-A (064), and 2-LS (004). One address on the controller can be saved by eliminating one 065 contact and joining the third leg to the middle of the second leg.

Solenoid A (012) is shown in Rung 4. It is energized through 2-CR-A (065) and 1-CR-A (064) in series.

This example shows how controller addresses can be saved by joining two legs of the same rung when both go through the same contact.

192

EXAMPLE 5 — FIGURE 3-26B, PAGE 62.

The controller diagram will require 6 rungs, 3 for the relays and 3 for the solenoid valve coils. All switching will be placed in the relay rungs and the valve solenoids will be energized from contacts on the relays.

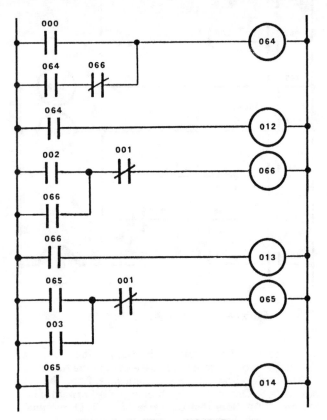

Example 5 — Figure 3-26B, Page 62

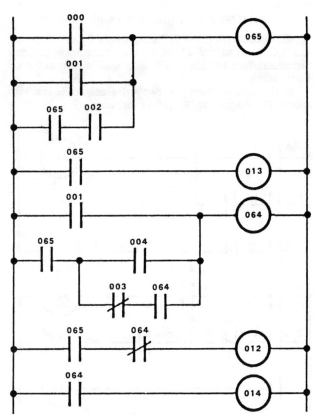

Example 6 — Figure 3-21B, Page 58

Relay 064 can be shown in Rung 1. There are two parallel paths from the left bus. One is through 1-PB (000). The other is through 1-CR-A (064) and 3-CR-C (066).

In Rung 2, Solenoid A can be energized from a set of contacts on Relay 1-CR (064)

Relay 066 can be shown in Rung 3. There are two parallel pathways, one through 2-LS (002) in series with 1-LS (001), the other through 3-CR-A (066) in series with 1-LS (001). The N.O. (not the N.C.) terminal on 1-LS should be assigned to input Terminal 001. This keeps 001 activated. Since this is opposite to the state of continuity required, 001 should be drawn N.C. in Rungs 3 and 5.

In Rung 4, Solenoid B can be energized from a set of contacts on Relay 3-CR (066).

Relay 065 can be shown in Rung 5. There are two parallel pathways, one through 2-CR-A (065) in series with 1-LS (001), the other through 1-PS (003) in series with 1-LS (001).

Finally, in Rung 6, Solenoid C can be energized from a set of contacts on 2-CR (065).

A safety feature which can easily be added to most controller diagrams is to disconnect 1-PB (000) pushbutton as soon as the cylinder moves far enough to release 1-LS (001). All that is necessary is to add one N.O. (001) contact to Rung 1 in series with 000.

EXAMPLE 6 — FIGURE 3-21B, PAGE 58.

Conversion of the remaining circuits in this section will not be shown in detail. The text will be limited to an explanation of any unusual features.

The Stop pushbutton in this application is considered as an emergency switch, so its N.C. terminal will be assigned to input Terminal 002. This keeps 002 normally activated. This is the same state of conductivity required in Rung 1. Draw 002 N.O. (not N.C.).

As in other circuits, where a switch (2-PB Reverse pushbutton 001) has more than one circuit, assign only one of its N.O. terminal to an input terminal. Since both circuits operate at exactly the same time period, the terminal number, 001, is all that is needed to add continuity or discontinuity at any place in the diagram.

Switch 1-LS has a N.C. action on the JIC diagram and is being held actuated before the cycle starts. Assign only its N.O. terminal to an input terminal (003). This keeps 001 activated. Since this is the opposite state of conductivity required in Rung 1, draw 003 as N.C.

EXAMPLE 7 — FIGURE 3-24B, PAGE 60.

The fork lever toggle switch, 1-TS, is actuated in both directions so has no N.O. and N.C. terminals. In this case we have assigned the terminal connected to Solenoid B to input Terminal 002. This will keep 002 normally de-activated. This is the opposite state of continuity required to Solenoid A (012) so 002 is drawn N.C. in Rung 2. It is the same state of conductivity required to Solenoid B (013) so 002 is drawn N.O. in Rung 3.

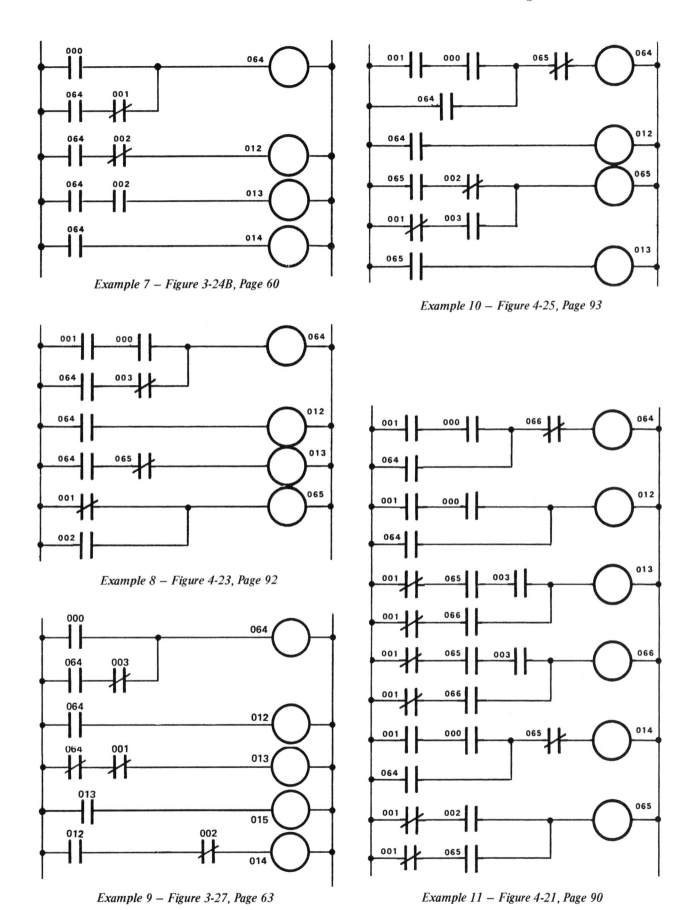

Example 7 – Figure 3-24B, Page 60

Example 10 – Figure 4-25, Page 93

Example 8 – Figure 4-23, Page 92

Example 9 – Figure 3-27, Page 63

Example 11 – Figure 4-21, Page 90

ENTERING A PROGRAM INTO A CONTROLLER

All controllers operate on the same generic principles but operating controls, keyboard layout and terminology, and order of procedure may vary from those described here for the Model S-6. It will be necessary to refer to your Operation Manual to relate the procedures described here to your particular brand and model.

The procedures in this section relate to the method of getting the electrical information from a ladder diagram into the memory of a controller. It is assumed that the fluid circuit and the electrical ladder diagram have been designed and have been checked to be sure the ladder diagram does not violate any of the circuit rules given in previous sections.

Each contact, relay coil, and valve solenoid shown on the ladder diagram must be keyed in, one at a time, into the RAM memory of the controller using a programming keyboard. Each of these bits of information occupies one "slot" or address in the memory. The memory capacity is limited so it may be important, when designing the ladder diagram, to arrange the circuit to use the least number of addresses. The memory capacity of the Model S-6 is 512 addresses. Circuits which require more addresses are beyond the capacity of this model and a larger model must be used.

Necessary Information About Each Entry . . .

If the next entry is a contact, the controller must be supplied with three bits of information and in this order:

(1). Whether the new contact is to be entered in series (AND) or parallel (OR) relationship with contacts or groups of contacts previously entered *in that same rung*.

(2). Whether the new contact is N.O. or N.C.

(3). The 3-digit identifying code which has been assigned to that contact.

If the next entry is the coil of one of the 40 internal relays or the 8 output relays (on the Model S-6), these are load devices and must be the last entry on the rung. The controller must be informed of the end of the rung with an OUT preceding the 3-digit identification of the coil. A typical entry could be: OUT-012-WRITE.

Detailed instructions will be described later on how to key in information about contacts and coils.

Data Storage Registers . . .

The Model S-6 used for illustration has two registers for temporarily holding data which has been keyed into the display until such time that it can be transferred into the controller RAM memory. When an operator keys in information about a contact, relay coil, or valve solenoid, this information shows on a data display and is held in the first, or working, register. When the operator is satisfied that he has entered the information correctly, he presses the WRITE key. This transfers the displayed information into the controller RAM memory at the next address. If he discovers the information is not correct, he can make a correction before it is transferred.

Quite often during programming, there may be places in the diagram where the next contact cannot be correctly combined either in series or parallel with preceding entries without producing an error in the finished program. In this example, after 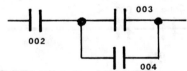 002 has been entered, if 003 were entered next, then 004 could not be combined correctly with those entries. If 004 were to be entered following 002, then 003 could not be correctly combined with 002 and 004. To handle this situation the controller has another "holding" register into which preceding contact entries on that rung can be temporarily transferred and held, while additional contacts down the rung are entered. When the operator reaches a place where they will correctly combine with the additional contacts subsequently entered, he can bring them out. In this example, 002 must be temporarily placed in the holding register while 003 and 004 are combined in parallel. Then 002 can be brought out and combined in series with the others. Procedure for transferring contacts into and out of the holding register is shown in examples to follow.

More than one contact or group of contacts can be held in the holding register at the same time. When brought out they will come out, one group at a time, in the reverse order to that in which they were entered, and can be joined in series or parallel with contacts presently in the working register.

Scan Time or Response Time . . .

When the controller is in operation on a machine, a "scanning" circuit "looks at" or scans the entire program continuously. An analogy of this scanning action is shown on Page 182. When one scan is completed the next scan immediately starts. On the Model S-6, if the entire capacity of 512 addresses is used, each scan requires about 10 milliseconds. Or the entire program is scanned about 100 times per second. If the entire capacity of the machine is not used, each scan requires less time. When an external switch is actuated, this change will be detected by the scanner in 10 milliseconds or less. The time required, on any controller, for one scan is called its "response" time.

THE USE OF A PROGRAMMING KEYBOARD

Every programmable controller will have a programming keyboard or console. Usually this keyboard can be mounted directly on the CPU or can be connected to it with a cable and operated from a few feet away. After programming has been completed, the keyboard can either be left in position to monitor operation of the machine, or can be disconnected and stored for future use.

There are many buttons on the programming keyboard. Some are used for entering a program into memory; some are used in various diagnostic checks to verify correctness of a program or to hunt for program errors or to aid in troubleshooting if the machine fails to run through a cycle as programmed. Other buttons are used to access internal counters, timers, and latching relays to enter them into the program and to set time on timers and count on counters. Various brands and models of controllers will have different capabilities and it will be necessary to study the Operation Manual to learn how to use all the features. However, all controllers will have basic buttons for entering a program. On the Model S-6 the programming buttons are listed below. All controllers will have these same buttons and their functions will be the same although their titles may vary from those shown.

| LD | Abbreviation for LOAD. This button is used to start each rung and imparts this information to the electronic scanner. It is also used, as described in the Operation Manual for the Model S-6, to move previous contact entries into and out of the "holding" register.

| 4 | Numerals from 0 through 9 for functions requiring numbers such as 3-digit identification numbers for contacts and relays, for setting the time on internal timers and the count on internal counters.

FIGURE 10-12.
Programming Keyboard for Model S-6.

| AND | Used as a prefix ahead of the 3-digit relay or switch identification when connecting a contact in series (AND) with a previously entered contact or group of contacts. |

| OR | Used as a prefix ahead of the 3-digit relay or switch identification when connecting a contact in parallel (OR) with a previously entered contact or group of contacts. |

| NOT | Used as a prefix ahead of the 3-digit relay or switch identification to tell the scanner that the contact about to be entered is a N.C. one. If this prefix is not used, the scanner assumes that the next contact is N.O. |

| OUT | This instruction is used as part of the programming of each relay "coil" to indicate to the scanner the completion of a rung. |

| WRITE | After the complete information on a contact is entered and is showing on the display panel, the operator presses this button to burn the displayed information into the CPU memory. This key must be pressed after each contact is set up on the display. |

| CLEAR | On the Model S-6 this button will return the display to the start of programming. The program can then be rolled up, one address at a time for review or corrections. |

| END | This button must be pressed after all rungs of the diagram have been entered. It indicates to the scanner the end of the program so it can skip the remaining addresses and start a new scan. If not pressed, the program will show an error when checked. |

The keyboard will contain many additional buttons, specific for that particular brand and model controller for making additions, deletions, or corrections to a completed program. There may be many additional components in the CPU such as electronic timers, counters, and latching relays. Buttons on the keyboard must be used for entering these components into a program and setting them to the desired time or count values. The number of these extra buttons and their functions will vary. Refer to your Operation Manual for specific details.

On the Model S-6 the keyboard console also contains a selector switch for placing the controller in modes for programming, running, monitoring, and for duplication of programs.

EXAMPLES OF CONTACT PROGRAMMING

The procedures give here are for the Model S-6. For other controllers they should be similar but may vary slightly in details. Exact procedures must be verified by your Operation Manual.

The following circuits show how various combinations of series (AND) and parallel (OR) contacts on the same rung are entered into the memory of a programmable controller. Circuitry shown here is limited to relay and switch contacts. Refer to your Operation Manual for programming of the internal counters, timers, latching relays, etc.

Before starting to program, any data stored in the controller RAM memory must be erased. The procedure for clearing the memory will be found in your Operation Manual. Put the programming keyboard into the programming mode. This keyboard must be plugged into the CPU, and input power must be supplied to the CPU. Leave input switches and output loads disconnected from the terminal boards. Get the keyboard display to the first address where information can be stored. On the Model S-6 this is done by pressing the CLEAR button.

CONTACTS IN SERIES (AND) ARRANGEMENT

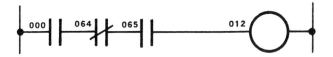

This is one rung of a ladder diagram. It has three contacts in series to energize one of the output relays. Always start a rung with the LD button. Enter Contact 000, the one nearest the left bus. The controller needs to know if it is N.O. or N.C. and its assigned terminal number. When the information is showing on the display, press the WRITE button to burn the information into the controller memory. Press these buttons:

LD-000-WRITE

Add the next contact 064, which is a N.C. type to be added in series (AND) with the first contact. Then burn it into memory with the WRITE button:

AND-NOT-064-WRITE

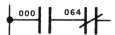

Then add the 3rd contact 065. This is a N.O. contact to be added in series with those previously entered. Press these buttons:

AND-065-WRITE

Finish the rung by connecting to the right bus through a relay. Press these buttons:

OUT-012-WRITE

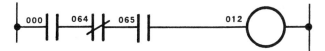

This completes the rung. Any number of series contacts, either N.O. or N.C. can be entered in this way. Start the next rung with the LD button.

CONTACTS IN PARALLEL (OR) ARRANGEMENT

This is another rung of the diagram in which 3 parallel contacts control the operation of a relay. Again, start with Contact 000, the top one, First use the LD button to start the rung. Press these buttons:

LD-000-WRITE

Then add the 2nd contact, 001 which is a N.C. one. Press these buttons:

OR-NOT-001-WRITE

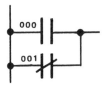

Then add the 3rd contact. This is N.O., and is to be added in parallel. Press these buttons:

OR-002-WRITE

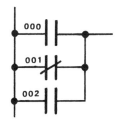

Finally, finish the rung through Relay 012 to the right bus. The OUT button must always precede the entry of the relay. Press these buttons:

OUT-012-WRITE

PARALLEL/SERIES CONTACT GROUPS

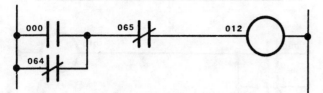

A group of series and parallel contacts in this kind of arrangement can be easily programmed. Again, start with Contact 000 at the left bus. Press these buttons:

LD-000-WRITE

The parallel contact, 064 must be added next. It would produce an error in the electrical action if 065 were to be entered before the two parallel contacts were combined. Press these buttons:

OR-NOT-064-WRITE

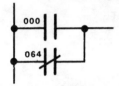

Now, the series contact 065 can be added without producing an electrical error. Press these buttons:

AND-NOT-065-WRITE

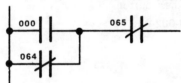

Finish the rung by completing the circuit through Relay 012. Be sure to use the OUT button to finish the rung. Press these buttons:

OUT-012-WRITE

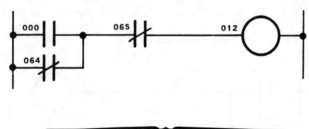

DIFFICULT SERIES/PARALLEL GROUP

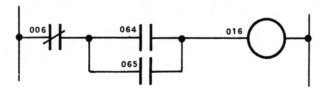

This combination of contacts presents a programming problem which must be handled with the aid of the holding register. Start at the left side of the diagram with N.C. Contact 006. Press these buttons:

LD-NOT-006-WRITE

Neither 064 nor 065 can be added either in series or parallel with 006 without producing an electrical error. In this case the previously entered contact, 006, must be transferred into the holding register until later in the programming when it can be combined with other contacts without error. In the Model S-6, the transfer is made simply by entering the next contact, 064, preceded by a LD symbol. This atuomatically transfers all preceding contacts or group of contacts into the holding register.

LD-064-WRITE

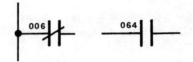

Leave 006 in the holding register and add 065 in parallel with 064. Press these buttons:

OR-065-WRITE

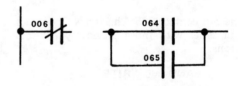

Now that 064 and 065 have been combined, 006 will combine correctly with them. Bring it out of the holding register by using the LD button preceded by instruction AND or OR according to how it is to be combined. In this case it must be combined in series, so use the AND button.

AND-LD-WRITE

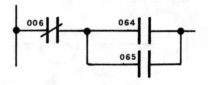

Finish the rung through Relay 016 to the right bus. Press these buttons:

OUT-016-WRITE

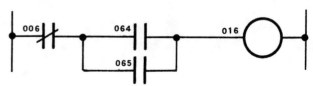

ANOTHER DIFFICULT SERIES/PARALLEL CIRCUIT

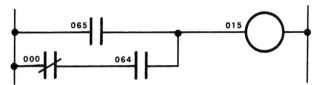

This is another contact grouping in which the holding register must be used. Start with Contact 065 at the left bus. Enter it by pressing these buttons:

LD-065-WRITE

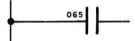

At this point neither 000 nor 064 can be entered in combination with 065 without producing an error in the finished program. Proceed to enter the next contact preceeded by LD. This automatically puts 065 into the holding register. Press these buttons:

LD-NOT-000-WRITE

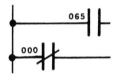

Leave 065 in the holding register and combine 064 with 000 by pressing these buttons:

AND-064-WRITE

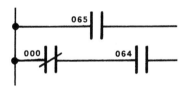

Now, 065 can be brought out of the holding register and will correctly combine with the other contacts. On the Model S-6 these buttons would be pressed:

OR-LD-WRITE

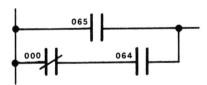

Finish the rung to the right bus through Relay 015. Press these buttons:

OUT-015-WRITE

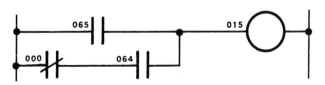

ANOTHER EXAMPLE, SERIES/PARALLEL CIRCUIT

This circuit further illustrates how groups of contacts are transferred into the holding register and how they are brought out and combined with other entries either in parallel using the OR-LD buttons or in series using the AND-LD buttons.

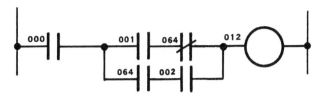

Start with Contact 000 by pressing these buttons:

LD-000-WRITE

None of the remaining contacts can be directly combined with 000 without producing an error in the finished program. Therefore, use the LD button preceding the next contact to put 000 into the holding register.

LD-001-WRITE

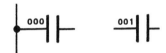

Leave 000 in the holding register and add N.C. 064 contact in series with 001 by using these buttons:

AND-NOT-064-WRITE

Here too, the next contact, 064 cannot be combined with previous contacts without producing an error. Previously entered contacts, 001 and 064, now in the working register must be transferred into the holding register. This is done automatically by entering the next contact, 064, preceded by LD. There are now two sets of contacts in the holding register.

LD-064-WRITE

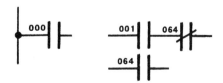

Then, add 002 in series with 064 by using these buttons:

AND-002-WRITE

(Continued on next page)

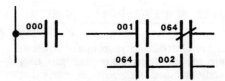

At this point the two groups of contacts in the holding register can be brought out and combined with the other contacts. They will come out in the reverse order that they were put in. The group of 001 and 064 will come out first and must be combined in parallel with the group of 064 and 002 which are now in the working register. Use these buttons:

OR-LD-WRITE

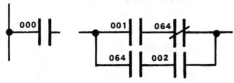

Now, Contact 000 can be brought out and combined in series with the other contacts. Use these buttons:

AND-LD-WRITE

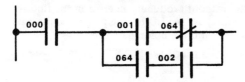

Finally, combine the entire group of contacts with Relay 012. Use these buttons to complete the rung:

OUT-012-WRITE

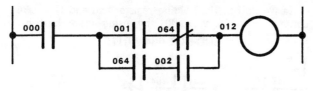

COMPLICATED PARALLEL CIRCUIT

This circuit is a good exercise in the use of the holding register — transferring contacts into it and then bringing them out and combining with previous entries in parallel or in series. Start with 000:

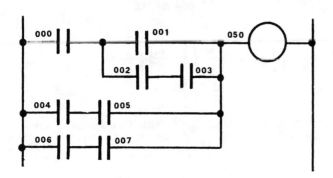

LD-000-WRITE

Before other contacts can be entered, 000 must be transferred to the holding register by entering the next contact.

LD-001-WRITE

This contact, too, must be placed in the holding register before programming can proceed:

LD-002-WRITE

Contact 003 can be combined with 002 in series:

AND-003-WRITE

At this point 001 can be brought out and combined in parallel with 002 and 003:

OR-LD-WRITE

Next, 000 can be brought out and combined in series with the other contacts:

AND-LD-WRITE

The group of four contacts must be placed in the holding register before any contacts in the other legs can be combined with them.

LD-004-WRITE

Next, add 005 in series with 004:

AND-005-WRITE

The first group of four contacts can now be brought out and will combine with 004 and 005:

OR-LD-WRITE

For the 4th leg, place all preceding entries into the holding register by entering 006:

LD-006-WRITE

Add 007 in series with 006:

AND-007-WRITE

Combine the last two entries with the group being retained in the holding register. Add them in parallel:

OR-LD-WRITE

All contacts have now been combined, and the rung can be completed to Relay 050:

OUT-050-WRITE

CIRCUIT SIMPLIFICATION

In the circuit above and to the left, the bottom leg consisting of 064 and 002 can be connected to the left bus through another 000 contact rather than to the junction between 000 and 001 on the top leg. See diagram below. This will not change the electrical action.

Sometimes a circuit can be simplified this way to make it easier to program or to save on the number of addresses required to program it. Each contact can be used an unlimited number of times and in as many rungs as the designer desires.

PROGRAMMING A COMPLETE LADDER DIAGRAM

We return to the application on Page 77, Figure 4-10. The JIC electrical diagram is on Page 78, Figure 4-11. On Page 190 it was converted into a ladder diagram suitable for programming. It is this diagram we will use here to illustrate the method of programming. A Model S-6 programmable controller previously described, will be used. A similar method should be applicable to other models and brands.

(1). Connect operating power to the CPU.

(2). Plug the programming keyboard into the CPU and set the mode switch for programming.

(3). Do not connect wires to any input or output terminals.

(4). Erase the RAM memory of any previous program or, in the case of a new unit, of any random entries caused by exposure to magnetic or electric fields. Refer to your Operation Manual for procedure for erasure and for setting the display to the first address at which information can be stored.

(5). Use the ladder diagram on Page 191 and enter the contacts into controller memory as follows:

RUNG 1:

Start with the top rung and at the left side of the diagram (left bus).

Press Buttons LD-002-WRITE. This connects the left end of the rung to the left power bus.

Press Buttons AND-005-WRITE. This combines Contact 005 in series with the preceding entry.

None of the remaining contacts can be combined either in series or parallel with preceding entries without producing an error in the electrical circuit. Put the preceding entries into the holding register as follows: Press Buttons LD-006-WRITE. This also enters the next Contact 006. See * note below.

Press Buttons AND-000-WRITE. This enters 000 in series with 006.

Press Buttons OR-064-WRITE. This combines 064 in parallel with the combination of 000 and 006.

Now, entries in the holding register can be brought out and combined in series with later entries. Press Buttons AND-LD-WRITE.

Finally, press Buttons OUT-064-WRITE. This connects internal Relay 064 to the right power bus.

RUNG 2:

Referring to the JIC diagram for this circuit on Page 74, Relay 064

and output Relay 012 are in parallel. The correct programming for a controller is to draw each relay on a separate rung. In this case, Relay 012 is placed in the second rung and activated by a contact on Relay 064 in the first rung. Or Relay 012 could be placed in the first rung and one of its contacts could activate 064 in the next rung.**

Press Buttons LD-064. This connects the rung to the left bus.

Press Buttons OUT-012-WRITE. This connects the rung to the right power bus. Proceed to Rung 3.

RUNG 3:

Press Buttons LD-064-WRITE. This connects Rung 3 to the left bus.

Press Buttons AND-001-WRITE. This connects 001 in series with 064.

Press Buttons AND-007-WRITE. This connects 007 in series with the two preceding entries.

Finally, press Buttons OUT-014-WRITE. This completes Rung 3.

RUNG 4:

Press Buttons LD-064-WRITE. This connects Rung 4 to the left bus.

Press Buttons AND-001-WRITE. This places 001 in series with 064.

Press Buttons AND-008-WRITE. This places 008 in series with the two preceding entries.

To complete the rung, press Buttons OUT-016-WRITE.

RUNG 5:

Press Buttons LD-003-WRITE. This connects Rung 5 to the left bus.

To complete Rung 5, press Buttons OUT-015-WRITE.

RUNG 6:

Press Buttons LD-004-WRITE. This connects Rung 6 to the left bus.

Press Buttons OUT-017-WRITE. This completes Rung 6.

RUNG 7:

Start at the left end. Press Buttons LD-002-WRITE.

Press Buttons AND-005-WRITE. This connects 005 in series with 002.

Press Buttons AND-NOT-006-WRITE. This connects N.C. Contact 006 in series with the two preceding entries.

Press Buttons AND-NOT-064-WRITE. This connects 064 in series with preceding entries.

Press Buttons OUT-013-WRITE. This completes the programming. Be sure to signal the end of the program by pressing the Buttons END-WRITE. If the END instruction is not entered, the program will show an error when it is checked by the controller, and it will not run.

*Note: To understand operation of the holding register, see Page 195. An example is given on Page 200 under "Another Example, Series/Parallel Circuit" of storing more than one group of contacts and bringing them out in reverse order to combine either in series (AND-LD) or in parallel (OR-LD) with contacts or groups of contacts presently in the working register.

**Note: The N.O. or N.C. continuity states of output relays, even though they are mechanically operated, can be programmed as many places and in as many rungs as needed.

PRACTICE EXAMPLES FOR PROGRAM WRITING

Write programs for ladder diagrams on the referenced pages and check with answers below.

EXAMPLE 10 – Page 194
```
LD-001-WRITE
AND-000-WRITE
LD-064-WRITE
OR-LD-WRITE
AND-NOT-065-WRITE
OUT-064-WRITE

LD-064-WRITE
OUT-012-WRITE

LD-065-WRITE
AND-NOT-002-WRITE
LD-NOT-001-WRITE
AND-003-WRITE
OR-LD-WRITE
OUT-065-WRITE

LD-065-WRITE
OUT-013-WRITE
```

EXAMPLE 11 – Page 194
```
LD-001-WRITE
AND-000-WRITE
LD-064-WRITE
OR-LD-WRITE
AND-NOT-066-WRITE
OUT-064-WRITE

LD-001-WRITE
AND-000-WRITE
OR-064-WRITE
OUT-012-WRITE

LD-NOT-001
AND-065-WRITE
AND-003-WRITE
LD-NOT-001-WRITE
AND-066-WRITE
OR-LD-WRITE
OUT-013-WRITE

LD-NOT-001
AND-065-WRITE
AND-003-WRITE
LD-NOT-001-WRITE
AND-066-WRITE
OR-LD-WRITE
OUT-066-WRITE

LD-001-WRITE
AND-000-WRITE
OR-064-WRITE
AND-NOT-065-WRITE
OUT-014-WRITE

LD-NOT-001-WRITE
AND-002-WRITE
LD-NOT-001-WRITE
AND-065-WRITE
OR-LD-WRITE
OUT-065-WRITE
```

EXAMPLE 2 – Page 191
```
LD-002-WRITE
AND-005-WRITE
LD-006-WRITE
AND-000-WRITE
OR-064-WRITE
OUT-064-WRITE

LD-064-WRITE
OUT-012-WRITE

LD-064-WRITE
AND-001-WRITE
AND-007-WRITE
OUT-014-WRITE

LD-064-WRITE
AND-001-WRITE
AND-008-WRITE
OUT-016-WRITE

LD-003-WRITE
OUT-015-WRITE

LD-004-WRITE
OUT-017-WRITE

LD-002-WRITE
AND-005-WRITE
AND-NOT-006-WRITE
AND-NOT-064-WRITE
OUT-013-WRITE
```

EXAMPLE 6 – Page 193
```
LD-000-WRITE
OR-001-WRITE
LD-065-WRITE
AND-002-WRITE
OR-LD-WRITE
OUT-065-WRITE

LD-065-WRITE
OUT-013-WRITE

LD-001-WRITE
LD-065-WRITE
LD-004-WRITE
LD-NOT-003-WRITE
AND-064-WRITE
OR-LD-WRITE
AND-LD-WRITE
OR-LD-WRITE
OUT-064-WRITE

LD-065-WRITE
AND-NOT-064-WRITE
OUT-012-WRITE

LD-064-WRITE
OUT-014-WRITE
```

EXAMPLE 3 – Page 191
```
LD-000-WRITE
LD-065-WRITE
AND-NOT-001-WRITE
OR-LD-WRITE
OUT-065-WRITE

LD-065-WRITE
AND-NOT-064-WRITE
OUT-012-WRITE

LD-065-WRITE
AND-004-WRITE
LD-065-WRITE
AND-NOT-003-WRITE
AND-064-WRITE
OR-LD-WRITE
OUT-064-WRITE

LD-064-WRITE
OUT-013-WRITE
```

EXAMPLE 5 – Page 180
```
LD-000-WRITE
LD-064-WRITE
AND-003-WRITE
OR-LD-WRITE
AND-NOT-005-WRITE
OUT-012-WRITE

LD-000-WRITE
OR-001-WRITE
LD-064-WRITE
AND-NOT-002-WRITE
OR-LD-WRITE
OUT-064-WRITE

LD-001-WRITE
LD-064-WRITE
AND-004-WRITE
OUT-013-WRITE

LD-064-WRITE
OUT-014-WRITE
```

EXAMPLE 7 – Page 194
```
LD-000-WRITE
LD-064-WRITE
AND-NOT-001-WRITE
OR-LD-WRITE
OUT-064-WRITE

LD-064-WRITE
AND-NOT-002-WRITE
OUT-012-WRITE

LD-064-WRITE
AND-002-WRITE
OUT-013-WRITE

LD-064-WRITE
OUT-014-WRITE
```

EXAMPLE 4 – Page 191
```
LD-000-WRITE
OR-001-WRITE
LD-065-WRITE
AND-NOT-002-WRITE
OR-LD-WRITE
OUT-065-WRITE

LD-065-WRITE
OUT-013-WRITE

LD-000-WRITE
LD-065-WRITE
LD-003-WRITE
LD-064-WRITE
AND-NOT-004-WRITE
OR-LD-WRITE
AND-LD-WRITE
OR-LD-WRITE
OUT-064-WRITE

LD-065-WRITE
AND-064-WRITE
OUT-012-WRITE
```

EXAMPLE 8 – Page 194
```
LD-001-WRITE
AND-000-WRITE
LD-064-WRITE
AND-NOT-003-WRITE
OR-LD-WRITE
OUT-064-WRITE

LD-064-WRITE
OUT-012-WRITE

LD-064-WRITE
AND-NOT-065-WRITE
OUT-013-WRITE

LD-NOT-001-WRITE
OR-002-WRITE
OUT-065-WRITE
```

EXAMPLE 9 – Page 194
```
LD-000-WRITE
LD-064-WRITE
AND-NOT-063-WRITE
OR-LD-WRITE
OUT-064-WRITE

LD-064-WRITE
OUT-012-WRITE

LD-NOT-064-WRITE
AND-NOT-001-WRITE
OUT-013-WRITE

LD-013-WRITE
OUT-015-WRITE

LD-012-WRITE
AND-NOT-002-WRITE
OUT-014-WRITE
```

PERMANENT STORAGE OF CONTROLLER PROGRAMS

From the preceding page it is easy to see how quickly a program can be set up in a programmable controller compared to many hours or days of labor in hard wiring the same system. However, the program can be damaged or lost if the memory chip should fail or if it should be damaged by exposure to a strong magnetic or electrical field such as lightning, causing the program to scramble. Since the controller memory is "volatile", it can be lost if power to the controller is lost.

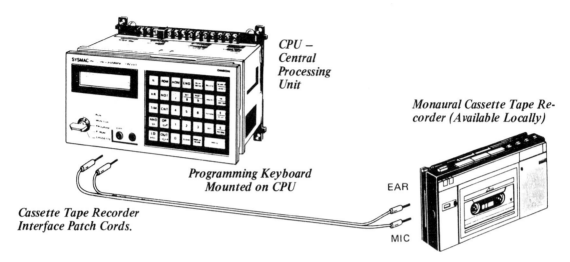

CPU — Central Processing Unit

Monaural Cassette Tape Recorder (Available Locally)

Programming Keyboard Mounted on CPU

EAR

Cassette Tape Recorder Interface Patch Cords.

MIC

FIGURE 10-13. A program can be transferred into and out of an audio cassette.

For these reasons, a permanent copy should be made as soon as a program has been entered and verified. A copy can be made on a standard audio cassette tape with a monaural tape recorder. The tape can be stored and the program can be played back into the controller memory at any time. A tape can be made at one location and mailed to another for programming a controller. Refer to your Operations Manual for instructions.

CPU— Central Processing Unit

PROM Writer

Memory Unit

Programming Keyboard

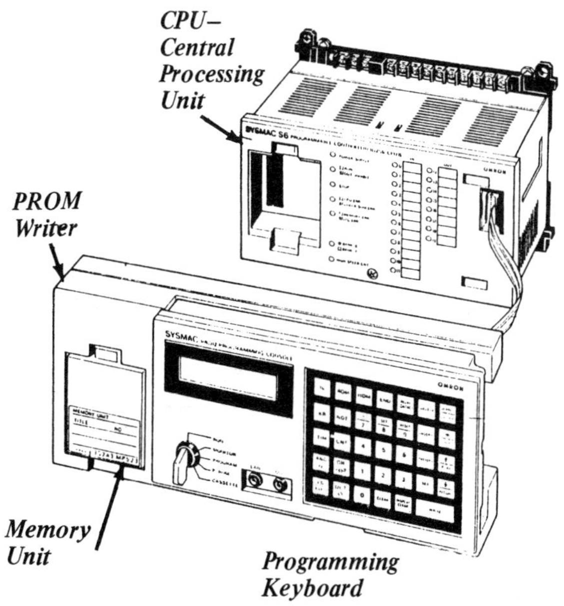

FIGURE 10-14. A program can be duplicated into the permanent memory of an EPROM chip with an auxiliary piece of equipment called a PROM Writer.

Perhaps a more convenient and permanent storage medium is a memory unit containing an EPROM chip. In this illustration a memory chip is plugged into an optional piece of equipment called a PROM writer. A program which has been entered into the RAM memory of the controller can be duplicated into the memory unit. The memory unit has a non-volatile memory and is impervious to most radiation except strong ultraviolet radiation. It will retain memory without power applied, and can be stored indefinitely.

The memory unit, after a program has been duplicated into it, can be plugged into the controller. It will supply the program or its program can be duplicated into the CPU memory. Some machines are designed to do several different jobs. A program for each job can be stored in memory units and the desired program can simply be plugged into the controller.

CHAPTER 11

Servo Valves and Systems

INTRODUCTION

Since a servo-controlled fluid power system is so different from one controlled with standard solenoid valves, the design technique is somewhat different. To properly use an electro-hydraulic servo valve, a designer must understand how such a valve works, the applications where it should or should not be used, how its size must be selected, and limitations on its use. A designer should understand how a servo valve must be matched to its cylinder (or hydraulic motor) load.

There are many brands of servo valves available and construction and appearance will vary from the examples shown in this book. They all produce similar results but internal operating principles and details of construction will vary. Details presented in this book may not be exactly those for a particular brand. But application principles are the same regardless of brand.

In this chapter we will show what servo valves are and on what kinds of applications they can be used. Hydraulic design of the applications is covered in other Womack textbooks.

WHAT IS A SERVO MECHANISM?

Webster's dictionary defines a servo mechanism as "an automatic device for controlling large amounts of power by means of very small amounts of input power, and automatically correcting performance of a mechanism". This is a very good, but broad, definition. But just how is a servo system different from an ordinary system? In an ordinary system, fluid power provides the "muscles" or power, and is controlled by electrical, electronic, or manual input. But in a servo system the valves themselves are a part of the "brain". Probably the key word in Webster's definition is "automatic".

Servo systems use well-known and long-established fluid power principles to handle several kinds of applications:

(1). To provide an accurate control of cylinder rod speed or hydraulic motor rotational speed.

(2). To provide very accurate positioning at specified points in a cylinder stroke or machine slide movement.

(3). To maintain a very accurate control of cylinder force (or hydraulic motor torque) either while the device is moving or when stalled.

(4). Other less common applications include accereration control, flow control, etc. These applications will not be considered in this book.

The first three kinds of applications are described in detail later in the chapter. In a conventional hydraulic system we have some degree of control over position, speed, and force, but not to the high degree of accuracy possible in a servo system, and not with automatic control.

To illustrate one difference between a servo system and an ordinary hydraulic system, consider the power steering on your automobile. A power steering system is a mechanically operated servo system of the "follower" type in which the angular position of the road wheels follows, but does not overrun the angular position of the steering wheel. An ordinary hydraulic system is entirely unsuited to such an application. The steering wheel would probably be attached to a 4-way rotary directional valve. The operator could turn the road wheels to the right or left by rotating the steering wheel ever so slightly. The road wheels would travel at full speed from their "straight-on" position to the "hard-over" position or until the operator centered the steering wheel. The road wheels would remain at this angle until jogged back toward straight-on position. The angle of the road wheels would have no relation to the angular position of the steering wheel. A manual lever 4-way valve would work just as well as a rotary valve for this kind of operation. The road wheels would have to be jogged back to the straight-on position. This kind of steering is sometimes suitable for slow-moving, off-the-road vehicles which usually travel in a straight line and where the travel direction may have to be slightly corrected from time to time. But this kind of system is entirely unsuited for any fast-moving vehicle traveling on a highway. The road wheels must be slaved to the steering wheels and their turning angle must be exactly related to the angle of the steering wheel. Only a servo system can do this.

BLOCK DIAGRAM OF AN ELECTRO-HYDRAULIC SERVO SYSTEM

Figure 11-1. The terminology in this diagram will be used throughout the chapter. The function of each main block is briefly described in the following paragraphs:

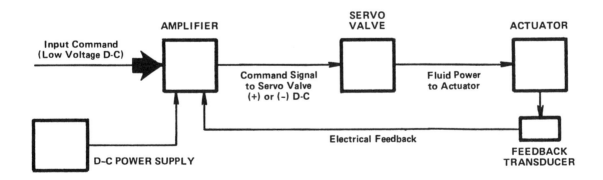

FIGURE 11-1. Closed loop electro-hydraulic servo system.

Input Command. System operation is always controlled with a low D-C voltage obtained either from external potentiometers (Pots), from limit or selector switches connected to taps on a voltage divider, from some kind of microprocessor (such as a programmable controller), or from a potentiometer manipulated by an operator. On some applications the input command will be different levels of voltage of the same polarity; on others it may be different levels of (+) and (–) polarity. The input command voltage must be connected to input terminals of an amplifier suitable for the application.

Amplifier. An amplifier is used on all servo applications. It is a solid state circuit board to serve several functions. (See Page 225). Each kind of application requires an amplifier designed specifically for it. For example, one designed for cylinder position finding could not be used for motor speed control.

The amplifier accepts the input command, compares it with the electrical feedback voltage from a transducer connected to the load, then delivers a control voltage of (+) or (-) polarity to the servo valve which instructs the valve main spool on which way to shift and how far to shift.

Servo Valve. Consider a 4-way servo valve designed for 10-volt operation and used on an application in which a cylinder moves to a designated position in its stroke and stops. If the control signal from the amplifier is +2.5 volts, the cylinder will extend to 1/4 of full stroke and stop. If the control signal is increased to +5.0 volts, the cylinder will extend to 1/2 of full stroke and stop. If the signal is increased to +10 volts, the full extension stroke will be made. Now, if the control signal is reduced to +5 volts, the cylinder will return to its 1/2 full stroke position. If the signal is reduced to 0 volts, the cylinder will completely retract.

In a hydraulic motor speed control application, if the control signal from the amplifier is +10 volts, the motor will run at full speed in CW rotation (for example). if the signal is changed to –10 volts, the motor will reverse and run at full speed in CCW rotation. If the signal is changed to –5 volts, the motor will run at 1/2 speed in CCW rotation.

In a pressure control application, if the control signal is +10 volts, the cylinder will extend with full system pressure. If the signal is +5 volts, the cylinder will extend but with only 1/2 full system pressure. A (-) control signal will retract the cylinder.

Actuator. Electro-hydraulic 3-way and 4-way servo valves are normally used to control hydraulic cylinders and low-slippage hydraulic motors. See Page 208.

Transducer. Some kind of feedback is required for all servo systems to tell the amplifier the position, speed, direction, or force of the actuator. Various transducers are described on the following pages.

Power Supply. The low voltage D-C power supply can be used to furnish power to the amplifier, to the servo valve, to the transducer, and sometimes as a source of voltage for the input command.

FLUID MEDIA FOR SERVO VALVES

Servo mechanisms of the kind described in this book are suitable only for hydraulics because satisfactory servo system operation depends greatly on "stiffness" or "rigidity" of the fluid for its accuracy. Air is compressible; it does not have the required rigidity. Hydraulic oil is also compressible but to a lesser degree. And because of its compressibility a hydraulic servo must be carefully designed to keep significant oil columns as short as possible, the most critical being the column between servo valve spool and the cylinder piston or motor working elements.

Proportional solenoid 4-way or pressure control valves, described in Chapter 12 can sometimes be used instead of servo valves and are far less expensive. They can be used on speed control of both cylinders and motors, and on pressure control in any hydraulic circuit. But they cannot be substituted for servo valves on applications for controlling the stop position of a cylinder.

For compressed air there are single-stage and two-stage servo valves having the same kind of torque motor as hydraulic servo valves. They may use a jet pipe nozzle or flapper nozzle shifted by a torque motor to direct an air flow out of one or a set of cylinder ports. But they cannot be used for the kinds of applications described in this book. They can deliver a variable air flow or air pressure in response to a variable command signal but cannot be used on position-finding applications.

DEFINITION OF AN ELECTRO-HYDRAULIC SERVO VALVE

An electro-hydraulic servo valve is a 3-way or 4-way spool-type directional valve with spool powered by a pair of D-C solenoid coils yoked to the armature of a torque motor. One polarity of voltage to the coils causes the spool to shift, from center neutral, toward one side position. Reversing polarity causes the spool to shift toward the other side position. The spool can be shifted against centering spring force to any distance up to full shift by varying voltage (and current) to the torque motor coils.

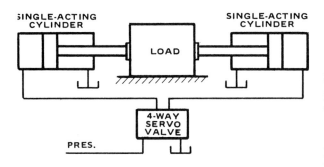

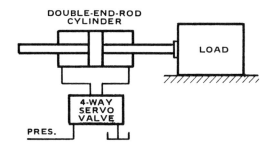

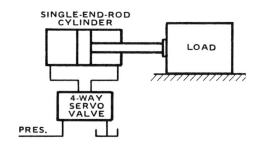

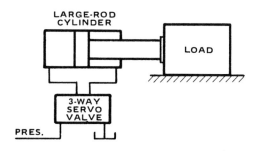

FIGURE 11-2. Servo system cylinder and valve combinations.

KINDS OF ACTUATORS

Single-Acting Cylinder. One such cylinder cannot be used by itself on a servo application. A cylinder for servo mechanisms must be powered in both directions to find the servo null position.

Two single-acting cylinders can be used as a pair with both yoked to the same load so they act like one double-acting cylinder. They can be controlled with one 4-way servo valve.

Double-End-Rod Cylinder. The preferred cylinder for most servo applications is a double-acting, double-end-rod type with equal size rods of minimum standard diameter. It will deliver equal force and speed in both directions, and can be controlled with a 4-way servo valve.

Single-End-Rod Cylinder. Some applications can use a standard double-acting, single-end-rod cylinder with smallest standard rod for its bore size. Force and speed are only slightly different in each direction. But because of unbalanced areas on opposite sides of its piston, the servo valve may have to have its "null" or neutral position mechanically adjusted slightly off true center. This will depend on the nature of the load, primarily how much load reaction is present when the valve is centered. It can be controlled with a 4-way servo valve.

Large-Rod Cylinder. If a cylinder with an oversize rod is used, its piston-to-rod area should be as close to a 2:1 ratio as possible. It should be controlled with a 3-way servo valve connected as in a regenerative circuit, with full pump pressure permanently connected to its rod end. The 3-way servo valve controls pressure only in the blind end, pressurizing it for extension and venting it for retraction.

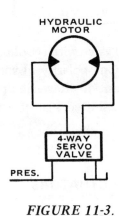

FIGURE 11-3.

Hydraulic Motors. Certain kinds of reversible hydraulic motors can be controlled with a servo valve. They can be used for position finding when driving a machine slide through a worm gear or a rack and pinion drive.

Motor slippage must be considered. Piston and high efficiency vane-type motors give the best performance because their slippage is low. A motor with high slippage will be less responsive to low level changes in command voltage.

Rotary actuators of the vane-type can be position controlled with a servo valve but must be operated within their pressure rating which is usually 1000 to 2000 PSI.

EFFECTS OF VALVE LOCATION

Figure 11-4. To have stability and fast response, a servo system must have as much "stiffness" as possible in the oil loop between valve and actuator. As a rule, hydraulic motors adapt better to servo systems because the system is easier to design with a short oil loop.

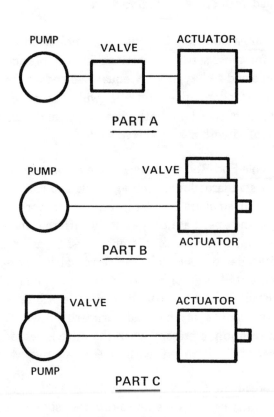

FIGURE 11-4. *Servo valve locations.*

Part A. The valve can be mounted separately with connecting lines to the actuator. The length of lines connecting valve spool to actuator is where compressibility can most affect performance. Keep these lines as short as possible. Line and cylinder diameter do not affect compressibility in the loop. Also, line length and diameter between pump and valve or between valve and tank are not a problem but should be no longer than necessary.

Line length to cylinders with more than 10 inches of stroke may be a problem on some applications, although other systems not requiring as much rigidity may work perfectly well with cylinders of longer stroke.

Part B. Maximum rigidity is obtained by manifolding the valve to the cylinder or motor. This may require the use of a special cylinder or valve designed for the application.

Part C. This is a servo-pump system with the valve manifolded to the pump. One advantage to this arrangement is that less plumbing is required. But since connecting lines in the critical oil loop are longer, the system is not as rigid as in Part A.

If the load moves linearly more than 10 inches, perhaps a hydraulic motor coupled to a lead screw or rack and pinion may be a better method than the use of a cylinder. A standard cylinder or hydraulic motor can sometimes be fitted with a special valve mounting bracket which will locate the valve very close to the cylinder or motor ports to reduce the effect of oil compression in the lines.

SPOOL LAP ON A SERVO VALVE

Servo valves use a closed center spool. A *full* open center or tandem center spool is never used. Full pressure should be maintained on the valve pressure inlet while the system is in operation, and this includes standby periods. This is necessary to allow the valve to hold the cylinder in exact position and to make a correction if it should drift out of position. The term "open center" as applied to a servo valve is simply an underlapped spool as described below. Pump unloading can be done best by using a variable displacement, pressure compensated pump. Since a servo system has slightly higher power losses and heat generation than a standard system of the same HP, connections should be provided, during construction, for addition of a heat exchanger if one should be necessary.

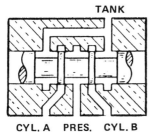  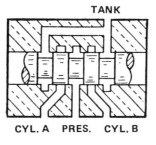 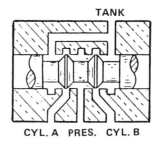

Part A. Zero-Lap Spool. *Part B. Overlapped Spool.* *Part C. Underlapped Spool.*

FIGURE 11-5. Spool lap on servo valves.

Zero-Lap Spool. Figure 11-5A. Spool lands are exactly the same width as body grooves. Most servo valves have a zero-lap spool to obtain a high degree of accuracy in finding and stopping at a precise position in a cylinder stroke. A zero-lap spool is very sensitive to the slightest change in level of command voltage.

Overlapped Spool. Figure 11-5B. Overlapping is a spool condition where the spool lands are slightly wider than the body grooves. Normally this is not a desirable situation because "hysteresis" or "backlash" will be produced, causing the action to be erratic when responding to low level current changes. For example, a cylinder traveling from left to right would stop at one position, but when traveling from right to left would stop at a different position (on the same command voltage).

Where the electrical circuit provides a "dither" — a very short lateral vibration to reduce spool friction — a small amount of overlap is sometimes designed into the spool. Overlap together with dither gives about the same effect as a zero-lap spool.

Underlapped Spool. Figure 11-5C. Sometimes called an "open center" spool. The valve is constructed with the spool lands slightly narrower than the body grooves. This results in a higher leakage of pump oil to tank in center position. Underlap must not be so great that the pump cannot supply this leakage and still maintain full or nearly full pressure at the inlet port. An "open center" servo spool is not equivalent to a *full* open center and cannot be used for pump unloading.

The purpose of underlap is to get a more rapid response on very low changes in the command voltage, but flow linearity in the low-flow region is affected. Ordinarily, a servo valve should have almost linear response. That is, the flow orifices opened up on the main spool should be proportional to the current on the torque motor coils. In a valve with underlapped spool, at very low flows, linearity cannot be achieved because spool orifices open up faster than they should.

POWER SOURCE FOR ELECTRO-HYDRAULIC SERVO VALVES

Electro-hydraulic servo valves must always be operated on D-C power, never directly on A-C power. They are usually designed for 10 to 20-volt operation. D-C power is essential because the distance of spool shift must be varied in proportion to the D-C command voltage. Only a D-C solenoid can do this. Usually only one magnetic structure is used and the main spool is shifted to the opposite side of center by reversing the polarity of the command voltage.

Valves can be operated from an A-C power source by using a power supply which converts 115 volts A-C to low voltage D-C. Power supplies are available from electronic supply houses. Valve manufacturers recommend that a regulated power supply be used. The correct D-C output voltage is maintained to high accuracy even though the A-C input voltage may vary widely.

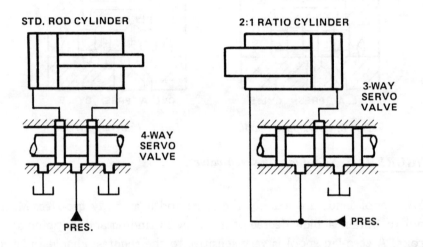

FIGURE 11-6. *Relation of body grooves and spool lands in a servo valve.*

VALVE CONSTRUCTION

Figure 11-6. In a 4-way servo valve, two spool lands cover the two cylinder ports line-to-line. As the spool moves to the left or right, the blind end or rod end is pressurized while the opposite end is vented.

In a 3-way servo valve, one spool land covers the cylinder port line-to-line. As the spool moves to the left or to the right, the cylinder is vented or pressurized.

CLOSED AND OPEN LOOP SERVO SYSTEMS

All servo systems must have some kind of feedback signal to the servo valve to tell it what to do. In closed loop systems this must be an electrical voltage produced by a transducer connected to the load to feed back a voltage proportional to the position, speed, or force of the load. Closed loop servo systems use an electro-hydraulic type of servo valve. Examples of three kinds of closed loop systems are given later in this chapter.

In an open loop system the operator himself provides feedback to the servo valve. He watches load movement and shifts the servo valve to provide more or less restriction, to reverse direction of the actuator, or to stop the actuator. A hydrostatic transmission with manual lever on pump or motor control head is an example of an open loop system because the operator, watching movement of the load, manually operates the control lever. But within the control head itself there is a closed loop system. The control lever operates a rotary servo valve and the angle of the pump cam plate is directly proportional to lever angle; there is internal mechanical feedback from cam plate to servo valve.

In general, a closed loop system uses an electro-hydraulic valve to control a system automatically. An open loop system, although it may or may not use an electro-hydraulic servo valve, is primarily a power boost system, multiplying an operator's effort to control a large mechanical load.

MECHANICAL SERVO SYSTEMS

Mechanical servos are used primarily for boosting power or force, and are sometimes called power boosters. They have been in use many years, long before the invention of the electro-hydraulic servo valve. One familiar example is power steering on an automobile where a small effort on the steering wheel is multiplied by hydraulic pressure from a pump into a much larger force to turn the road wheels. Large trucks, buses, and road machinery would be impractical without power steering.

The servo valve is usually built into or mounted on the end of the cylinder to increase system rigidity and to decrease cost.

Another example is the small control lever on a hydrostatic transmission pump or motor. The lever operates a rotary servo valve to develop up to 800 lbs. on the control head cylinder to tilt the cam plate for changing pump displacement.

Still another example is a tracing machine in which a servo head with a tracer stylus follows the contour of a pattern and, in turn, controls the movement of a large hydraulic cylinder which moves cutting tools to duplicate the pattern contour.

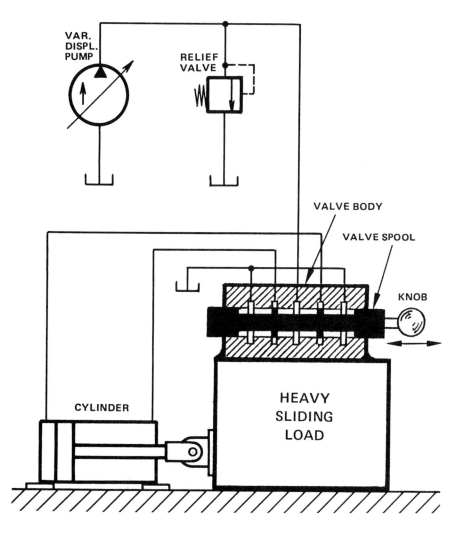

Figure 11-7. Mechanical Servo. Most mechanical servos are the "follower" type. The operator can push or pull on the valve knob with a few ounces of force. A massive sliding load, powered by a hydraulic pump and cylinder, will follow along but will not overrun the operator.

The servo valve body is anchored to and moves with the load. When the operator pulls on the knob, the spool, attached to the knob, is displaced with respect to the valve body. This opens porting inside the body, causing pump oil to flow to the blind end of the cylinder. The load starts to move and as soon as it catches up with the neutral spool position, pump flow is cut off and the cylinder stops. If the operator should push the knob, the spool is displaced in the opposite direction and the load moves

FIGURE 11-7. Example of a "follower type" mechanical servo.

to the left. The maximum load speed, regardless of how fast the operator moves the knob, is determined by the maximum flow from the pump, but the operator, by moving the knob fast or slowly, can control travel speed up to the maximum.

The pump shown is a variable displacement type with a pressure compensator. It will produce only the volume of oil, while the servo valve is centered, to make up spool leakage and maintain full pressure on the valve inlet.

The hydraulic pump and cylinder are sized in the usual way, according to the force and speed required by the load.

Because of zero or a very small overlap of spool lands over body grooves, there is usually a small amount of spool leakage in a servo valve. This leakage is expected and does not affect performance. In fact, a small amount of leakage is beneficial to maintain pressure across both sides of a cylinder piston while the valve spool is centered and is holding a reactionary load. But leakage must not be so great that the system pump cannot maintain full or nearly full pressure at the valve inlet while the spool is centered. If there were no leakage the spool might "hunt" back and forth across center.

ELECTRO-HYDRAULIC SERVO VALVES

Figure 11-8 shows a typical electro-hydraulic servo valve. Flow ratings range from about 3 to over 100 GPM. Most servo valves are built in two stages, with a pilot section mounted on top of and controlling spool movement in the main body. The main body will have a closed or open center servo spool, either spring or pilot pressure centered. The main spool, for most applications will have a zero lap spool (Figure 11-5A). Servo valves can provide directional control in addition to flow metering.

Conventional double solenoid 4-way valves have two individual solenoids connected to opposite ends of a pilot spool. But servo valves have only one magnetic structure. Four-way directional control is by reversing polarity on the D-C solenoid coils. Usually there are two identical and independent coils on one armature structure. The two coils (or windings) can be connected in parallel, in series aiding, or in series opposing (push-pull). With no current in the coils, or with equal but opposing current in the case of a push-pull connection, the main spool is spring or pilot centered. Applying D-C to the coils will cause the main spool to shift to a side position a distance proportional to coil current. Reversing polarity on the coils will cause the main spool to shift to the opposite side position. The user has a choice of two voltages on which to operate (with a choice of a parallel or series connection).

FIGURE 11-8. Electro-hydraulic servo valve.

Valve Variations. Some servo valves have a 3-way main spool, but these can be used only for operation of a large-rod cylinder in a regenerative fashion. They should not be used for operation of small-rod cylinders, double-end-rod cylinders, or hydraulic motors. Single-acting cylinders can only be used in pairs as shown in Figure 11-2.

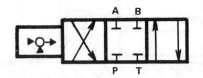

Graphic Symbol

Servo valves designed for flows less than 3 to 5 GPM may be built with only the pilot stage. Valves for high flows, over 100 GPM or those designed for faster response, may be built in three stages. Other variations are mentioned throughout the chapter.

Detailed Description. Figure 11-9. The valve construction shown in this illustration is but one of several ways in which a servo valve can be built. Most valves use a torque motor but it may operate a jet pipe nozzle or flapper nozzle instead of the pilot spool shown here. But regardless of the mode of construction, all 2-stage valves produce the same end result.

The torque motor produces movement in the pilot spool. The pilot spool produces movement in the main spool. Mechanical feedback through a linkage from main spool to pilot spool "nulls" the pilot spool as soon as the main spool has reached the same position as the pilot spool.

Pilot Stage. Item 1, Figure 11-9. Control voltage from the amplifier (Page 207) connected to the torque motor coils produces current in the coils and magnetism in the armature. One end of the armature is attracted by one coil and repelled by the other (in a parallel or series connection). Deflection of the armature pushes or pulls on the pilot spool. Armature torque is the sum of torques from both coils. When current is removed from the coils the armature and pilot spool return to normal center position. If voltage polarity on the coils is reversed, the armature and pilot spool are shifted in the other direction. (Note: Actuator direction is determined by polarity of voltage on the torque motor coils (not on polarity of input command voltage); cylinder position, motor speed, or pressure level to the actuator is controlled by the level of D-C voltage into the torque motor coils.

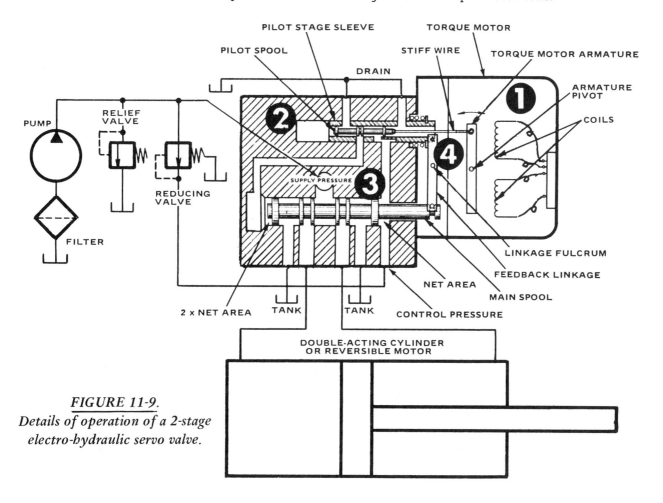

FIGURE 11-9.
Details of operation of a 2-stage
electro-hydraulic servo valve.

214

If the two coils are connected in series opposing (push-pull), the torque produced by one coil is opposed by equal torque from the other coil and the armature remains centered. To produce a movement of the armature, the current in one coil must be increased while current in the other is decreased by an equal amount. In a push-pull connection, command voltage polarity is never reversed.

A torque motor is used in most servo valves because it is virtually frictionless. The movement of the armature is very slight, only enough to produce a movement of a few thousandths of an inch in the pilot spool. Because of the extremely small rotary movement, the linear motion of the pilot spool is very nearly proportional to the current through the coils.

Pilot Spool. Item 2, Figure 11-9. Rotary movement of the torque motor armature is transmitted through a stiff wire to the pilot stage spool, which in this case is a 3-way spool surrounded by a movable pilot stage sleeve. When the spool and the pilot stage sleeve are in neutral alignment, as they should be when there is no current through the coils, the spool in the main body (below) should be in its closed center position. The "null" adjustment on the pilot stage is a means of adjusting the pilot stage sleeve to be in perfect alignment with the pilot spool. Sometimes, as described later, the null position must be adjusted slightly off true center in order to cause the output actuator (cylinder or motor) to hold stationary against a reactionary load.

Second Stage. Item 3, Figure 11-9. The 4-way main spool in this particular valve is operated by a 3-way pilot spool in a regenerative action. Other servo valves may have a 4-way pilot spool operating a spring or pilot centered main spool.

The main spool in Figure 11-9 is powered to either side position by low hydraulic pressure (control pressure) obtained from the pump through a pressure reducing valve. The spool is designed with a 2:1 area ratio between left and right ends. The left end has full area for control pressure to work against. The right end has one-half the area because of the large diameter spool shaft which extends to the outside. Shifting action is the same as in a regenerative circuit where a 2:1 ratio cylinder is operated in both directions with 3-way valve action.

With the pilot spool in its neutral position, the main spool is oil-locked into its closed center position because the oil in the left end is blocked by the pilot spool. Control pressure is maintained permanently on the right end of the spool. When the pilot spool is moved by the torque motor to the left of its normal position, control pressure is admitted to the full area on the left end of the spool. This causes the main spool to be shifted toward the right, against the pressure maintained on its right end. When the pilot spool is moved by the torque motor to the right of its normal position, the left end of the main spool becomes vented to tank. Control pressure working on the right end moves the spool to the left. The distance moved by the main spool is controlled by feedback as described in the next section.

Lands on the main spool exactly cover the body port grooves, and any slight movement of the main spool to the right or left will open flow passages to and from the cylinder.

Feedback. Item 4 on Figure 11-9. The main spool is servo controlled by the pilot section, so there must be some means of position feedback from the main spool. This is usually a mechanical link, and in this particular valve, the link mechanically couples the main spool to the pilot stage sleeve. When the valve is energized, the pilot spool moves a distance related to the magnitude of coil current. It is the job of the main spool to find and stop at the same relative position. When the main spool moves, the linkage shifts the position of the pilot stage sleeve. When the sleeve arrives at "null" position relative to the pilot spool, oil pressure to the main spool is cut off and the spool stops at this position.

If the command voltage is raised or lowered, the pilot spool will move to a new position and the main spool will follow it. If polarity of the command voltage is reversed, the torque motor armature will be deflected in the opposite direction and the main spool will follow the pilot spool across center and will operate the cylinder in reverse.

The "null" adjustment of a servo valve is usually some means of changing the physical position of the linkage fulcrum.

To make a cylinder operated by the system sensitive to very small changes in voltage level of the command signal, the main spool should have zero overlap porting. (Figure 11-5A). For greater sensitivity to low level voltage changes, the spool can be slightly underlapped. Machining of the spool requires a high degree of manufacturing precision. Not only must the spool lands be exactly the same width as the body grooves, but the locations of lands along the spool must exactly match the location of body grooves.

MAXIMUM POWER TRANSFER IN A SERVO SYSTEM

While the cylinder is moving, the ideal pressure relation through the system is to allow a pressure drop of 1/3rd system pressure across the servo valve spool, leaving the remaining 2/3rds across the load. This gives maximum power transfer from pump to actuator and gives the servo valve good control of load speed. The servo valve size should be selected which will meet these conditions. Of course, when the actuator stalls, full pressure will appear across the load but there will be no power transfer. In a non-servo system using flow control valves for speed control, the 4-way valve is sized so as much as possible of the 1/3rd drop is across the flow control valves and as little as practical across the valve spool and plumbing restrictions.

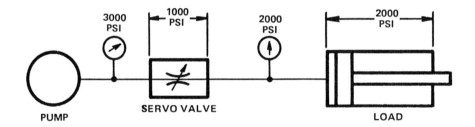

FIGURE 11-10. Division of pump pressure in a servo system.

One of the basic functions of a servo system is flow metering through the servo valve. The spool is shifted with a D-C solenoid controlled by the magnitude of current supplied to it. The spool can be shifted from full side position to any metering position either side of center neutral by regulating the D-C voltage (and current) to its torque motor. Flow control valves should not be used in a servo system. Flow metering is done in the valve itself through spool orifices. In such a system it can be shown mathematically (by calculus) that there is a maximum transfer of power from the pump to the actuator when pressure drop through valve spool orifices is 1/3rd of system pressure. Two-thirds of the pressure is then available to the actuator, cylinder or motor. This means the servo valve size must be carefully selected and this can only be done with reference to the flow and pressure curves published by the valve manufacturer. Pressure losses are usually somewhat higher in a servo system than in a non-servo system and oil heating may be a little greater. During construction it is good practice to provide connections for future addition of a heat exchanger if one should be needed.

If the servo valve is either oversize or undersize to create the 1/3rd pressure drop there will be a reduction in power transfer, but this may be significant only if the mis-match is more than 25%.

FLOW AND PRESSURE RATINGS OF ELECTRO-HYDRAULIC SERVO VALVES

When selecting an electro-hydraulic servo valve you will find them rated for flow capacity at a pressure drop of 1000 PSI. For example, a valve used with a 3000 PSI pump should be selected with a 1000 PSI pressure drop at the rated system GPM flow. Nearly all servo valve manufacturers rate their valves at 1000 PSI pressure loss because 3000 PSI is the most popular working pressure for a servo system. The valve can be used at lower or higher pump pressures but its flow rating should be adjusted for the working pressure as related to its standard rating at 3000 PSI. Re-rating a servo valve will be covered later.

A servo valve is not selected by pipe size. The correct model can only be selected by reference to performance curves published by the valve manufacturer. A correction will usually be necessary for viscosity of your fluid compared to the viscosity used for the performance curves. The performance data will have viscosity correction factors.

If a valve model is not available with the exact flow rating required, the next larger catalog model may be a better match than the next smaller size.

PRESSURE AND FLOW CONDITIONS IN A SERVO CIRCUIT

Figure 11-11. If valve is correctly sized, the pressure drops in a servo system, while the valve is shifted, should be approximately as shown. Starting with 3000 PSI at the pump outlet port, there should be a total of 1000 PSI pressure loss across the valve divided equally between outgoing and return passages. This leaves a maximum of 2000 PSI available for the load while the load is in motion. If the load should stall and if the servo valves remains in shifted position, the entire 3000 PSI will appear across the actuator. The 1000 PSI pressure drop across the servo valve is necessary, while the load is in motion, not only to get maximum power transfer but to give the servo valve the best control over the actuator.

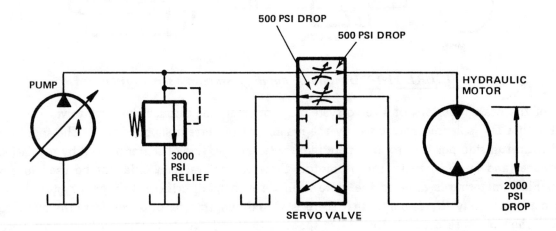

FIGURE 11-11. Expected pressure drops through spool orifices of a servo valve.

When the actuator is running unloaded, system pressure drops to a low value and there is minimum power transfer, maximum speed (with the valve fully shifted), minimum input power, minimum power loss, and minimum oil heating.

When the servo valve spool is centered, about half the system pressure, 1500 PSI should appear across each of its cylinder ports caused by internal spool leakage. However, if there is a reactionary load against the cylinder when stopped, pressure across valve ports will be unequally divided. The valve should be nulled. See Page 227.

OPERATION ON SYSTEM PRESSURES OTHER THAN 3000 PSI

Although most electro-hydraulic systems operate at 3000 PSI, for which most servo valves are pressure rated, sometimes a system must be designed for a different pressure, usually lower than 3000 PSI. The catalog flow rating at 3000 PSI must be re-adjusted for a flow rating at the new pressure. For example, a valve rated for 5 GPM at 3000 PSI, with a pressure loss of 1000 PSI, will have a lower flow rating at 2000 PSI system pressure. The objective is to re-adjust catalog ratings so a valve can be selected with the correct flow rating at the new pressure.

An approximate conversion can be made by using the orifice theory which states that through a perfect orifice the flow through it will change in proportion to the square root of the change in pressure across it.

Example: Using a valve rated for 20 GPM flow on a 3000 PSI system, suppose this valve is to be used on a 2000 PSI system. What will its adjusted flow rating be?

For maximum power transfer and best valve control, 1333 PSI should be available to the actuator and 667 PSI should be pressure drop across the valve. The ratio of pressure reduction is 2000 ÷ 3000 = .667. Take the square root of .667 = .816. This means the new flow rating of the valve is 81.6% of 20 GPM = 16.32 GPM. Adjust also for viscosity difference between your fluid and fluid used in the catalog rating.

SELECTING COMPONENTS FOR A SERVO SYSTEM

Actuator. As with any hydraulic system, design should be started by selecting an actuator which will provide the force or torque needed. On a 3000 PSI servo system, 2000 PSI will be the working pressure to the actuator when maximum power is being transferred, but about 5% of this will be lost to cylinder friction. On a hydraulic motor system, about 15% of the port-to-port pressure will be lost to friction and porting losses. Select motor displacement to produce the necessary maximum torque at about 1700 PSI (on a 3000 PSI system). Force and speed calculations are the same as for any system and are covered in the other Womack textbooks.

Remember that if the actuator is allowed to stall and the servo valve is still shifted, the full pump pressure of 3000 PSI will be applied to the actuator.

Hydraulic Pump. Select displacement of the pump to supply the GPM needed for the specified speed. Remember that full pressure should be maintained on the valve inlet at all times the system is in operation, whether or not the actuator is moving. Systems using a servo valve with underlapped spool may have a high rate of leakage while the spool is centered. Be sure the pump has sufficient flow to supply this leakage and still maintain full pressure on the inlet.

On a 3000 PSI system, calculate pump drive HP at full 3000 PSI and rated pump GPM even though the actuator is working at 2000 PSI. Because a servo valve spool has a closed center, a variable displacement piston pump with pressure compensator or load sensing control will work best on most systems.

The pressure compensator should be adjusted slightly above 3000 PSI to prevent flow cut-off when pressure reaches 3000 PSI. We recommend that a small, direct-acting relief valve, be used on the pump line and set for a cracking pressure of about 3500 PSI to protect the system against momentary pressure spikes before the compensator has time to reduce pump displacement.

Heat Exchanger. Oil heating may be a little greater than in a conventional system of the same HP. Servo valve spool leakage produces extra heat, plus the fact that full pressure is maintained even when the actuator is not moving. Oil temperature should not exceed 150° F. During construction, connections should be provided for addition of a heat exchanger if it should be needed.

Servo Valve. Most servo valve catalogs rate valve flow at a 1000 PSI pressure drop when working with 3000 PSI pump pressure. For example, on a valve rated for 16 GPM flow, this means that the maximum power can be transferred from pump, through the servo valve, and to the actuator when the flow is 16 GPM because the nominal pressure drop will be 1000 PSI. Usually, maximum power transfer will occur when the valve spool is at or near its full shift. The valve will handle higher or lower flows but with slightly less power transfer if the pressure drop is more or less than 1000 PSI.

Select a valve with a flow rating close to the design GPM of the system. If it is not possible to exactly match system flow use the model with next larger flow rating. Size selection is not extremely critical. A mismatch of as much as 20% will cause only a slight sacrifice in performance.

Frequency Response. There are some applications on which the D-C input command voltage must be varied or reversed in polarity at a rapid rate such as 20, 100, 200 or more times per second. The torque motor and main valve spool must be able to respond to these rapid changes and produce full output. The maximum rate at which a valve can keep up with these changing inputs is called its frequency response. On applications where this is an operating condition, the required frequency response is a part of the specifications when purchasing a valve.

ELECTRICAL THEORY AS APPLIED TO SERVO VALVES

Electro-hydraulic servo valves have two coils, or windings, on the same magnetic core. Coil leads are brought out through a DIN, MS, or AN connector. Mating plugs and sockets can be purchased from the valve manufacturer or from an electronic supply house. The windings can be connected in user's choice of parallel for lower voltage, higher current operation or series aiding for higher voltage, lower current operation. See Page 220. The effects of both coils are additive. Windings designed for series opposing (push-pull) operation oppose each other. The magnetic attraction on the torque motor armature is proportional to the difference in current between the two windings.

The valve manufacturer offers a choice of coil resistances. The best choice of coil resistance depends on the nature and level of the control voltage. A high resistance coil has many turns of fine wire and is designed to operate from a higher voltage and a lower current. A low resistance coil has fewer turns of larger wire and is designed to operate from a lower voltage at a higher current. But all coils, whether of high or low resistance should have the same "ampere-turns" and should produce the same magnetic pull when supplied with the proper voltage.

Coil Current. The magnetic force is produced by the number of amperes (or milliamperes) and the number of turns on the windings. Voltage is only significant because the amount of current through a winding is proportional to the voltage pushing it through. Servo valve coils operate at very low power and low current, so the current is usually expressed in milliamperes, abbreviated ma. One ampere is equal to 1000 ma., or 1 ma = .001 ampere. Servo valve coils usually operate in the range of 10 to 100 ma., depending on coil resistance selected.

Coil Voltage. Voltage, current, and resistance in a D-C circuit are proportionally related to each other. Voltage is the electrical pressure or force which pushes current through wire and coil resistances.

While it is current which produces the magnetic effect, it takes a related amount of voltage to push it through. For a specific amount of power on a coil, voltage and current are inversely proportional to one another: as voltage goes up, current must come down and vice versa. The relation of voltage, current, and resistance is expressed by Ohm's Law: I (current) = E (voltage) ÷ R (resistance), or one of its variations: E = I x R, or R = E ÷ I.

<u>Power.</u> Electrical power in a D-C circuit is calculated from the formula: P = E x I, where P is power in Watts, E is voltage, and I is current in amperes. Variations of this formula are: P = I² x R, or P = E² ÷ R.

SERVO VALVE COIL CONNECTIONS

Electro-hydraulic servo valves which use a torque motor input, have two coil windings on a common solenoid armature. This not only balances the torque motor but gives a choice of two operating voltages by the way the coils are connected. In these illustrations we will use as an example a valve which has two 200-ohm windings, each of which is rated for a full current of 40 ma (0.04 amps) at 7.5 volts. If both coils are connected in parallel their combined resistance is 100 ohms, and they will require 80 ma at 7.5 volts. Each coil will supply one-half of the total power required by the torque motor. If connected in series aiding, each coil will supply one-half of the total power but a power supply of 15 volts at 40 ma will be required. Power for each coil is calculated by multiplying E (voltage) x I (current).

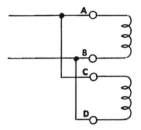

PARALLEL (AIDING)

Two coils can be connected in series opposing (push-pull), but each coil will have to have twice the strength of a coil used in a parallel or a series aiding arrangement, since one coil, by itself, must furnish the power for full spool shift.

Coil terminals are usually marked A, B, C, and D which is standard for some manufacturers.

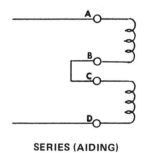

SERIES (AIDING)

Parallel Coil Connection. Figure 11-12. Coil Terminals A and C must be wired together and connected to one side of the control circuit. Terminals B and D must be wired together and connected to the other side of the control circuit. When control (command) voltage is reduced to zero, current through the coils will be zero and the pilot spool will be in its closed center position. If the top line is (+) and the bottom line is (–), the main spool will shift in one direction. If full 7.5 volts is applied, the main spool will fully shift and provide maximum flow orifice size. If voltage is reduced to one-half, to 3.75 volts, the coil current will decrease from 80 to 40 ma, and the main spool will move to a position which will provide flow orifices of one-half maximum. If the valve is accurately built, the orifice area through the spool will be proportional to coil current.

PUSH-PULL (OPPOSING)

FIGURE 11-12.
Possible coil connections

Now, if the control voltage polarity is reversed, with the top line negative (–) and the bottom line positive (+), the spool will move to the opposite side of its center neutral and will open flow orifices proportional to coil current.

With a parallel coil connection the net resistance is one-half the resistance of one coil alone, or 100 ohms. Maximum current required for both coils is 80 ma, or 40 ma per coil. D-C power required on each coil is P = E x I, or P = 7.5 volts x 0.04 = 0.30 watts. Total power, both coils, 0.60 watts.

Series Coil Connection. Figure 11-12. Terminals B and C must be wired together but not connected to either side of the control circuit. Command voltage is applied to Terminals A and D. Power requirement is the same, 0.60 watts, but at 15 volts and 40 ma. Total coil resistance is now 400 ohms.

Operation is the same as described for the parallel connection, but a series connection permits operation from a source of higher voltage at lower current.

Push-Pull Connection. Figure 11-12. Terminals B and D must be wired together and connected to the center tap of the control circuit command voltage. This terminal should be connected to earth ground in the driving amplifier.

When in series or parallel the coils are aiding. But in push-pull they are opposing. Each coil must be capable of supplying full power to the torque motor. Coils on an existing system cannot be simply reconnected from series or parallel to push-pull.

When equal voltage of the same polarity (3.75 in this case) is applied to both coils the torque motor armature is centered. The torque motor armature will move in one direction if voltage is raised on one coil and lowered the same amount on the other. It willl move in the opposite direction if voltage is lowered on the first and raised on the second. Full armature shift is by applying 7.5 volts on one coil and 0 volts on the other. Polarity is never reversed with a push-pull connection.

A push-pull connection is preferred when practical to use it. Any change in coil resistance due to temperature or other cause is cancelled by the other coil. This minimizes "null" drift. A push-pull connection is practical only for amplifier operation, and not for direct battery operation.

CLOSED LOOP ELECTRO-HYDRAULIC SERVO SYSTEMS

A closed loop servo system is one in which a voltage signal is required from a transducer connected to the load. The signal is a voltage proportional either to actuator position, speed, or force, depending on the type of system. It is connected to the amplifier (see Page 225) and the amplifier tells the servo valve how to respond. An open loop system is one in which there is no voltage feedback from the load; the operator provides the feedback information to the amplifier.

The majority of servo systems are closed loop. Although they can be adapted to many control processes, only the three basic and most common kinds of applications will be covered in this book. These are: (1), position-finding in which the input command is varied to tell a cylinder how far to travel before it stops; (2), speed control in which the input command is varied to tell the actuator (usually a hydraulic motor) how fast to rotate and in which direction; and (3), pressure control in which the input command is varied to tell a cylinder how much force to exert against a load, or a hydraulic motor how much torque to produce.

Servo systems of the kind described in this book work from a variable low voltage D-C input command. On some applications, the polarity of the input command must be reversed to cause the actuator to operate in the reverse direction for directional as well as position or speed control.

Transducers. Feedback voltage from the load is required on all closed loop applications. It is produced by some kind of a transducer. Many kinds are available and the right one to use is determined

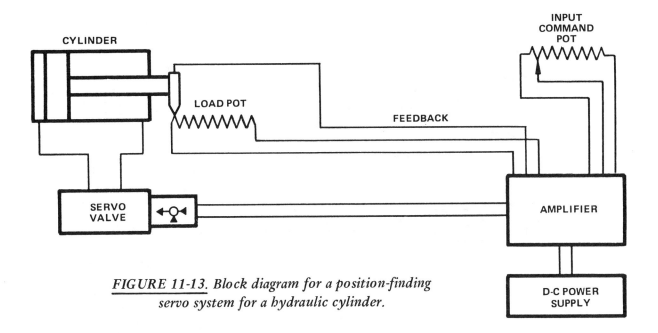

FIGURE 11-13. Block diagram for a position-finding
servo system for a hydraulic cylinder.

by the nature of the application. A transducer is a device which converts one form of force or energy into another kind of force or energy. Some may convert mechanical movement into a variable voltage feedback signal. These are the kind used on position-finding applications. Other transducers convert rotary motion into a variable A-C or D-C voltage, and are used for motor speed control. Still others convert fluid or mechanical force into a variable voltage, and are used for pressure control.

An electro-hydraulic servo can be a very accurate means of handling massive loads such as machine slides, and positioning them for metal cutting operations. System accuracy depends on several factors including accuracy of the servo valve itself, length of pressurized oil column between servo valve and actuator, accuracy of the transducer used, accuracy and adjustment of the amplifier, and mechanical and hydraulic resonance of the system or machine. Accuracies in position-finding for example, up to 0.00001" have been achieved with specially designed systems, but an accuracy of 0.0005" to 0.002" is more common.

Position-finding is the most common type of application for a servo system because speed control and pressure control can often be done with sufficient accuracy and far cheaper with proportional solenoid valves, or by other means.

Position-Finding Systems. Figure 11-13. Machine slides, grinding and milling tables, planers, and other heavy loads which must be moved and stopped at a designated position with a high degree of accuracy can be moved with a cylinder controlled with a servo valve. But if the cylinder stroke exceeds 10 inches (depending on rigidity required) the movement may become erratic, inaccurate, or unstable because of oil compressibility. A more accurate system for long movements is to use a hydraulic motor working through a worm gear or rack and pinion arrangement to produce linear movement. The mechanical parts must be machined to close tolerances to reduce inaccuracy caused by "backlash".

In Figure 11-13, for demonstration, the input command is shown coming from a potentiometer or (Pot), although it can come from any source which can deliver an accurate D-C voltage. The feedback signal is produced by a linear Pot the same length as the cylinder stroke. The cylinder, or a moving member of the machine, moves the slider along the pot as the cylinder extends. A voltage signal is produced which is proportional to the stroke position. If the input command is set at

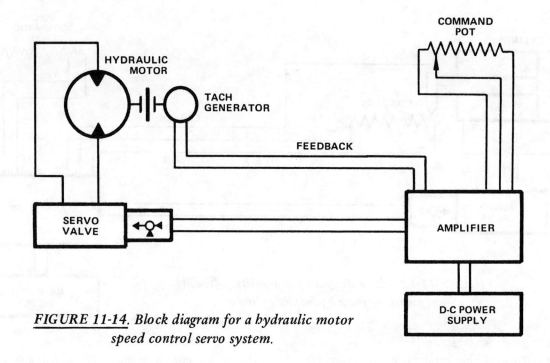

FIGURE 11-14. Block diagram for a hydraulic motor speed control servo system.

5 volts, for example, the cylinder will extend until the feedback voltage reaches the equivalent of 5 volts. At this position the amplifier will instruct the servo valve main spool to center and the cylinder to stop. This arrangement is sometimes called a "Pot-Pot" system.

To extend the cylinder to a new position, input command must be increased. To retract to a new position, input command must be reduced while keeping the same polarity. See Page 207. The amplifier will reverse polarity to the servo valve to cause it to shift across center until the cylinder has found the new position and stopped.

Feedback transducers used with cylinders for position finding may also include multi-turn rotary pots with rack and pinion drive, and LVDT (linear variable differential transformers). An LVDT works by induction. An iron core is moved by the cylinder through a long coil of wire (equal to the cylinder stroke). A low voltage A-C is supplied to the coil. A voltage proportional to the depth of penetration of the core into the coil is produced and is fed to the amplifier.

A D-C power supply of the specified voltage must be connected to the amplifier. It can also serve as a source of power for the input command pot and transducer, if needed.

Speed Control Servo Systems. Figure 11-14. On this application for speed control of a hydraulic motor, a tachometer generator, driven from the motor, provides a feedback to the amplifier. The tach generator is a small A-C or D-C generator which delivers a voltage proportional to its shaft speed. If, for example, the input command pot is set at 5 volts, the hydraulic motor will accelerate until the tach generator produces the equivalent of 5 volts. The amplifier will then instruct the servo valve to shift its spool to smaller orifices to prevent motor speed from increasing further. The servo valve will modulate flow to the motor to keep its speed constant. Increasing the input command to 6 volts will allow the motor to accelerate to and maintain a higher speed.

Polarity of the input command can be reversed to cause the hydraulic motor to rotate in the opposite direction. An A-C tach generator can operate in either rotation and will produce the same voltage in proportion to speed.

223

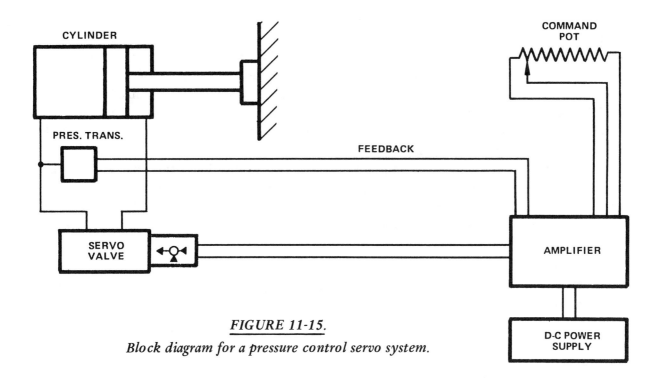

FIGURE 11-15.

Block diagram for a pressure control servo system.

It is difficult to apply a feedback transducer to control cylinder speed, especially on short strokes. Instead, a proportional solenoid 4-way or flow control valve may have sufficient accuracy for the application and will make a less expensive system.

Pressure Control Systems. Figure 11-15. A servo valve can automatically maintain close control of the maximum force exerted by a cylinder against a load while the load is moving. It can also control the maximum torque of a hydraulic motor against a running load.

Sensing of force against a load by a cylinder can be done by installing a piezo-electric (quartz crystal) transducer in the hydraulic cylinder port. Hydraulic fluid pressure against the face of the crystal will produce a very small voltage proportional to stress in the crystal produced by fluid pressure. The voltage is fed to the amplifier where it is amplified and matched against the input command. A crystal is subject to temperature drift and must be operated at low to moderate temperatures.

Or, strain gauges can be attached to surfaces of the load to detect minute deflections caused by force exerted on the load. The torque from a hydraulic motor can also be regulated by either method. Tensioning and crowding applications are typical.

It is important on all servo applications, but especially on those for pressure control, to maintain full pressure on the valve inlet at all times while the system is functioning.

A servo valve limits pressure to an actuator *while in motion* by positioning its spool to reduce flow orifice size. Excess pressure above that called for by the input command is dissipated across the servo valve spool. In any servo system heat power loss can be reduced by using a variable displacement, pressure compensated pump to avoid discharging excess oil flow across the system relief valve.

For directional control, polarity of the input command must be reversed. Pressure or flow in the reverse direction will be uncontrolled unles a duplicate transducer and amplifier, or a special amplifier are used. Proportional solenoid pressure and/or reducing valves are available and may be a more economical way of controlling pressure if they have sufficient accuracy for the job.

AMPLIFIERS FOR ELECTRO-HYDRAULIC SERVO VALVES

A servo system operates from a low voltage D-C input command. By varying this voltage up and down, the servo system actuator can be controlled. All systems, whether position-finding, speed control, or pressure control operate from the same kind of input command voltage.

The power requirement to the windings of a servo valve torque motor is quite low, and a valve could theoretically be operated from a battery and a potentiometer or any device which could deliver a varying low D-C voltage. But in practice the benefits provided by an amplifier make its use almost mandatory on most applications. An amplifier is a solid state circuit board or "card" containing components to enhance valve operation. Amplifiers are built for applications other than position-finding, speed control, and pressure control, but study in this book will be limited to those three kinds.

An amplifier specifically suited for the kind of application under design can be furnished by the valve manufacturer and can be purchased along with the servo valve. Some of the major advantages provided by an amplifier are these:

(1). It can amplify a feedback voltage to a level where it can be matched to the input command voltage. Some transducers, the piezo-electric type for example, deliver such a minute voltage that it must be greatly amplified before it can be used.

(2). By amplifying the feedback voltage, the accuracy to which the system can respond is greatly increased. However, if the amplification or gain is too high the system becomes unstable. On most amplifiers the gain is adjustable.

(3). An amplifier can provide a "dither" signal to the main spool of the servo valve. Dither causes the spool to vibrate back and forth over a very short distance and at a high frequency, to reduce spool friction and hysteresis. See more information on Page 226.

(4). The range on input command voltage can be spread over the full spool travel of the servo valve. This makes variation of the input command less critical and increases system accuracy.

(5). An amplifier can protect the windings of the servo valve torque motor by preventing excessive current to be accidentally applied.

(6). An amplifier can compensate for some of the errors caused by changes in ambient conditions or changes in resistance of the copper wire in the windings, to improve linearity of the servo valve output with respect to changes of the input command.

Magnetism in the servo valve torque motor is proportional to current through the windings, not to applied voltage. If coil resistance should change as ambient temperature changes, this would change spool movement even though the applied input command remained the same.

Components in the servo system will include, as a minimum, the servo valve, a D-C power supply, an amplifier designed for the kind of application, and a feedback transducer operated by the load. Input command voltages are obtained from a source outside the servo system.

AMPLIFIER AND SYSTEM ADJUSTMENTS

Usually, system adjustments must be made when the system is put into operation. Briefly, the procedure should be as follows:

Phasing. This is a test to be sure the cylinder (or motor) moves in the right direction in response to a command voltage. Connect all components but reduce the hydraulic pressure to a low level, just high enough to barely move the cylinder. Apply a command voltage and see if the cylinder moves in

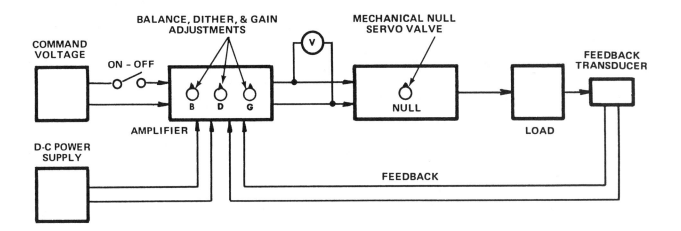

FIGURE 11-16. Trim adjustments on a servo system.

the right direction. If not, reverse polarity of electrical connections either on the command signal, on electrical connections to the servo valve, on the feedback transducer, or reverse hydraulic connections between servo valve and cylinder.

Amplification or Gain. If the gain control on the amplifier is set too high the system will be unstable and will go into oscillation. Connect the entire system including both electrical and hydraulic components. Raise the hydraulic pressure to its normal level. See that the hydraulic system responds to an input command even though it may not be correctly adjusted at this time. Start with the gain control at minimum or to a low setting and increase the setting until the system becomes erratic or starts to oscillate. Back down the gain control to about one-half this setting and be sure there is no tendency for erratic motion or instability. This is the best gain setting for most systems.

If it appears to be impossible to set the gain control properly because of excessive unbalance of amplifier or valve, leave the gain setting near minimum and proceed with a temporary null adjustment. Then, later, go back and increase the gain.

Dither Adjustment. An oscillator in the amplifier provides a small override voltage which causes the valve main spool to vibrate back and forth over a very small distance. This reduces spool friction, reduces the valve deadband, makes the valve more sensitive to low level input commands, and reduces hysteresis of the spool.

First, reduce the load to one-half or less of maximum. Increase setting of dither control until vibration can barely be felt while the load is stopped. Back down the control to about one-half this setting.

Next, to reduce hysteresis to a minimum, apply full load to the cylinder. Move the load, first approaching a designated stop position from the left, then from the right. Measure the difference in position where the cylinder stops. Increase dither, a little at a time, until the error is minimum. Use no more dither than necessary. Too much dither will not reduce hysteresis further and will increase spool wear. Dither frequency is usually set at the factory and cannot be easily changed in the field.

Amplifier Null. There is a "null" or "balance" adjustment on both the servo valve and the amplifier. Start with the balance adjustment on the amplifier.

<u>(1)</u>. Connect a low range voltmeter across the amplifier output as shown in Figure 11-16. Using a multi-range voltmeter start with a higher range, then change to a lower range for greater sensitivity.

<u>(2)</u>. Turn on the amplifier but switch off the command voltage. Turn off the hydraulic system. Adjust the balance control on the amplifier for minimum voltage. For valve torque motors rated at 10 to 15 volts, the voltage should be virtually zero on the 3-volt meter range.

This balances the amplifier. If the system null must be adjusted slightly off true center to offset an unbalanced load, this must be done on the servo valve, not the amplifier.

Servo Valve Null. Turn the entire system on, including the command voltage, and with the system regulating a position, turn the null adjustment on the servo valve until the voltmeter again reads zero or minimum. This adjustment may place the null slightly off true center, either to provide more pressure on the rod end of a single-end-rod cylinder to offset its smaller area, or to provide more pressure on one end of the cylinder to resist reaction from a load when the cylinder is stopped. If necessary, go back and re-set the gain adjustment on the amplifier.

FILTERING IN SERVO SYSTEMS

Most servo valves have a small, built-in, micronic filter to clean the oil which goes into the pilot spool. But it is also important to have good filtering in the entire hydraulic system, to 5 to 10 μm. If the main flow is not finely filtered, the micronic filter in the servo valve may become clogged in a short time, causing the valve to malfunction.

CHAPTER 12

Proportional Solenoid Valves

DESCRIPTION

A spool-type proportional solenoid valve is one in which the spool can be shifted by low voltage D-C solenoids against a return spring or centering springs. By regulating current to the solenoids, the spool can be moved from its normal position, against spring force, to any distance up to full spool travel. Proportional valves can be used instead of conventional 4-way directional control valves for controlling both direction and speed of an actuator by variable electrical control. As the spool shifts, the flow orifices opened up are directly proportional to command voltage and to spool displacement.

A poppet-type proportional solenoid valve can be used instead of a conventional pressure control valve (of any kind) for remote electrical control of poppet cracking pressure.

Flow metering through a proportional solenoid 4-way valve is similar to flow metering with a manual bank valve, and its purpose is to control both speed and direction of the actuator. A proportional solenoid valve can be used for speed control while the actuator is moving, but it cannot duplicate the action of a servo valve in seeking and stopping the actuator at a designated position.

APPLICATIONS FOR PROPORTIONAL SOLENOID VALVES

Proportional valves are more costly than standard solenoid valves and they require an electronic amplifier, so they are not the best selection for every application, but should be considered in place of standard A-C operated valves on applications like these:

(1). Where electrically controlled 4-way valves must be operated remotely but where the operator must be able to vary cylinder or motor speed as well as direction, much like manually operated bank valves are used to control direction and to modulate speed of cylinders. Before the introduction of proportional solenoid control, electrical operation had to be an ON-OFF function without the capability of also controlling flow through the circuit.

(2). Where a cylinder or cylinders are controlled by signals coming from a microprocessor such as a computer or programmable controller, and must go through a cycle in which speed changes are required at certain points in the cycle. Cylinders may be required to extend and retract all or part of their stroke several times before the cycle is complete, and the speed may be different during these phases. Maximum pressure in different parts of the cycle can be varied, but only while the cylinder is in motion. Changes in speed or direction are initiated by various switches and sensors placed at appropriate points along cylinder strokes. One advantage in proportional control on these applications is the reduction in number and cost of components required.

(3). Where it may be necessary to override the operator to automatically change force or speed at certain points in a cylinder stroke.

(4). On systems which must be shockless. Shock can be almost entirely eliminated from the hydraulic circuit of machines controlled with proportional solenoid valves, yet the system can be adjusted for maximum acceleration and deceleration just short of a shock condition. Sometimes cycle time can actually be reduced because the cylinder can be programmed, not only to accelerate faster without shock, but to travel faster during parts of the cycle where this is acceptable.

(5). Where high horsepower and high flow must be handled with directional control and speed control exercised through a small electrical joystick with small operator effort.

PROPORTIONAL SOLENOID ACTION

The principle of proportional solenoid control can be used in any hydraulic spool-type or poppet-type valve including 4-way directional, pressure relief, pressure reducing, by-pass, unloading, sequence, and flow control valves. The principle as applied to any spool-type valve is to control the distance the spool moves from its normal position against spring force. As applied to poppet valves, the principle is to control the spring tension which holds the poppet on its seat. A proportional valve must always work against spring force, a return spring or centering springs. For this reason, proportional control cannot be applied to 2-position, no spring, valves.

Solenoid directional valves are no longer limited to three positions. They could be built with four or more working positions and the spool could be shifted to any of these positions by application of the correct command voltage. These would be highly special valves and could not be used for flow control, only for directional control.

Solenoid Action. Proportional solenoids which operate spool-type directional and similar valves are called "stroke controlled" solenoids because the length of stroke, against a return spring, is controlled by the amount of current to the solenoid. On a D-C solenoid, armature movement is approximately proportional to coil current only over a limited distance. Therefore, pilot spools for proportional valves are designed for a very short stroke, usually 3 to 5 mm (0.075 to 0.225 inches) from their normal, unactivated position. Stroke controlled solenoids are also used on spool-type, pressure compensated, flow control valves and have essentially the same action as those used on 4-way valves.

When used on a poppet-type pressure control valve, the proportional solenoid is called a "force controlled" solenoid. Force of the solenoid holds a poppet on its seat until pressure builds high enough to unseat the poppet against solenoid force. Opening pressure can be set remotely by electrical control. Proportional relief valves described later in this chapter can be used for sequence, counterbalance, or by-pass service by properly providing internal or external pilot pressure and/or drain.

Operating Power. Proportional solenoids must always be operated on D-C, never on A-C power. Operating voltage is usually 12 or 24 volts from a battery or from a regulated D-C supply connected to 115 volts A-C. An A-C solenoid, because of the fluctuating and reversing state of the voltage cannot be used on other than its rated operating voltage. The inrush current when an A-C solenoid is first energized can be up to five times its normal rated current until the armature has made its *full* stroke and closed the air gap by completing the magnetic loop. Unless the armature can seat quickly, the solenoid coil may burn out from excessive current.

Comparison to Servo Valve. There are some similarities between a servo valve and a proportional solenoid valve. Both must operate from low voltage D-C. Directional control is by reversing polarity of the command voltage into the amplifier controlling the valve. Both use closed center spools on 4-way directional valves – the lands on a servo valve spool open up flow area abruptly when the spool moves slightly away from neutral; those on a proportional valve open up flow areas gradually and continue to open wider during full spool travel.

However, a servo valve operates in closed loop while a proportional valve operates in open loop. On most applications a servo valve seeks a stop position or an operating condition for the actuator where the closed loop feedback voltage equals the command voltage. On most applications, a proportional valve seeks an actuator speed proportional to the command voltage; and it will control direction as well. It can be set for choice of actuator speed but if actuator load should change, it cannot make automatic corrections, unless pressure compensation is added. (See Page 236). It cannot find and automatically stop the actuator at a designated position. So the two kinds of valves are used for different kinds of applications.

Coil Temperature. One problem with proportional solenoid valves is the effect of temperature on solenoid coils. Copper wire resistance increases with temperature, and although the same command voltage may be applied to the coils when cold as when warm, the solenoids will have less force at higher temperatures because the increased coil resistance will reduce coil current (at the same applied voltage). The increase in resistance can be considerable. For example, there is about a 50% increase over the range of –6 to +300° F. As the current becomes less at higher temperatures, the solenoid will have less force and will not move the valve spool as far (on the same command voltage). The amplifier can correct for these errors due to temperature changes. This is one reason why an amplifier is essential to good control of a proportional valve.

Metering Orifices. As the spool on a proportional solenoid valve moves from its normal position, it should open up approximately equal spool metering areas both into and out of the actuator. One-half the total pressure drop across the valve should appear in each cylinder line. Standard spools are designed for control of equal-area actuators – hydraulic motors, double-end-rod cylinders, and rotary actuators. They will work nearly as well with single-end-rod cylinders which have smallest size rod for their bore diameter. With pressure drop approximately equal in each cylinder line, this gives a combination of meter-in and meter-out speed control.

To operate single-end-rod cylinders with rod larger than standard, the valve must be ordered with a special spool in which spool metering areas opened up to the blind end are twice as large as those opened up to the rod end of the cylinder. These are called "2:1 ratio" spools.

Flow Control Valves. External flow control valves are not used with proportional solenoid valves. All speed control metering is done inside the valve. For smooth control of cylinder speed, virtually all the flow resistance between pump and actuator should be inside the proportional solenoid valve where it can be varied by electrical control. External flow resistance in plumbing lines should be kept reasonably low.

Fluid Media. Proportional solenoid valves can be used on the same liquids (with their manufacturers approval) as used in other hydraulic systems – petroleum base oil, water base fluids, and chemical fluids. The valves described in this book cannot be used on gases, but the same principles can be applied for building gas valves to meter the flow of gas in proportion to command voltage.

PROPORTIONAL SOLENOID VALVES FOR DIRECTIONAL CONTROL

Figure 12-1. This is a block diagram of the units which comprise a proportional solenoid valve system for combined speed and directional control of a hydraulic cylinder or motor. Although this is typical, individual systems could vary in certain details.

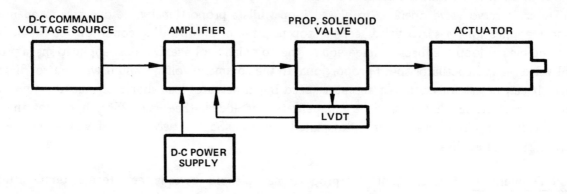

FIGURE 12-1. Block diagram of a proportional solenoid system for direction and speed control.

D-C Command Voltage. Control of the system comes from a D-C voltage connected to terminals on the amplifier. Command voltage can come from a manually operated electronic joystick, from a potentiometer, from a microprocessor such as a computer or programmable controller, or from a limit switch connected to a tap on a precision voltage divider. The actuator will move in one direction when a command voltage is applied and will move in the opposite direction when polarity is reversed.

Amplifier. Sometimes called a "circuit card" or "circuit board". Theoretically a proportional solenoid valve could be operated directly with a potentiometer from a battery or D-C power supply. But in practice, an amplifier should be used on all applications because of the necessary functions it performs. Each size and kind of proportional solenoid valve must be operated from the amplifier designed specifically for it. An amplifier can be purchased from the valve manufacturer. See a more complete description of amplifiers on Page 235.

D-C Power Supply. Power to operate the system must be from a low voltage power supply, usually 12 or 24 volts. For mobile applications a battery can be used. For industrial applications a regulated D-C supply operating from 115 volts A-C. One power supply can serve for all low voltage D-C components in the system including amplifier, joysticks, command voltage, and for the solenoids of the proportional valve.

Proportional Solenoid Valve. A 4-way valve, usually a double solenoid model with closed center spool will serve for applications of combined direction and speed control. It must be carefully sized in relation to system pressure and flow so it will have a pressure drop within certain operating limits to be able to smoothly control actuator speed over the desired range. It must be sized from manufacturers flow curves. See additional information on valve sizing on Page 237.

LVDT. Abbreviation for linear variable differential transformer. This is a variable inductor contained within a proportional solenoid structure for producing a feedback voltage to the amplifier to indicate valve spool position. This allows the amplifier to correct the current supplied to the valve solenoids so the spool will move to the exact position in which it should be. Usually, an LVDT is used only on direct-acting solenoid models, and is particularly useful on applications where the cylinder is out of view of the operator. It is seldom needed on models which are used on applications where an operator is visually monitoring cylinder movement.

System Capability. Please remember that 4-way proportional solenoid valves are used only on applications for combined control of direction and speed of hydraulic cylinders and motors by D-C command voltages. Direction is selected by polarity of command voltage; speed is controlled by level of D-C command voltage. Position finding or pressure control of a cylinder or torque of a motor is not within the practical capability of the system, although proportional solenoids can be used on pressure relief or reducing valves for remote selection of system pressure as described later in this chapter.

CONTROL OF A PROPORTIONAL SOLENOID VALVE

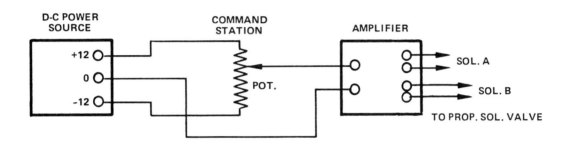

FIGURE 12-2. Block diagram for basic control of a proportional solenoid system.

Figure 12-2. Magnitude and polarity of the D-C command voltage fed into the amplifier will control actuator speed and direction. In this block diagram, a 24-volt D-C power supply with center tap will furnish a +12 to –12 command voltage. A Pot (potentiometer) is wired across the power supply voltage. When the Pot slider is at center position, command voltage to the amplifier is zero and the valve spool will be in center position. As the Pot slider is moved upward toward the side position, voltage level to the amplifier will increase up to a maximum of +12 volts. The main valve spool will move from its center position a distance proportional to the voltage (and current) supplied to the amplifier input. If the Pot slider is moved downward to the other side of center, the increasing voltage, up to a maximum of –12 volts will cause the valve spool to move to the opposite side of its center position.

This simple illustration is only one of many sources from which command voltage can be obtained.

FOUR-WAY PROPORTIONAL SOLENOID VALVES

Sliding spool construction is used on 4-way proportional valves. The solenoid pushes a spool against a return or centering spring. When the solenoid is de-energized, the spool returns to its normal position. The force from a D-C solenoid is proportional to coil current only over short distances, so the spool stroke must be limited to a few millimetres.

The spool is notched in such a way that the flow area opened up by spool movement is proportional to the distance of spool movement. For example, with one-half of maximum command voltage on the system, the spool will shift to one-half its maximum stroke, and the flow areas opened up will be one-half the flow areas at full spool shift. The amplifier which operates the valve can be adjusted to spread the maximum command voltage evenly across full spool travel.

Total pressure drop through the valve, with the spool shifted to full side position should be at least 150 PSI. However, this is subject to valve manufacturers specification. A pressure drop of this magnitude is essential to give the valve smooth control over the full range of actuator speed.

FIGURE 12-3.
Direct-acting proportional solenoid valve.

DIRECT-ACTING 4-WAY VALVES

Figure 12-3. To correct spool positional errors primarily caused by resistance change of solenoid coils due to temperature, this model has a built-in LVDT which can be seen extending from the end of the left solenoid. It is effective for spool movements both sides of center neutral.

The LVDT is an inductive device energized with low voltage A-C from the amplifier. An iron core attached to the spool, causes an A-C voltage to be induced which is exactly proportional to spool position. This induced voltage is fed back to the amplifier and compared to the position where the spool should be for the level of command voltage. The amplifier changes current to the solenoid and causes it to move to the correct position.

This model, with LVDT, should be used on applications where input command voltages are not monitored by an operator and where spool position must be accurate for applied command voltage. Another similar model without LVDT is available for those applications where the positional error is not important, that is, where an operator is watching actuator movement and controlling it manually.

PILOT-OPERATED PROPORTIONAL SOLENOID VALVES

Figure 12-4. Pilot-operated models are available from at least one manufacturer to handle flows to 100 GPM, in both single solenoid and double solenoid models. Obviously, proportional valves are not

FIGURE 12-4.
Pilot-operated proportional solenoid valve.

available in double solenoid, no spring, models. The return spring or centering springs are a most necessary part of proportional operation. They provide a linear resistance for the spool to work against when activated by the proportional solenoid.

An LVDT (linear variable differential transformer) as shown on the direct-acting model above is not necessary on pilot-operated models. Spool forces which would produce positional errors are relatively small compared to the very large forces which power the spool. The correction provided by an LVDT would be almost insignificant.

Like standard A-C solenoid 4-way valves, proportional valves can be furnished, or can

233

be converted in the field to choice of internally or externally drained and piloted operation. Consult specification sheet for your valve.

Main Body. The main body is very similar to one used for a standard A-C solenoid valve. However, the main spool is notched to spread the variable range of orifice areas over the entire main spool travel.

Pilot Section. The pilot or "piggy-back" valve is special. It is not just a direct-acting proportional solenoid valve mounted on top of the main body. The two solenoids of a double solenoid model are not mechanically connected. Each one operates separately, and is a D-C solenoid which provides force against the poppet of a miniature pressure reducing valve. Pressure from the reducing valve delivers pilot pressure to one end of the main spool which is proportional to solenoid current. Therefore, the main spool moves a distance against its centering spring which is proportional to pilot pressure from the reducing valve and this, in turn, is proportional to solenoid current.

The pilot section may be rated for a lower operating pressure than used on the main valve. In this case, a suitable pilot pressure can be brought in from an external source and connected to the external pilot port on the valve subplate. Or, pilot pressure can be obtained from the pressure line to the main body by installing a sandwich-type pressure reducing valve between the pilot section and the main body. A minimum pilot pressure is required for full main spool shift. Consult valve specification sheet.

Hysteresis. Hysteresis can be up to 6% on pilot-operated, spool-type, proportional valves. This means there may be up to 6% difference in actuator speed when the command voltage causes the valve main spool to move toward a metering position from the left as compared to when it moves to the same position from the right (on the same command voltage but of opposite polarity).

Repeatibility. Repeatibility may be about 3%. This means that on successive cycles there could be up to 3% difference in actuator speed when the spool is shifted from neutral to the metering position with the same command voltage and polarity.

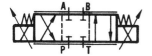

Direct-Acting Double Solenoid
Valve, Closed Center, Without
Linear Inductive Transducer

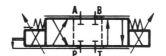

Direct-Acting, Double Solenoid
Valve, Closed Center, With
Linear Inductive Transducer

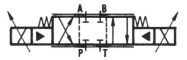

Pilot-Operated, Double Solenoid
Valve, Closed Center Spool

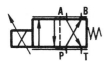

Direct-Acting Single Solenoid
Valve Without Linear Inductive Transducer

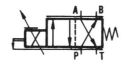

Direct-Acting, Single Solenoid
Valve With Linear Inductive
Transducer

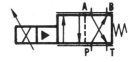

Pilot Operated, Single Solenoid
Valve

FIGURE 12-5. Graphic symbols for 4-way valves with proportional solenoids.

AMPLIFIERS FOR SOLENOID PROPORTIONAL VALVES

All proportional solenoid valves should be operated through an amplifier, called a "circuit card" or "circuit board". See Figures 12-1 and 12-2. This is a printed circuit electronic board, usually designed and manufactured by the valve manufacturer for specific valves. Each type of valve requires its own special amplifier. It provides an interface between the source of command voltage and the proportional solenoid valve, and contains electronic circuits, sometimes many circuits, to enhance valve performance and to bridge between command voltage and valve. One amplifier is required for each proportional solenoid valve, but both solenoids of a double solenoid valve can be operated from one amplifier board. For directional control, selection of Solenoid A or Solenoid B is by reversing polarity of the D-C command voltage. However, several joystick or limit switch signals can be fed into one amplifier for control of a valve from several sources or from several locations.

FIGURE 12-6.
Typical Amplifier Card.

FIGURE 12-7.
Card holder with 32
available terminals.

Amplifiers basically are printed circuit boards with transistors, diodes, capacitors, resistors, terminal boards, and sometimes inductors, relays, and other components. They can be individually mounted by plugging them into a card holder (see Figure 12-7). A number of card holders can be mounted in a card rack (see Figure 12-8). The plug and jack assembly on a card holder is usually the Eurocard standard used in Europe and which will probably be adopted as the SI standard in the U.S.A. Card holders have screw terminals for connecting into other components. All standard amplifier cards will fit the standard card holder which has 32 terminal connections. Not all connections are used in every amplifier. If electrical trouble should develop in a system, a spare amplifier card can be plugged in to determine if the problem is electronic. Defective amplifiers can be returned to the manufacturer for repair.

Some of the important and necessary functions performed by the amplifier are these:

(1). It can amplify the command voltage to match the rating of the proportional valve. Amplification increases sensitivity and accuracy.

(2). It can be adjusted to "spread" the command voltage range over the full spool travel of the valve.

(3). It adds PWM (pulse width modulation) to the signal it delivers to the proportional solenoid valve. PWM causes the amplifier output voltage, rather than being a steady D-C voltage, to be delivered in short pulses at a frequency compatible with the valve being controlled. One manufacturer uses a pulse rate of 83 Hz (cycles per second). Pulse frequency can be changed but usually must be done at the factory. Amplitude of the pulses does not change; it is constant regardless of amplitude of command voltage, but in order to produce a variable current in the solenoid coil, the width or duration of ON to OFF time of each pulse is varied.

The effect on the solenoid of varying the pulse width is the same as if the current level were being varied. Pulsing (ON-OFF) operation of the output transistors reduces the time during which they are delivering power and allows them to work with less heating. This eliminates the need for a "heat sink" on the amplifier board. PWM almost eliminates the effect of spool friction on spool position. When spool friction is reduced, "hysteresis" is reduced

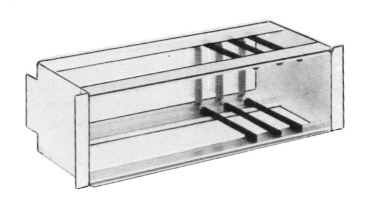

FIGURE 12-8.
Card rack for mounting several amplifiers.

and "repeatibility" is improved. Refer to Page 234 for more information on these characteristics.

(4). Most amplifiers provide a fixed or adjustable "ramp", or choice of several adjustable ramps. A ramp is a more gradual build-up or decay of current in a proportional solenoid coil to "soften" its action and reduce shifting shock. Small potentiometers are provided on the amplifier board for adjustment of steepness of the ramps.

Some amplifiers provide additional benefits. Please refer to specifications on model you intend to use.

PRESSURE COMPENSATION FOR PROPORTIONAL SOLENOID VALVES

Figure 12-9. Although the flow through a proportional solenoid valve can be varied by electrical control, the flow will fluctuate with changes in system load just as it will if ordinary needle-type flow control valves are used. On some applications this change in flow with changes in load is no problem.

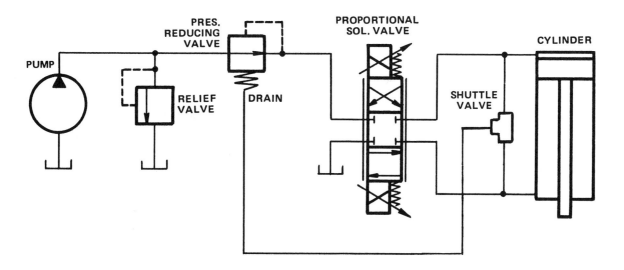

FIGURE 12-9. Adding pressure compensation to a proportional solenoid 4-way valve.

But if it is, pressure compensating components can be added. Then the flow, when once set by adjusting current to the solenoids, will remain constant at this flow regardless of load changes.

A full size pressure reducing valve in the inlet line, in combination with spool orifices, make a pressure compensated flow control. The reducing valve serves to keep a constant pressure difference across spool orifices, hence keeping flow across the orifices at a constant value. For an understanding of this compensating action, please refer to the Womack book "Industrial Fluid Power – Volume 2" on the topic of pressure compensated flow control valves.

The pressure reducing valve should be set to its lowest adjustment, as low as 50 PSI if possible. Its drain line, instead of being connected to tank, should be connected through a check valve either to cylinder Port A or B on the valve – to the one in which flow is to be compensated. If flow in both lines is to be compensated, use a shuttle valve connected as in the figure.

SELECTION OF VALVE SIZE

Size selection of a proportional solenoid valve is not made by pipe size, and is not made by selecting an overly large size with too low a pressure drop for good speed control.

Pressure drop through the valve is quite high as the spool starts its travel from neutral position. The pressure drop decreases as the spool moves farther. By the time the spool has reached full shifted position the pressure drop should have reached its minimum of no less than 150 to 200 PSI. Pressure drops and selection of proper size can only be made by using the flow curves published by the manufacturer, and taking into account any difference in oil viscosity from the viscosity used in preparing the flow curves.

If valve size is too large for the application, the pressure drop will have reached a minimum before the valve spool reaches full shift. This will cause the entire range of speed control to be concentrated near one end of spool travel instead of being spread evenly over the entire travel. Speed adjustment will be more critical and actuator speed may tend to be less stable.

If valve size is too small for the application, power losses and oil heating will be greater than they need to be. One manufacturer offers a choice of several spools with different notch sizes which fit the same size body. The user may choose the spool which, on his oil flow, will give *at least* 150 PSI at full spool shift. If necessary, the next smaller (rather than larger) notch size can be selected.

APPLICATION FOR JOYSTICK CONTROL

Figure 12-10. The advantages of using proportional solenoid valves to operate several cylinders or motors and controlling them with electronic joysticks rather than using conventional bank valves are (1), large valves handling high HP can be controlled with a very small operator effort, (2), control can be exercised from a remote location or from several locations without running large plumbing lines, and (3), with single hand control an operator can divide the pump flow between two or three circuits and operate all actuators at the same time.

Electronic joysticks are available in single-axis, 2-axis, and 3-axis models for controlling 1, 2, or 3 independent cylinders. A 2-axis joystick can be moved forward and back or from side to side. By moving diagonally, an operator can divide flow between two circuits. The third axis is up and down, and all three axes can be used at the same time by a skilled operator.

The proportional solenoid valve manufacturer can sometimes furnish the electronic joysticks, or he can furnish amplifiers to operate some other brand of joystick, or the joystick manufacturer can furnish amplifiers for his joysticks to feed into several brands of proportional valves.

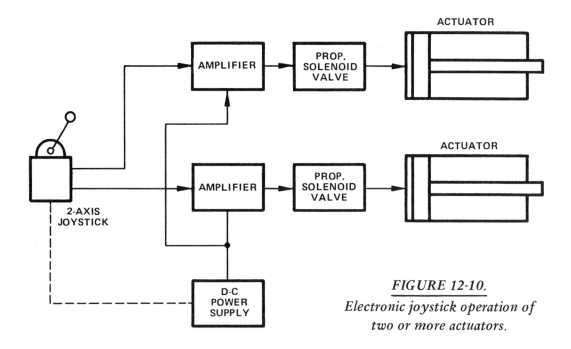

FIGURE 12-10.
Electronic joystick operation of two or more actuators.

One proportional solenoid valve and the amplifier to operate it are required for each actuator. The valves are closed center and can be connected in parallel across the pump line. A common D-C power supply can be used for all circuits requiring D-C power.

Two or more electronic joysticks can be connected in parallel for operation from more than one location or by more than one operator.

OPERATION FROM AUTOMATIC CIRCUITS

Figure 12-11. The command signals which control actuator speed and direction through the proportional valve can come from various sources and applied in various ways according to the model and brand equipment being used. Usually, signals which change actuator speed come from limit switches placed at appropriate positions along the cylinder stroke. These switches can be directly connected to the amplifier if the amplifier is one having built-in electronic circuits to provide reduced coil current for reduced speed. The amplifier may have several available circuits for this purpose. The command voltage from each circuit is adjustable with a small Pot on the amplifier chassis.

If the amplifier does not provide internal circuits to accept limit switch signals, the circuits can be provided externally with (in this case) adjustable Pots 1-P and 2-P connected to a source of D-C voltage. Limit Switches 1-LS and 2-LS can be connected to these pots to provide adjustable signals to the amplifier input when the switches are actuated.

Limit Switch 1-LS, for example, is connected to Pot 1-P. The normal position for 1-LS is to provide full (+) voltage to the amplifier for full extension speed. When 1-LS is actuated, a lower command voltage for slower speed is switched to the amplifier input.

In general, any method is acceptable which will supply a D-C command signal of the right voltage and polarity (+) for extension and (–) for retraction. No provision needs to be made in the external circuits for acceleration or deceleration (to prevent shock) at any place where the cylinder stops or reverses direction. Ramp adjustments in the amplifier can be set for the maximum acceleration or deceleration short of a shock condition.

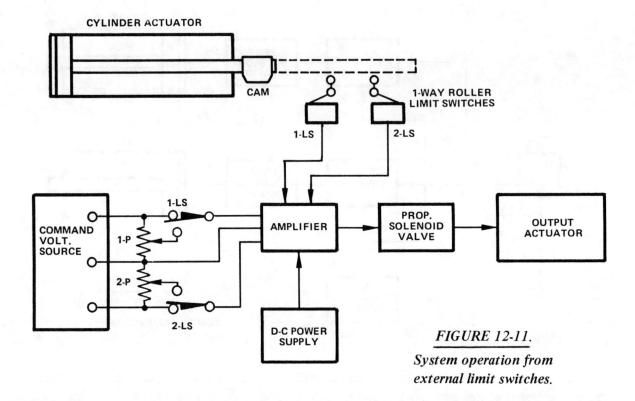

FIGURE 12-11.

System operation from external limit switches.

Limit switches placed along the cylinder stroke to change speed can be actuated by cams whose length is equal to the distance in which speed is to remain reduced. Where more than one speed change switch is used, separate cams should be used for each. Switches can also be momentarily actuated as the cylinder passes them. The momentary switching signal from the switch can be maintained by a holding relay for the distance desired, then the relay can be released. Limit switches fitted with a one-way roller actuator will be actuated by a cam approaching from one direction but will not be actuated on the return movement of the cam. See information on Page 19.

OPERATION FROM A PROGRAMMABLE CONTROLLER

Programmable controller operation will be demonstrated for the small Model S-6 controller described in Chapter 10. Drawing a ladder diagram for programming the entire electrical circuit has been described. In this example, only the components and connections related to speed and direction control of the cylinder are shown.

Figure 12-12. Hydraulic Diagram. This cylinder, and possibly others, is to be operated from a program in a controller, and its speed is to be automatically reduced at a certain point during its extension stroke and again at another point during its retraction stroke. Limit Switch 1-LS has been placed at the proper point in the extension stroke and 2-LS at the proper point in the retraction stroke. Both of these switches have one-way roller actuators of the kind described on Page 19. Each switch will actuate when a cam approaches from one direction but will not actuate on the return movement of the same cam. Each switch can be operated from a separate cam which has sufficient length to keep the switch actuated during the length of stroke where reduced speed is wanted.

(Text continues on Page 241)

239

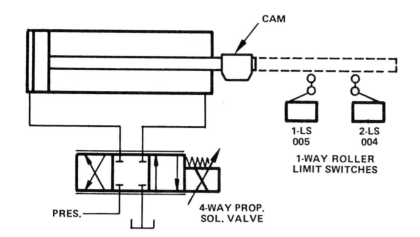

FIGURE 12-12.

Hydraulic diagram for programmable controller circuit shown below.

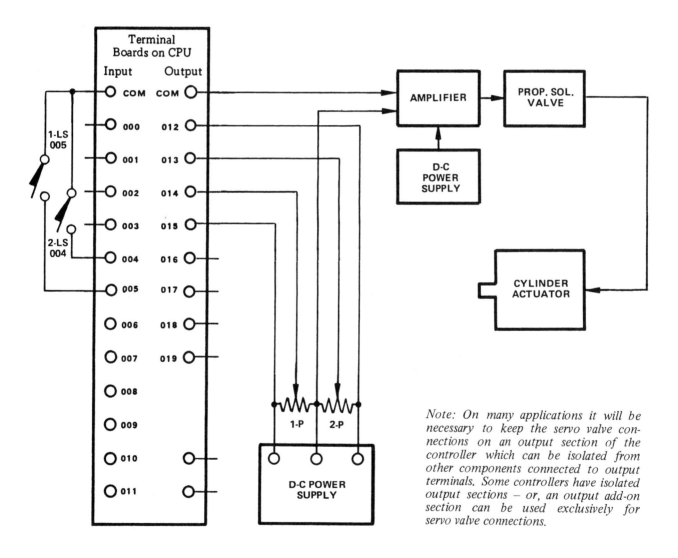

Note: On many applications it will be necessary to keep the servo valve connections on an output section of the controller which can be isolated from other components connected to output terminals. Some controllers have isolated output sections – or, an output add-on section can be used exclusively for servo valve connections.

FIGURE 12-13. *Block diagram – operation of a servo valve from a programmable controller.*

Figure 12-13. Electrical Circuit. The input and output terminal boards of the Model S-6 have been reproduced from Page 173. Proportional valve connections should be on a terminal board section which can be isolated from other output components. For example, an output add-on section can be used.

If the amplifier has internal circuits for setting cylinder speeds, Switches 1-LS and 2-LS should be connected, not to input terminals on the programmable controller, but directly to amplifier terminals, and the speed setting can be adjusted with pots on the amplifier. If the amplifier does not provide this function, the switches can be connected to controller input terminals as shown in the diagram and external pots provided for setting speed when each limit switch is actuated.

If a conventional double solenoid A-C valve were used to operate the cylinder, each of the two solenoids would be connected to one of the output terminals. When operating servo valves or proportional solenoid valves the problem is different because the valve has only one D-C solenoid coil. Energizing this coil with (+) polarity causes the cylinder to extend, energizing it with (–) polarity causes the cylinder to retract. Remember that each output terminal is simply an ON/OFF switching circuit; it does not supply power for operation of load devices.

In constructing a ladder diagram, signals from switches to start, reverse, and stop the cylinder must be connected to the input terminals. Among other switches, 1-LS and 2-LS have been assigned in this diagram to Terminals 005 and 004. Actuation of a switch will activate the terminal to which it is connected. On the output terminal board, the signal to start the cylinder in rapid advance must be programmed from a starting switch (not shown on the diagram), through a rung of the diagram to Terminal 019. The signal from 1-LS to reduce speed must be programmed from input Terminal 005, through another rung to Terminal 018. The signal to retract at full speed must be programmed from a limit switch at the end of the stroke (not shown on the diagram) through a rung to Terminal 016. The signal from 2-LS to reduce speed must be programmed from input Terminal 004 through a rung to Terminal 017. Potentiometers 1-P and 2-P are external components not a part of the controller. They must be pre-set to the reduced speeds needed.

If other cylinders must be controlled, each cylinder will require a proportional solenoid valve and its amplifier, connected to other input and output terminals in a like manner. In the Model S-6, to increase system capacity, input and/or output modules can be added.

One D-C power supply can serve all D-C circuits including amplifiers for all proportional valves and all potentiometers for reduced speed voltages.

PROPORTIONAL SOLENOID VALVES FOR PRESSURE CONTROL

FIG. 12-14

On machines where the maximum system pressure must automatically be changed during certain parts of every cycle, this can be done either with conventional solenoid relief valves or with proportional solenoid pressure relief or reducing valves.

Pressure Relief Valves. Figure 12-14. Changing pressure is cheaper by using conventional solenoid relief valves if they will produce the desired action. Circuits have been shown in the Womack book "Industrial Fluid Power – Volume 2". A pilot-operated relief valve is used across the pump. One or more small solenoid valves and miniature relief valves can be connected in the main relief valve vent line. Several pressure levels can be remotely selected by switches controlled by the operator, or by limit switches mounted at appropriate places along the path of cylinder or machine movement.

Probably the greatest advantage of using a proportional solenoid relief valve is that it not only can be controlled remotely but can be infinitely adjusted for pressure level by a rheostat or potentiometer on an operator's panel.

The D-C solenoid on a proportional relief valve is essentially the same as that used on directional control valves but acts as a "force controlled" solenoid. The force produced by current in the solenoid holds a pilot poppet on its seat. When hydraulic pressure under the poppet exceeds solenoid force, the pilot poppet raises to prevent a further rise in pressure on the main poppet. The relieving action is identical to that in a pilot-operated relief valve with manual spring adjustment of pilot poppet cracking pressure. Pressure control valves usually do not have a knob for manual adjustment.

An amplifier must be used and it must be one specifically designed for the valve to be controlled. Main functions of the amplifier are:

(1). To amplify the command voltage to a level which will operate the solenoid coil.

(2). To provide a "dither" to the solenoid to reduce the error caused by friction in the solenoid armature. This improves repeatability – the ability to arrive at the same pressure setting on successive cycles of operation, using the same command voltage. See more on Page 234.

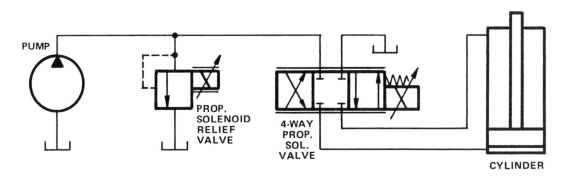

FIGURE 12-15. Hydraulic circuit —proportional solenoid direction, speed, and pressure control.

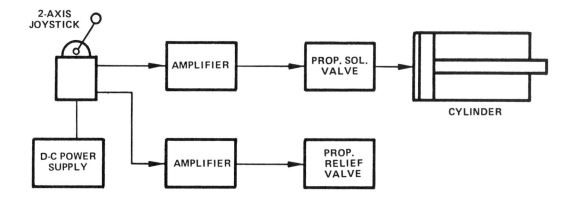

FIGURE 12-16. Block diagram of electrical control for above hydraulic circuit.

(3). To provide an adjustable delay (ramp) for pressure build-up or decay to reduce shock.

(4). To provide adjustments for pre-set maximum and minimum pressure levels.

(5). To offset the error produced by coil temperature (and resistance) changes by automatically adjusting voltage supplied to the solenoid to hold coil current to the correct level in relation to the command voltage.

Command signals often come from pre-adjusted Pots. Limit switches placed along a cylinder stroke connect Pot voltage to the input of the amplifier.

Joystick Control. Figure 12-15 and 12-16. A manually operated 2-axis electronic joystick can give complete control over direction, speed, and force of a hydraulic cylinder. The forward and backward axis movement controls both direction and speed. The side-to-side axis controls maximum pump pressure. The joystick can be moved along both axes at the same time.

Pressure Reducing Valves. Figure 12-17. A reducing valve is never used as the main pressure control of a system. It is always used to reduce the pressure in a branch circuit while allowing full pressure in the main circuit. Reducing valves are controlled in the same way as a relief valve — from D-C command voltages controlled by limit switches actuated by a cylinder, or from a manually variable Pot by the machine operator. Usually the same amplifier used for a relief valve can also be used to control a pressure reducing valve, and will provide the same functions described on the preceding page.

FIGURE 12-17.
Pressure Reducing Valve

PROPORTIONAL SOLENOID FLOW CONTROL VALVES

Figure 12-18. One manufacturer produces a spool-type pressure compensated flow control valve with proportional solenoid control of metering orifice size. A stroke controlled solenoid is used which is the same kind used in directional control valves. It is controlled through an amplifier specifically developed for it.

To avoid errors caused by coil heating and spool friction as described earlier in this chapter, spool position is detected by a "linear inductive transformer" which continually feeds back this information to the amplifier. Circuits in the amplifier compare this position voltage with the command voltage to see if the spool is where it should be for that level of command voltage. If not, it will adjust the voltage applied to the proportional solenoid to bring its coil current (and position) to where it should be.

One important use for this kind of valve is in a system using conventional A-C solenoid 4-way valves and in which it is necessary to vary the flow by electrical control from a remote location.

For speed control of a cylinder this valve can be installed between the 4-way valve and one of the cylinder ports, and connected for either meter-in or meter-out remote speed control.

FIGURE 12-18. Pressure Compensated Flow Control Valve.

APPENDIX
REFERENCE INFORMATION

GRAPHIC SYMBOLS FOR FLUID POWER DIAGRAMS

Common symbols are shown here. A complete list of approved ANSI (American National Standards Institute) graphic symbols can be obtained from the National Fluid Power Association. Ask for Publication ANSI Y32.10-1967.

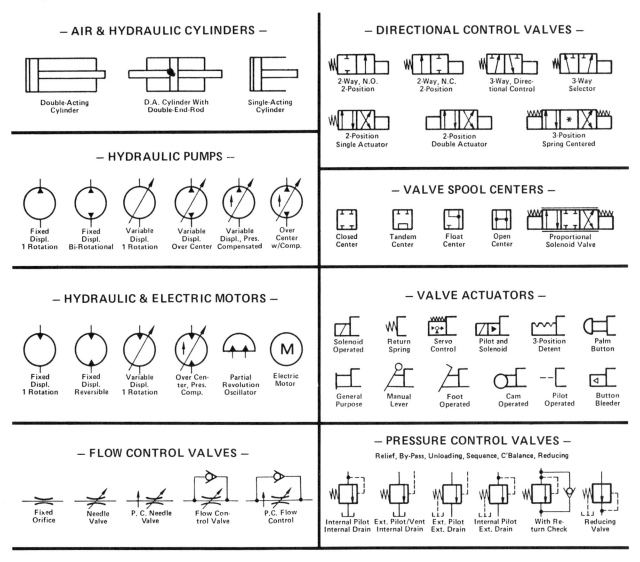

— AIR & HYDRAULIC CYLINDERS —

Double-Acting Cylinder | D.A. Cylinder With Double-End-Rod | Single-Acting Cylinder

— HYDRAULIC PUMPS —

Fixed Displ. 1 Rotation | Fixed Displ. Bi-Rotational | Variable Displ. 1 Rotation | Variable Displ. Over Center | Variable Displ., Pres. Compensated | Over Center w/Comp.

— HYDRAULIC & ELECTRIC MOTORS —

Fixed Displ. 1 Rotation | Fixed Displ. Reversible | Variable Displ. 1 Rotation | Over Center, Pres. Comp. | Partial Revolution Oscillator | Electric Motor

— FLOW CONTROL VALVES —

Fixed Orifice | Needle Valve | P. C. Needle Valve | Flow Control Valve | P.C. Flow Control

— DIRECTIONAL CONTROL VALVES —

2-Way, N.O. 2-Position | 2-Way, N.C. 2-Position | 3-Way, Directional Control | 3-Way Selector

2-Position Single Actuator | 2-Position Double Actuator | 3-Position Spring Centered

— VALVE SPOOL CENTERS —

Closed Center | Tandem Center | Float Center | Open Center | Proportional Solenoid Valve

— VALVE ACTUATORS —

Solenoid Operated | Return Spring | Servo Control | Pilot and Solenoid | 3-Position Detent | Palm Button

General Purpose | Manual Lever | Foot Operated | Cam Operated | Pilot Operated | Button Bleeder

— PRESSURE CONTROL VALVES —

Relief, By-Pass, Unloading, Sequence, C'Balance, Reducing

Internal Pilot Internal Drain | Ext. Pilot/Vent Internal Drain | Ext. Pilot Ext. Drain | Internal Pilot Ext. Drain | With Return Check | Reducing Valve

—MISCELLANEOUS AIR & HYDRAULIC COMPONENTS —

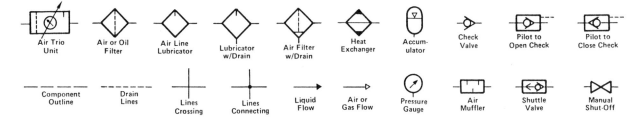

Air Trio Unit | Air or Oil Filter | Air Line Lubricator | Lubricator w/Drain | Air Filter w/Drain | Heat Exchanger | Accumulator | Check Valve | Pilot to Open Check | Pilot to Close Check

Component Outline | Drain Lines | Lines Crossing | Lines Connecting | Liquid Flow | Air or Gas Flow | Pressure Gauge | Air Muffler | Shuttle Valve | Manual Shut-Off

JIC STANDARD GRAPHIC SYMBOLS FOR ELECTRICAL LADDER DIAGRAMS

These graphic symbols are the ones most often used on ladder diagrams for fluid power electrical control circuits. They are standard JIC (Joint Industrial Council) symbols as approved and adopted by the NMTBA (National Machine Tool Builders Association). They have been extracted from the Appendix of the NMTBA Specification EGP1-1967. Remember that JIC standards are advisory only. Their use in industry or trade is entirely voluntary.

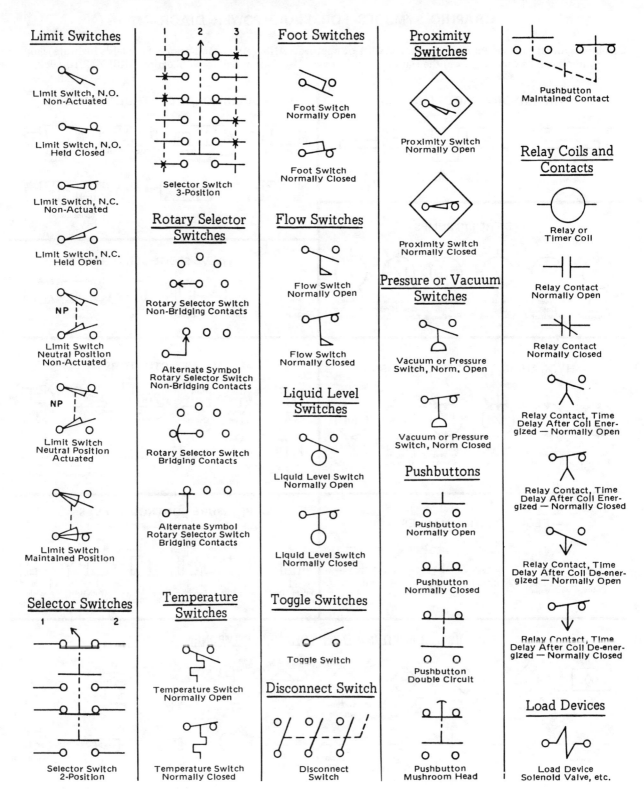

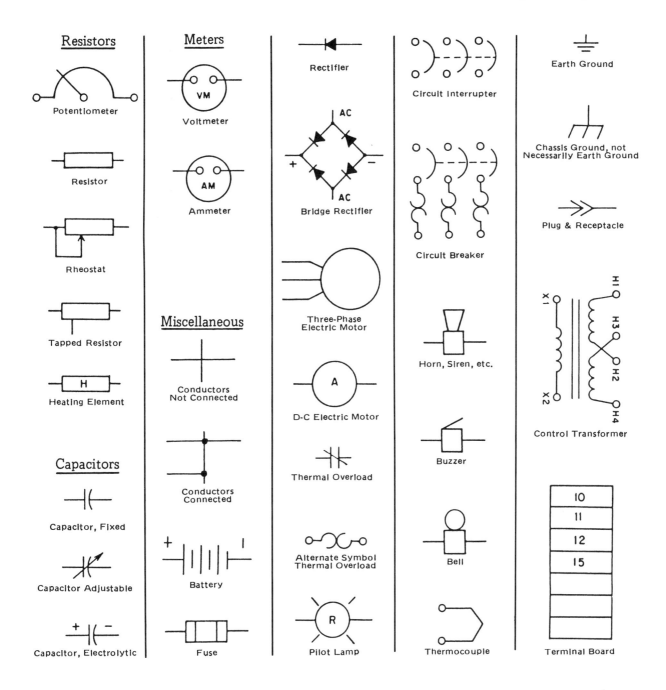

DEVICE DESIGNATIONS

These abbreviations are intended for use on diagrams in connection with the corresponding symbol from the charts on this and the preceding page, to amplify information on the function of a device. Suitable prefix numbers (1, 2, 3, etc.) may be added to distinguish between several similar devices. Suffix letters (A, B, C, etc.) may be added to distinguish between several sets of contacts on the same device. Examples: 1-CR-A, 1-CR-B, 1-CR-C, etc.

AM- Ammeter	CR - Control relay	FLS - Flow switch	RECEP - Receptacle
CAP - Capacitor	CS - Cam switch	FS - Float switch	RES - Resistor
CB - Circuit breaker	CTR - Counter	FTS - Foot switch	RH - Rheostat
CI - Circuit interrupter	F - Forward	HTR - Heating element	RSS - Rotary sel. sw.
CON - Contactor	FB - Fuse block	FU - Fuse	S - Switch
		GRD - Ground	SOC - Socket
		LS - Limit switch	SOL - Solenoid
		LT - Pilot light	SS - Selector switch
		M - Motor starter	T- Transformer
		MTR - Motor	TAS - Temp. actuated sw.
		PB - Pushbutton	TB - Terminal block
		POT - Potentiometer	T/C - Thermocouple
		PRS - Proximity switch	TGS - Toggle switch
		PS - Pressure switch	TR - Time delay relay
		R - Reverse	VM - Voltmeter
		REC - Rectifier	VS - Vacuum switch

246

NEMA FRAME ASSIGNMENTS – 3-PHASE INDUCTION-TYPE ELECTRIC MOTORS

Open Dripproof Motors			*Totally Enclosed Motors*			*Shaft Data for All Motors*			
HP	Speed, RPM	NEMA Frame	HP	Speed, RPM	NEMA Frame	NEMA Frame	Shaft Diam.	Shaft Length	Shaft Height
1	1200	145T	1	1200	145T	143T	7/8	2-1/4	3-1/2
1	1800	143T	1	1800	143T	145T	7/8	2-1/4	3-1/2
1½	1200	182T	1½	1200	182T	182T	1-1/8	2-3/4	4-1/2
1½	1800	145T	1½	1800	145T	184T	1-1/8	2-3/4	4-1/2
1½	3600	143T	1½	3600	143T	213T	1-3/8	3-3/8	5-1/4
2	1200	184T	2	1200	184T	215T	1-3/8	3-3/8	5-1/4
2	1800	145T	2	1800	145T	254T	1-5/8	4	6-1/4
2	3600	145T	2	3600	145T	256T	1-5/8	4	6-1/4
3	1200	213T	3	1200	213T	284T	1-7/8	4-5/8	7
3	1800	182T	3	1800	182T	284TS	1-5/8	3-1/4	7
3	3600	145T	3	3600	182T	286T	1-7/8	4-5/8	7
5	1200	215T	5	1200	215T	286TS	1-5/8	3-1/4	7
5	1800	184T	5	1800	184T	324T	2-1/8	5-1/4	8
5	3600	182T	5	3600	184T	324TS	1-7/8	3-3/4	8
7½	1200	254T	7½	1200	254T	326T	2-1/8	5-1/4	8
7½	1800	213T	7½	1800	213T	326TS	1-7/8	3-3/4	8
7½	3600	184T	7½	3600	213T	364T	2-3/8	5-7/8	9
10	1200	256T	10	1200	256T	364TS	1-7/8	3-3/4	9
10	1800	215T	10	1800	215T	365T	2-3/8	5-7/8	9
10	3600	213T	10	3600	215T	365TS	1-7/8	3-3/4	9
15	1200	284T	15	1200	284T	404T	2-7/8	7-1/4	10
15	1800	254T	15	1800	254T	404TS	2-1/8	4-1/4	10
15	3600	215T	15	3600	254T	405T	2-7/8	7-1/4	10
20	1200	286T	20	1200	286T	405TS	2-1/8	4-1/4	10
20	1800	256T	20	1800	256T	444T	3-3/8	8-1/2	11
20	3600	254T	20	3600	256T	444TS	3-3/8	8-1/2	11
25	1200	324T	25	1200	324T	445T	3-3/8	8-1/2	11
25	1800	284T	25	1800	284T	445TS	2-3/8	4-3/4	11
25	3600	256T	25	3600	284TS				
30	1200	326T	30	1200	326T				
30	1800	286T	30	1800	286T				
30	3600	284TS	30	3600	286TS				
40	1200	364T	40	1200	364T				
40	1800	324T	40	1800	324T				
40	3600	286TS	40	3600	324TS				
50	1200	365T	50	1200	365T				
50	1800	326T	50	1800	326T				
50	3600	324TS	50	3600	326TS				
60	1200	404T	60	1200	404T				
60	1800	364TS	60	1800	364TS				
60	3600	326TS	60	3600	364TS				
75	1200	405T	75	1200	405T				
75	1800	365TS	75	1800	365TS				
75	3600	364TS	75	3600	365TS				
100	1200	444T	100	1200	444T				
100	1800	404TS	100	1800	405TS				
100	3600	365TS	100	3600	405TS				
125	1200	445T	125	1200	445T				
125	1800	405TS	125	1800	444TS				
125	3600	404TS	125	3600	444TS				
150	1800	444TS	150	1800	445TS				
150	3600	405TS	150	3600	445TS				
200	1800	445TS							
200	3600	444TS							
250	3600	445TS							

Larger sizes are not standard.

The most widely used type of electric motor for hydraulic pump drive is the 3-phase, squirrel cage induction motor with Design B electrical characteristics. It is available in open dripproof, totally enclosed, and explosion proof frames. Information on this page is concerned only with frame assignments and with dimensions of shaft length, diameter, and height above base, which have to do with selection of a pump coupling and with the height of a pump mounting bracket. Please refer to other pages in this Appendix for information on wire and fuse sizes.

Shaft dimensions in the columns above apply to both open and totally enclosed motors which have the indicated frame assignment.

Note: Symbol TS indicates standard short shaft for direct drive. Symbol T, standard long shaft may be preferred for side drive from belt or gear.

WIRE SIZE AND FUSE RATINGS FOR 3-PHASE ELECTRIC MOTORS

Motors should be protected by both fuses (or circuit breakers) and by heater coils in a magnetic motor starter. Fuses will open the circuit quickly in case of a short circuit or a sudden massive overload. Heater coils do not give this kind of protection. They provide a delay and open the circuit if the average current over a period of time is greater than the circuit or motor is designed to handle. Fuses cannot give this kind of protection.

In some cases it may be necessary to use delayed action fuses. These provide a delay of a few seconds before blowing. This prevents them from blowing until a motor can get started and reach full speed.

Current values in this chart, are approximate, and are compiled from data published by several motor manufacturers. They could be slightly high or low for a specific brand or size motor. For selection of magnetic starter heater coils it is better to go by the nameplate current rating of the actual motor rather than depending on this or any other table.

Wire and fuse sizes are listed for reference only, and may vary with the type of insulation, number of conductors in a cable or raceway, the ambient temperature, and other factors. On a new design, requirements of the NEC (National Electrical Code) should be followed. A copy of the code book can be ordered through any book store. Other local ordnances may also apply.

HP	Speed RPM	230-Volt Service			460-Volt Service			HP	Speed RPM	230-Volt Service			460-Volt Service		
		Full Load Amps	Wire Size	Fuse Amps	Full Load Amps	Wire Size	Fuse Amps			Full Load Amps	Wire Size	Fuse Amps	Full Load Amps	Wire Size	Fuse Amps
1	1200	3.76	14	10	1.88	14	6	25	1200	65.6	3	120	32.8	6	180
1	1800	3.56	14	10	1.78	14	6	25	1800	64.8	3	120	32.4	6	80
1	3600	2.80	14	10	1.40	14	6	25	3600	60.8	3	120	30.4	6	80
1½	1200	5.28	14	15	2.64	14	10	30	1200	78.8	1	150	39.4	6	80
1½	1800	4.86	14	15	2.43	14	10	30	1800	75.6	1	150	37.8	6	80
1½	3600	4.36	14	15	2.18	14	10	30	3600	73.7	1	150	36.8	6	80
2	1200	6.84	15	20	3.42	14	10	40	1200	102	0	200	50.6	4	110
2	1800	6.40	14	20	3.20	14	10	40	1800	101	0	200	50.4	4	110
2	3600	5.60	14	20	3.00	14	10	40	3600	96.4	0	200	48.2	4	110
3	1200	10.2	14	25	5.12	14	15	50	1200	126	000	250	63.0	3	120
3	1800	9.40	14	25	4.70	14	15	50	1800	124	000	250	62.2	3	120
3	3600	8.34	14	25	4.17	14	15	50	3600	120	000	250	60.1	3	120
5	1200	15.8	12	30	7.91	14	20	60	1200	150	000	300	75.0	2	150
5	1800	14.4	12	30	7.21	14	20	60	1800	149	000	300	74.5	2	150
5	3600	13.5	12	30	6.76	14	20	60	3600	143	000	300	71.7	2	150
7½	1200	21.8	10	40	10.9	14	20	75	1200	184	300	350	92.0	0	200
7½	1800	21.5	10	40	10.7	14	20	75	1800	183	300	350	91.6	0	200
7½	3600	19.5	10	40	9.79	14	20	75	3600	179	300	350	89.6	0	200
10	1200	28.0	8	60	14.0	12	30	100	1200	239	500	500	120	000	250
10	1800	26.8	8	60	13.4	12	30	100	1800	236	500	500	118	000	250
10	3600	25.4	8	60	12.7	12	30	100	3600	231	500	500	115	000	250
15	1200	41.4	6	80	20.7	10	40	125	1200	298	- - -	- - -	149	0000	300
15	1800	39.2	6	80	19.6	10	40	125	1800	293	- - -	- - -	147	0000	300
15	3600	36.4	6	80	18.2	10	40	125	3600	292	- - -	- - -	146	0000	300
20	1200	52.8	4	110	26.4	8	60	150	1200	350	- - -	- - -	174	300	350
20	1800	51.2	4	110	25.6	8	60	150	1800	348	- - -	- - -	174	300	350
20	3600	50.4	4	110	25.2	8	60	150	3600	343	- - -	- - -	174	300	350

For selecting ampere rating of heater coils for magnetic motor starters, select the standard coil with rating closest to the rating on the motor nameplate. However, if motor operates in a cold environment, the coil with next lower rating may be preferred. If in a hot environment, the coil with next larger current rating may work better.

For copper wires in a cable or raceway, the NEC recommends the maximum current shown in this table where there are no more than 6 current carrying wires in the cable. The first column is continuous ampere flow, the sceond column is wire size, B & S or MCM.

MINIMUM SIZE OF COPPER CONDUCTORS

Amps	Size	Amps	Size	Amps	Size
15	14	60	4	175	3/0
20	12	70	4	200	4/0
25	10	80	3	225	250
30	10	90	3	250	300
35	8	100	2	300	400
40	8	110	1	350	500
45	6	125	1	400	750
50	6	150	0	450	1000

SELECTION GUIDE FOR ELECTRIC WIRE SIZE

Two Factors to be Considered ... When choosing conductor size for electric wiring, TWO important factors must be considered: (1), the safe current-carrying capacity without overheating, and (2), keeping voltage loss to an acceptable minimum.

On short wiring runs, say up to 20 feet, the voltage loss is usually negligible and need not be considered. Wire size should be selected solely for current rating. See Chart 1.

On longer runs, say several hundred feet or more, the voltage loss may be too high, even though the wire size will carry the current without overheating. In this case, a wire of larger diameter should be used which will keep the voltage loss to an acceptable minimum. Voltage loss per 1000 feet is shown in Chart 2 according to wire size.

Permissible Voltage Loss ... There will be a voltage loss on any wiring run, and the designer must decide how much loss can be tolerated without seriously affecting performance. He must select a wire size accordingly. Electric motors generally should not be operated at full load on less than 90% of nameplate voltage.

When deciding on acceptable voltage loss in the wiring, the minimum voltage available from the power line at certain periods of the day must be considered. For example, a motor rated at 230 volts should not be run under full load at less than 208 volts. If line voltage may sometimes drop as low as 220 volts, the wiring should be designed for no greater than 12 volts loss.

A rule-of-thumb is to design the wiring of sufficient size to limit voltage drop to 5% of the input voltage.

Chart 1 – Wire Ampacity for Short Wiring Runs

"Ampacity" means ampere capacity. Chart 1 is for runs of less than 20 feet. Figures in the chart are recommended maximum current flow. They are taken from NEC (National Electrical Code) for No. 14 and larger sizes. The current capacity also depends on type of insulation, how the wire is installed – whether in the open or in a raceway, and the ambient temperature. The chart is based on low temperature insulation (140°F). Wire with high temperature insulation will carry higher current Consult NEC code for capacity of larger wires.

(Figures in the body of this chart are recommended maximum current ratings, in amperes)

Wire Size, B & S	18	16	14	12	10	8	6	4	3	2	1	0	00	000	0000
In Raceway or Cable	6	9	15	20	30	40	55	70	80	95	110	125	145	165	195
In Open Air	8	12	20	25	40	55	80	105	120	140	165	195	225	260	300

Chart 2 – Voltage Loss on Long Wiring Runs

Chart 2 is for long runs, several hundred feet or more. Decide on operating conditions before using this chart, including the following:

(1). Current flow in the line must be determined.

(2). The amount of voltage loss which is acceptable must be decided,

(3). Length of wiring run must be measured or calculated using the sum of outgoing and return wire lengths.

On 3-phase devices such as electric motors, each of the three main wires must carry the current shown on motor nameplate but the length of wiring run is the sum of lengths of only two, not three, connecting wires.

Read across the top of the chart to find the column which matches the amperage rating of the load. Figures in this column show voltage losses per 1000 feet of wire length, the sum of outgoing plus return. If, for example, total wire length is 250 feet, losses would be 1/4th the chart figure, etc.

(Figures in the body of this chart are voltage losses per 1000 feet of wire length)

Wire Size B & S	Current Flow, Amperes											
	10	15	20	25	30	40	50	60	70	80	90	100
18	65.10	97.65	130.2	162.8	195.3	260.4	325.5	390.6	455.7	520.8	585.9	651.0
16	40.94	61.41	81.88	102.4	122.8	163.8	204.7	245.6	286.6	327.5	368.5	409.4
14	25.75	38.63	51.50	64.38	77.25	103.0	128.8	154.5	180.3	206.0	231.8	257.5
12	16.19	24.28	32.38	40.48	48.57	64.76	80.95	97.14	113.3	129.5	145.7	161.9
10	10.18	15.27	20.36	25.45	30.54	40.72	50.90	61.08	71.26	81.44	91.62	101.8
8	6.405	9.608	12.01	16.02	19.22	25.62	32.03	38.43	44.84	51.24	57.65	64.05
6	4.028	6.042	8.056	10.07	12.08	16.11	20.14	24.18	28.21	32.24	36.27	40.30
4	2.533	3.800	5.068	6.335	7.602	10.14	12.68	15.22	17.75	20.29	22.82	25.36
3	2.009	3.014	4.020	5.025	6.030	8.040	10.05	12.07	14.08	16.09	18.10	20.11
2	1.593	2.390	3.184	3.980	4.776	6.368	7.960	9.552	11.14	12.74	14.33	15.92
1	1.264	1.896	2.528	3.160	3.792	5.056	6.320	7.584	8.848	10.11	11.38	12.64
0	1.002	1.503	2.004	2.505	3.006	4.008	5.010	6.012	7.014	8.016	9.018	10.02
00	0.796	1.193	1.592	1.990	2.388	3.184	3.980	4.776	5.572	6.368	7.164	7.960
000	0.630	0.945	1.260	1.575	1.890	2.520	3.150	3.780	4.410	5.040	5.670	6.300
0000	0.500	0.750	1.000	1.250	1.500	2.000	2.500	3.000	3.500	4.000	4.500	5.000

ELECTRIC MOTOR TERMINAL MARKINGS

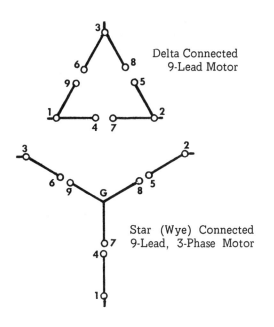

Delta Connected
9-Lead Motor

Star (Wye) Connected
9-Lead, 3-Phase Motor

NEMA Standard Terminal Markings and Connections for 9-Lead, 3-Phase Motors

These diagrams show which motor leads must be wired together inside the motor junction box for operation of the motor on its highest or lowest voltage as stated on its nameplate. Normally, on a star connected motor the center point of the windings is brought out for connection to ground.

DELTA CONNECTION

Voltage	Line 1	Line 2	Line 3	Together
Low	1&6&7	2&4&8	3&5&9	None
High	1	2	3	4 & 7, 5 & 8, 6 & 9

STAR (WYE) CONNECTION

Voltage	Line 1	Line 2	Line 3	Together
Low	1 & 7	2 & 8	3 & 9	4 & 5 & 6
High	1	2	3	4 & 7, 5 & 8, 6 & 9

CHARACTERISTICS OF COPPER WIRE

No. AWG	Diam., Mils	Area, Circ. Mils	Lbs. per 1000 Ft. *	Ohms per 1000 Ft. **	Feet per Ohm	No. AWG	Diam., Mils	Area, Circ. Mils	Lbs. per 1000 Ft. *	Ohms per 1000 Ft. **	Feet per Ohm
0000	460	211,600	640.5	.05901	19,643	19	35.9	1,288	3.900	8.361	119.6
000	410	167,800	508.0	.06419	15,579	20	32.0	1,024	3.099	10.52	95.1
00	365	133,100	402.8	.08097	12,350	21	28.5	812.3	2.459	13.26	75.4
0	325	105,600	319.7	.1019	9,814	22	25.3	640.1	1.937	16.83	59.4
1	289	83,500	252.7	.1290	7,752	23	22.6	510.8	1.546	21.09	47.4
2	258	66,500	201.5	.1618	6,180	24	20.1	404.0	1.223	26.66	37.45
3	229	52,440	158.7	.2054	4,869	25	17.9	320.4	.9697	33.63	29.71
4	204	41,620	126.0	.2588	3,864	26	15.9	252.8	.7650	42.57	23.48
5	182	33,120	100.2	.3253	3,074	27	14.2	201.6	.6101	53.45	18.71
6	162	26,240	79.43	.4105	2,436	28	12.6	158.8	.4806	67.84	14.74
7	144	20,740	62.78	.5194	1,925	29	11.3	127.7	.3866	84.35	11.85
8	128	16,380	49.60	.6574	1,521	30	10.0	100.0	.3027	107.8	9.28
9	114	13,000	39.35	.8286	1,207	31	8.9	79.2	.2398	136.0	7.36
10	102	10,400	31.48	1.036	965.2	32	8.0	64.0	.1937	168.2	5.94
11	90.7	8226	24.90	1.309	763.9	33	7.1	50.4	.1526	213.6	4.68
12	80.8	6,529	19.76	1.650	606.1	34	6.3	39.7	.1201	271.1	3.69
13	72.0	5,180	15.68	2.080	480.7	35	5.6	31.4	.09493	342.5	2.919
14	64.1	4,109	12.44	2.621	381.5	36	5.0	25.0	.07568	431.7	2.315
15	57.1	3,260	9.866	3.304	302.6	37	4.5	20.3	.06130	532.1	1.880
16	50.8	2,581	7.812	4.174	239.5	38	4.0	16.0	.04843	671.5	1.488
17	45.3	2,052	6.213	5.249	190.5	39	3.5	12.3	.03708	872.3	1.147
18	40.3	1,624	4.914	6.636	150.7	40	3.1	9.6	.02909	1128	0.888

Temperature Correction. The chart shows wire resistance at 25°C (77°F). The following formula can be used to find resistance at other wire temperatures:

$$R_c = R_t[1 + 0.00385(t - 25)]$$

where: R_c is the resistance at the new temperature; R_t is the resistance value from table; t is the wire temperature in degrees C.

*Weight of bare wire.   **At 25°C (77°F).

FINDING THE CAUSE OF SOLENOID COIL BURN-OUT

Perhaps occasionally a solenoid valve coil may burn out because of a defect in its manufacture. But usually the cause can be traced to an abnormal condition either in operating conditions of the machine on which the valve is used, or to unusual environmental conditions. This becomes evident if the burn-out should occur more than once on the same coil and under the same operating conditions.

CHECKLIST FOR A-C SOLENOID VALVES

Burn-out is more common on valves with A-C coils than on those with D-C coils because of high inrush current at the moment the coil is energized. Until the armature on an A-C solenoid becomes fully seated, closing the air gap in the magnetic loop, the current is often 5 times the normal, steady state or holding current. On a D-C solenoid, the inrush is about the same as the holding current. Here are some likely causes of burn-out on an A-C solenoid:

1. Coil Does Not Match Operating Voltage . . .

Improper match between the electrical source and the coil rating is sometimes a cause for burn-out.

a. Voltage Too High. The operating voltage should be no more than 10% above the coil voltage rating. Excessive voltage causes excessive current, and excessive current causes excessive heating.

b. Voltage Too Low. Operating voltage should be no more than 10% below coil voltage rating. Low voltage causes low current, and low current reduces the mechanical force of the solenoid. If unable to pull completely in, it will draw more current than its steady state rating and it will soon burn out.

A test for low voltage should be made by measuring the voltage directly on the coil wires while the solenoid is energized but is blocked open so it will draw inrush current. Energize the solenoid just long enough to take a voltage reading. Also, take a no-load reading on the feed wires while they are disconnected from the solenoid. A difference of more than 5% between these two readings indicates excessive resistance in the wiring circuit, or insufficient volt-ampere capacity in the control transformer if one is used.

c. Frequency. Operation of a 60 Hz coil on 50 Hz will cause the coil to draw higher than normal current. Operation of a 50 Hz coil on 60 Hz will cause the coil to draw less than normal current and it may burn out from inability to seat its armature.

2. Overlap In Energization . . .

On some double solenoid valves, if both solenoids are energized at the same time and held in this state for a short time, the last coil to be energized will be unable to seat its armature and will burn out from excessive current.

The burn-out condition described above will occur only on double solenoid valves where the two solenoids are yoked to opposite ends of a common spool. If each solenoid operates a separate spool, both of them can be energized at the same time without danger of burn-out.

Careful attention should be given to electrical circuit design to make certain that an operator, through an accident, cannot energize both solenoids at the same time. Interlocking circuits can be used on pushbuttons, and these are described on Page 149.

Even with correct circuit design and interlock circuits a relay with sticking contacts or slow release can be responsible for a momentary overlap of energization on each cycle and eventual coil burn-out. This condition can only be detected with the use of an oscilloscope.

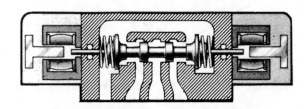

On an A-C solenoid valve where two solenoids are yoked to opposite ends of a common spool, energizing both solenoids at the same time will cause one of them to burn out.

3. Too Rapid Cycling . . .

Since the inrush can be 5 times the holding current, a standard A-C coil on an air-gap solenoid can overheat and burn out if required to cycle too frequently. Because of the high current during inrush periods, the average current over a period of an hour or so will be greater than the steady state current rating. Heat will accumulate and gradually build up in the windings. This could burn out a coil after a few hours operation.

High cycling applications can be roughly defined as those where the solenoid is energized more than 5 to 10 times per minute. On those applications, oil immersed solenoid structures or those with high temperature coils should be used.

In plants where instrumentation is available, a thermocouple can be placed on the surface of the winding on two identical valves. One valve can be cycled for several hours at the proposed cycle rate while the other valve solenoid remains continuously energized. A difference of more that 10 to 20°F in surface temperature of the two coils indicates the need for an oil immersed solenoid.

During the design stage, electrical circuits can be designed to use D-C valves. These valves can be cycled as often as needed without overheating.

4. High Electrical Transients . . .

If current for the solenoid valves is taken directly from a power line which is supplying large inductive devices such as electric motors, the switching of these motors may cause high transient voltages which may break down the coil insulation on solenoid coils. If this appears to be a problem, a "thyrector" can be placed across the coil of each solenoid to "short circuit" these momentary high transients. Thyrectors are available at electrical supply houses.

251

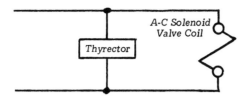

On A-C solenoids a thyrector placed across the coil will short circuit momentary high transient voltages which otherwise might damage coil insulation.

5. Dirt in Oil or Atmosphere . . .

A small particle lodging under the armature of a solenoid may keep it from fully seating. The solenoid may appear to be working properly but its steady state current will be above normal. If this is suspected, measure the coil current and compare with the coil rating.

On valves with loose dust covers, be sure these covers remain tightly in place to exclude atmospheric dust.

Small dirt particles in the oil may lodge on the surface of the spool, glued there by "varnish" circulating in the oil, or the varnish itself may cause excessive spool drag and excessive average current. "Varnish" forms in systems where the oil is allowed to run too hot. Heat accelerates unwanted chemical reactions. Reduce oil temperature with a heat exchanger.

6. Environmental Conditions . . .

Abnormally high or abnormally low ambient temperatures to which a solenoid is exposed for an extended time may cause a solenoid to burn out.

<u>a.</u> High Temperature. Coil insulation may be damaged and one layer of wire may short to the next layer. A heat shield or baffle will give some protection against radiated heat. High temperature or oil immersed solenoids are the best protection against heat conducted either through metal surfaces or from surrounding high temperature air.

<u>b.</u> Low Temperature. Cold ambient temperatures cause oil to become more viscous, possibly overloading solenoid valve capacity (see Item 9). Mechanical parts of the valve or solenoid structure may distort, causing the valve spool to stick and burn out the solenoid coil. Use an oil more suitable for the low temperature, or use an oil immersed or high temperature coil to handle the greater load imposed by the abnormally low ambient temperature.

7. Dead End Service . . .

Fluid circulating through a solenoid valve helps to carry away electrical heat. Some valves depend on fluid flow to keep excesive heat from accumulating, and if used on dead end service, and the solenoid remains energized for long periods without fluid flow, this effect, possibly in combination with other causes may burn out a coil.

8. Atmospheric Moisture . . .

High humidity coupled with frequently changing ambient temperature, may form corrosion on metal parts of the solenoid structure, causing the armature to drag or the spool to stick. Humidity also tends to deteriorate standard solenoid coils, causing shorts in the windings.

Change to molded coils or oil immersed solenoids.

Keep solenoid covers in place, and perhaps seal the electrical conduit openings after the wiring is installed.

9. Excessive Flow Through Valve . . .

Pressure drop through the spool of a direct-acting solenoid valve due to excessive flow may cause a force unbalance (Bernouilli's Principle) tending to cause the spool to move in an axial direction with extra load on the solenoid.

In circuit design, be very careful not to overload a valve above its manufacturer's flow rating. In fact, it should be de-rated when used with fluids of higher viscosity or those having a higher specific gravity (fire resistant fluids, etc).

CHECKLIST FOR D-C VALVES

A-C solenoid valves are far more common for in-plant industrial applications, but D-C solenoids may in some cases offer a specific advantage. A-C current can be run through a full wave rectifier to obtain a D-C supply. A filter capacitor may have to be added to eliminate chatter or hum.

<u>a.</u> Inrush Current. On D-C solenoids, inrush is about the same as holding current. Therefore, some of the burnout conditions previously described may not apply.

<u>b.</u> Fast Cycling. Because of lower inrush current, D-C solenoids can usually be cycled at higher rates without overheating the coil.

<u>c.</u> Repeatability. Shifting time on a valve with a D-C solenoid repeats accurately from cycle to cycle. On A-C valves, shifting time may vary each cycle according to the state of the line current at the moment the valve is energized — whether at maximum, minimum, or in between.

<u>d.</u> Limit Switch Contacts. D-C solenoids may burn up switch contacts faster than do A-C solenoids. Energy stored in the coil inductance must dissipate when the coil is disconnected, causing an arc across switch contacts on their break. Much of this energy can be safely dissipated by wiring a diode across the coil, with + on diode connected to + side of coil voltage. The diode should be rated for at least 2 to 3 times the D-C supply voltage.

A capacitor wired across the switch contacts on A-C or D-C solenoids will help absorb released energy. The best value of capacitance can be determined by trial, either by observing intensity of the arc, or by measuring the voltage spike with an oscilloscope as various capacitors are tried.

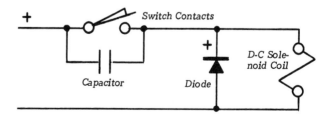

Contact arcing on A-C and D-C solenoids can be reduced by placing a capacitor across the contacts. On D-C solenoids a diode placed across the coil will help to dissipate stored coil energy when the switch contacts are opened.

HOW TO SELECT A PRESSURE SWITCH FOR YOUR APPLICATION

Part of the information on diaphragm and bourdon tube pressure switches was adapted from information published by the Barksdale Division of Delaval.

Several types of pressure switches are available. A designer should choose a type which can be expected to give the most satisfactory results on his application.

Basic Types . . .

At low pressures (compressed air, vacuum, and very low hydraulics), diaphragm and bellows movements, and sometimes bourdon tube, are most often used. At high pressures, piston and bourdon tube movements are more common. Snap action contacts seem to be universally used except in switches with tilting mercury contacts actuated with a bourdon tube. See Page 20.

Expected Service Life . . .

Expected life is usually limited by the type of pressure sensing mechanism — bourdon tube, diaphragm, piston, belleville spring, etc. The snap action contacts are presumed to have greater life than the sensing mechanism.

If the service life (number of cycles the switch is expected to operate) is less than 1 million, a bourdon tube or diaphragm type is indicated. If more than 1 million cycles, a piston type should be used. An exception is when the pressure change in a system is small (20% or less, of the adjustable range). Under such a condition a bourdon tube or diaphragm switch can be used up to 2½ million cycles before metal fatigue or contact failure.

Speed of Cycling . . .

In addition to service life, the cycling speed must be considered. If a switch is to cycle more than once every 3 seconds, a piston switch is preferred. The metal in any bourdon tube or diaphragm acts as a spring which will heat and fatigue on extremely high cycle rates, thus reducing switch life expectancy.

Accuracy . . .

Diaphragm and bourdon tube pressure switches generally have greater accuracy than piston switches, and are preferred where accuracy is important provided they meet requirements for service life and speed of cycling.

Switches with belleville (snap action) spring seem to provide the greatest repetitive accuracy, but the manufacturer should be contacted on life expectancy of the spring.

Adjustable Range . . .

The term "working range" defines the pressure range a switch may see under normal working conditions. This is normally the adjustable range.

For greater accuracy the set point should fall in the upper 65% of the adjustable range. But for the most favorable life factor, the set point should be in the lower 65% of the adjustable range. Therefore, the most favorable combination of accuracy and life factor lies in the middle 30% of the adjustable range, and this is illustrated in the diagram. This general rule applies only to bourdon tube and diaphragm pressure switches. Piston switches have a more nearly uniform accuracy and life factor over their entire adjustable range.

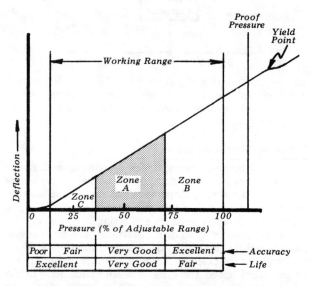

On switches with diaphragm or bourdon tube movements, greatest accuracy is in the upper 65%, best life factor in the lower 65%, and the best combination is usually in the middle 30% of its working range.

Types of Switch Action . . .

(1). Standard pressure switches sense a single pressure source and open and close a single set of contacts.

(2). Differential pressure switches have two connections and sense the difference across a circuit.

(3). Dual switches sense a high and low limit on the same pressure source, and actuate two sets of electrical contacts.

Wide range dual pressure sensing can be accomplished with two standard pressure switches connected to a holding relay. See Womack Data Sheet 20.

Fluid Media . . .

The fluid compatibility with materials of construction must be considered. Consult manufacturers catalog.

Proof Pressure . . .

Proof pressure is the highest pressure the switch will stand without permanent deformation, and usually defined as 1½ times maximum working range. Although a pressure gauge in the switch circuit may show a constant operating pressure, there may be momentary pressure spikes (dampened by the gauge snubber) which would damage the element in a pressure switch. For this reason the working range should extend well above the actual operating pressure point.

Electronic Pressure Switching . . .

For the ultimate in accuracy, range, and life expectancy, electronic pressure switching uses a strain gauge type of pressure transducer connected into electronic circuits to operate either solid state switching or a mechanical action relay.

ELECTRIC MOTOR HP TO DRIVE A HYDRAULIC PUMP

Figures in the body of this table show the horsepower needed to drive a hydraulic pump having an efficiency of 85%. Most positive displacement pumps (gear, vane, piston) fall in the range of 80 to 90% efficiency so this chart should be accurate to within 5% for almost any pump. The table was calculated from the formula:

$$HP = PSI \times GPM \div [1714 \times 0.85]$$

For pumps with efficiency other than 85%, the forula can be used, substituting actual efficiency, in decimals, in place of 0.85.

Using the Table: The range of 500 to 5000 PSI covers most hydraulic systems, but power requirements can be determined for conditions outside the range of this table, or for intermediate values. For example, power at 4000 PSI will be exactly 2 times the figure shown for 2000 PSI. At 77 GPM, power will be the sum of the figures shown in the 75 and the 2 GPM lines, etc. For systems operating below 500 PSI, horsepower calculations tend to become inaccurate because mechanical friction losses become a greater proportion of total power input.

Rules-of-Thumb. Approximate HP requirement can be estimated by our "Rule of 1500" which states that 1 HP is required for each multiple of 1500 when multiplying PSI x GPM. For example, a 5 GPM pump at 1500 PSI would require 5 HP, or at 3000 PSI would require 10 HP. A 10 GPM pump at 1000 PSI would require 6-2/3rds HP or the same pump at 1500 PSI would require 10 HP, etc.

Another rule-of-thumb states that about 5% of the pump maximum rated HP is required to idle the pump when it is "unloaded" and the full flow is circulating at near 0 PSI. This amount of power may be consumed in flow losses plus mechanical friction losses in bearings and friction in pumping elements.

Figures in Body of Table are HP's Required to Drive a Hydraulic Pump (A Pump Efficiency of 85% is Assumed)

GPM	500 PSI	750 PSI	1000 PSI	1250 PSI	1500 PSI	1750 PSI	2000 PSI	2500 PSI	3000 PSI	3500 PSI	4000 PSI	5000 PSI
3	1.03	1.54	2.06	2.57	3.09	3.60	4.12	5.15	6.18	7.21	8.24	10.3
5	1.72	2.57	3.43	4.29	5.15	6.00	6.86	8.58	10.3	12.0	13.7	17.2
7½	2.57	3.86	5.15	6.43	7.72	9.01	10.3	12.9	15.4	18.0	20.6	25.7
10	3.43	5.15	6.86	8.58	10.3	12.0	13.7	17.2	20.6	24.0	27.5	34.3
12½	4.29	6.43	8.58	10.7	12.9	15.0	17.2	21.4	25.7	30.0	34.3	42.9
15	5.15	7.72	10.3	12.9	15.4	18.0	20.6	25.7	30.9	36.0	41.2	51.5
17½	6.01	9.01	12.0	15.0	18.0	21.0	24.0	30.0	36.0	42.0	48.0	60.1
20	6.86	10.3	13.7	17.2	20.6	24.0	27.5	34.3	41.2	48.0	54.9	68.6
22½	7.72	11.6	15.4	19.3	23.2	27.0	30.9	38.6	46.3	54.1	61.8	77.2
25	8.58	12.9	17.2	21.4	25.7	30.0	34.3	42.9	51.5	60.1	68.6	85.8
30	10.3	15.4	20.6	25.7	30.9	36.0	41.2	51.5	61.8	72.1	82.4	103
35	12.0	18.0	24.0	30.0	36.0	42.0	48.0	60.1	72.1	84.1	96.1	120
40	13.7	20.6	27.5	34.3	41.2	48.0	54.9	68.6	82.4	96.1	110	137
45	15.4	23.2	30.9	38.6	46.3	54.1	61.8	77.2	92.7	108	124	154
50	17.2	25.7	34.3	42.9	51.5	60.1	68.6	85.8	103	120	137	172
55	18.9	28.3	37.8	47.2	56.6	66.1	75.5	94.4	113	132	151	189
60	20.6	30.9	41.2	51.5	61.8	72.1	82.4	103	124	144	165	206
65	22.3	33.5	44.6	55.8	66.9	78.1	89.2	112	134	156	178	223
70	24.0	36.0	48.0	60.1	72.1	84.1	96.1	120	144	168	192	240
75	25.7	38.6	51.5	64.3	77.2	90.1	103	129	154	180	206	257
80	27.5	41.2	54.9	68.7	82.4	96.1	110	137	165	192	220	275
85	29.2	43.8	58.3	72.9	87.5	102	117	146	175	204	233	292
90	30.9	46.3	61.8	77.2	92.7	108	124	154	185	216	247	309
100	34.3	51.5	68.6	85.8	103	120	137	172	206	240	275	343

Power to Drive a Cylinder

Note: The HP obtained from this chart is that to drive a hydraulic pump to produce the GPM flow at the PSI pressures shown along the top of the chart. If the pump supplies a hydraulic cylinder, additional pressure will be required from the pump, over and above the pressure to just equal load resistance, to make up pressure losses through the system. A way of estimating system losses is given in Appendix A of "Volume 1 – Industrial Fluid Power". See also Pages 162 through 165 of this book for information on electric motor overloading.

Engine Pump Drive

This chart can also be used to estimate the HP from an engine to drive a hydraulic pump. Caution! An engine will lose compression and HP output with age. We reccommend that a new engine be capable of supplying 10 to 25% more HP than actually needed to compensate for aging. Remember, too, that unlike an electric motor, an engine cannot supply an overload torque, even momentarily, without stalling unless it is equipped with a heavy flywheel. An engine will not supply its rated HP at elevations of more than 3000 to 4000 feet.

HORSEPOWER TO COMPRESS AIR

This 3-part table shows the horsepower required to compress 1 SCFM (standard cubic foot per minute) of air from atmospheric pressure (0 PSIG) to the elevated pressures shown in the table.

Values are shown for single-stage, two-stage, and three-stage piston-type air compressors operating at 85% efficiency, and supplied with intake air at standard conditions. Compression conditions intermediate between adiabatic and isothermal have been assumed. (See explanation of these terms below). We believe this most nearly represents the condition which exists in the average plant air system. The table was prepared from information in Machinery's Handbook. Please refer to your copy of the Handbook for additional information on air compression and for formulae from which the table was calculated.

Horsepower has been calculated for compressors with 85% efficiency. If the efficiency of your compressor is different, an allowance should be made in table values.

Explanation of the Table

The table is useful either in determinimg the HP for a new application or for checking the capacity of an existing system for addition of more equipment to operate from the compressor.

NOTE: Figures are HP's to compress *1 SCFM* from 0 PSIG to the pressures shown. Calculation of air consumption of cylinders will be found in the Appendix of the Womack book "Industrial Fluid Power — Volume 1".

Adiabatic Compression. Defined as compression which takes place without allowing the escape of any of the heat of compression. Obviously this is a theoretical condition because cooling starts immediately as air is compressed.

Isothermal Compression. Defined as compression which takes place over a time period which allows escape of all heat of compression. This is also a theoretical condition.

In calculating the table we have chosen a compression condition intermediate between adiabatic and isothermal.

*Horsepower Required to Compress Air

Single-Stage Compressor, 85% Eff.		Two-Stage Compressor, 85% Eff.		Three-Stage Compressor, 85% Eff.	
PSIG	HP*	PSIG	HP*	PSIG	HP*
5	.021	50	.116	100	.159
10	.033	60	.128	150	.190
15	.056	70	.138	200	.212
20	.067	80	.148	250	.230
25	.079	90	.155	300	.240
30	.089	100	.164	350	.258
35	.099	110	.171	400	.269
40	.108	120	.178	450	.279
45	.116	130	.185	500	.289
50	.123	140	.190	550	.297
55	.130	150	.196	600	.305
60	.136	160	.201	650	.311
65	.143	170	.206	700	.317
70	.148	180	.211	750	.323
75	.155	190	.216	800	.329
80	.160	200	.220	850	.335
85	.165	210	.224	900	.340
90	.170	220	.228	950	.345
95	.175	230	.232	1000	.290
100	.179	240	.236	1050	.354
110	.191	250	.239	1100	.358
120	.196	260	.243	1150	.362
130	.204	270	.246	1200	.366
140	.211	280	.250	1250	.370
150	.218	290	.253	1300	.374
160	.225	300	.255	1350	.378
170	.232	350	.269	1400	.380
180	.239	400	.282	1450	.383
190	.244	450	.289	1500	.386
200	.250	500	.303	1550	.390

*Horsepower to compress 1 SCFM free air from 0 PSIG to the values shown in the chart.

CONVERSION OF ALL FORMS OF POWER INTO (SI) INTERNATIONAL STANDARDS UNITS

Charts for converting many other U.S. units into SI metric units will be found in Appendix D of the Womack book "Industrial Fluid Power — Volume 1".

Exponents tell whether to move the decimal point to the right (for a + sign) or to the left (for a - sign), and how far to move it. Example: 1.356×10^{-3} is the same as 0.001356, or 7.783×10^2 is the same as 778.3, etc.

The International Standard (SI) unit for all forms of power is the kilowatt, shown in the first column. Equivalent values of other units are shown on the same line. Look down the column of the unit to be converted and find the line on which "1" appears. Then move to the right or left to the column of the desired conversion. That figure is a multiplier. Example: Look down the Horsepower column to the "1" line. The chart shows "1" HP = 7.461×10^{-1} or 0.7461 kilowatt, etc.

Kilowatt	Watt, Joules/Sec, and N-M/Sec.	U.S. & U.K Horsepower	Foot-Pounds per Minute	Foot-Pounds per Second	BTU per Hour	BTU per Min.
1	1000	1.340	4.425×10^4	7.376×10^2	3.412×10^3	56.862
1×10^{-3}	1	1.340×10^{-3}	44.254	7.376×10^{-1}	3.412	5.686×10^{-2}
7.461×10^{-1}	746	1	3.300×10^4	5.500×10^2	2.545×10^3	42.44
2.260×10^{-5}	2.260×10^{-2}	3.029×10^{-5}	1	1.667×10^{-2}	7.710×10^{-2}	1.285×10^{-3}
1.356×10^{-3}	1.356	1.817×10^{-3}	60	1	4.626	7.710×10^{-2}
2.931×10^{-4}	2.931×10^{-1}	3.928×10^{-4}	12.971	2.162×10^{-1}	1	1.667×10^{-2}
1.759×10^{-2}	17.586	2.357×10^{-2}	7.783×10^2	12.971	60	1

255

General Index

Other Womack Books
on Industrial Fluid Power & Machine Tooling

VOLUME 1 – INDUSTRIAL FLU ID POWER. This book was first published in 1984 and is now in its Third Edition. Volume 1 focuses on basic instruction in air and hydraulic fluid power. It's used as a classroom text by hundreds of vocational/technical schools. In addition to basic instruction there are numerous tables and charts with design data and troubleshooting information. The metric international standard (ISO) units are explained. Charts are included for interchange between ISO metric and English units, and for sizing metric bore cylinders. The text follows a simple and practical format which has made this textbook so popular.

This is an excellent textbook for home study. It has been accepted as a training manual by the NFPA (National Fluid Power Association), by the FPS (Fluid Power Society), and has been adopted by the FPDA (Fluid Power Distributors Association) as their official training manual to accompany their audio cassette program for training members of the Association.

VOLUME 2 – INDUSTRIAL FLUID POWER. This is one of the more advanced textbooks. It uses the foundation laid in Volume 1 and goes on into certain subjects to a greater depth. Covers both hydraulic and air fluid power.

Some of the subjects include: how to calculate many types of cylinder loads, vertical, horizontal, and at an angle. Direction, force, and speed control of cylinders using some of the more sophisticated types of 4-way directional, pressure compensated flow control, and pressure control valves such as sequence, by-pass, unloading, reducing, and counterbalance valves. Pressure intensification with piston type and rotary type intensifiers. Sample circuit diagrams, design charts, and formulae are shown for each application. This book is limited to applications using air or hydraulic cylinders to deliver power output. Rotary mechanical output is covered in Volume 3.

Other material includes a chapter on air-over-oil circuits in which compressed shop air is used for power to produce a hydraulic oil flow. The last chapter shows many ideas, some novel, for the use of cylinders.

VOLUME 3 – INDUSTRIAL FLUID POWER. Although covering many advanced applications which require rotary mechanical output, the presentation is simple as it is in all the Womack books, and can easily be understood by anyone with mechanical or electrical aptitude. Mathematics are limited to very simple formulae, and in most cases the charts and tables can be used instead of the formulae

The format includes first an explanation of each component and how it works, using photos and sectional views. Then circuit diagrams plus design charts show how to design the component into circuits.

Among the components covered in this particular book are common types of hydraulic motors - gear, vane, and piston types. Shows how to match a hydraulic motor to its load; circuits for direction and speed control; closed loop hydrostatic transmissions; motor starting and running torque, efficiency, HP, life expectancy, and installation; air motor operation and circuit design; power steering design; rotary and spool-type flow dividers and how to use them; bootstrapping principles and circuits for saving power; and many other topics.

FLUID POWER IN PLANT AND FIELD. This book is a collection of everyday useful tips, suggestions, and ideas for improving performance in a system; for preventing premature failures; and correcting malfunctions and breakdowns of fluid power equipment in the industrial plant or on mobile equipment.

A great deal of this information has been compiled from our own notes and experience in helping our customers with design and troubleshooting problems. We have sorted out and grouped the information under appropriate chapter headings to make it easier to find. Topics include cylinders, valves, pumps and motors, oil reservoirs, accumulators, heat exchangers, air line conditioning units, air dryers, and vacuum pumps. This book can be useful as a reference while studying the other books.

SELECTED TOOLING TREASURES. The newest addition to the Womack Library of useful and practical textbooks offers ideas for tooling and special machine building. It's written in layman's language and can help business owners, accountants, purchasing people, and maintenance personnel to understand the value of simple, inexpensive tooling. It will also be a valuable asset to machine designers and engineers.

This book contains numerous original, one-of-a-kind, practical ideas. It can help you build simple tooling machines that will allow you to sell the product you build for less than your competitors, using traditional CNC machines, can build their product. It illustrates how to build multi-spindle machines that cost a fraction of the price of a standard, single spindle CNC machining center, but will turn out ten times the amount of product.

The author, with 55 years of tooling experience, helps you avoid many common problems and pitfalls. A number of safety tips are covered to help make your present and new machines safer and more efficient.

FUNDAMENTALS OF INDUSTRIAL CONTROLS & AUTOMATION. Womack Educational Publications newest textbook, "Fundamentals of Industrial Controls and Automation" focuses on a beginner's study of electricity, electronics, control components and automation as related to industrial controls.

Modern manufacturing techniques are only possible because of dependable electrical control systems. This textbook explores the proper use of electrical controls to maximize productivity, minimize downtime, simplify maintenance, improve safety and provide information to effectively manage operations.

Topics covered in the seven chapters include: Electrical Fundamentals, Input Devices – Sensors and Switches, Logic Devices – Timers and Counters, Output Devices, Schematic Diagrams and Logic, Programmable Logic Controllers and Accessories, and Temperature Control Systems.